Total War on PTSD

by
Courtenay Nold

Charitable Not-for-Profit benefiting from 100% of author proceeds for this book.

Operation Fetch began as a non-profit that performs Planned Acts of Community Kindness to further appreciation, education & awareness about service dogs PTSD, and dogs for visible and invisible wounds. We have dedicated ourselves to hundreds of missions since 2013. What began as fun social media microblogging has evolved into an important, positive and completely voluntary community of caring individuals worldwide who are committed to working dogs and their handlers, veterans, and other community members who care for and about each other without thought of reward through Planned Acts of Community Kindness (PACKs). No salaries are paid and no one profits from any of our activities.

Examples of our activities:

Education and awareness seminars and visits about service dogs, PTSD, suicide prevention and invisible disabilities to over 400 school, hospitals, and community service organizations
Helped veterans and survivors of physical, emotional, war or environmental trauma with short term needs; emergency housing, cards and letters, assistance with service dog placement, compassionate visits, short term medical needs for handlers and dogs not covered by the VA or personal insurance
Guided dozens of trauma survivors to long term and meaningful assistance
Created two national conferences to educate first responders, community leaders, businessmen and women and the general public about assistance animals, the laws that apply to them and the importance of service dogs in the lives of people with disabilities.
Traveled to 39 states and played TAPS 365 days in a row. Read the names of 22 soldiers lost to suicide. https://www.nbcdfw.com/multimedia/bugler-and-his-dog-honor-veterans_dallas-fort-worth/44814/
Created an anthology of dog stories (In Dogs We Trust) by world class authors that has been read globally and continues to move and inspire people to celebrate the human-canine connection.
Helped directly/indirectly raise over $3,000,000 for other groups: rescues, service dog agencies, and other non-profits...
Distributed over 3,000 coats and survival bags to homeless veterans and others in need. We do a coat drive annually.
Sent thousands of pounds of coffee to forward deployed troops. Each year Hansa Roasters in Libertyville, Illinois sells bags of Gander's Choice coffee meant to be sent overseas. Funds raised help Fetch and LZ-Grace warriors retreat in Virgina.
Helped reunite soldiers with their war dog battle buddies.
Provided adaptive equipment, appliances, cars, telephones and more to people in need.
Trained several national and local business and helped develop disability access straegies: Walmart, Hospitality International, Vantage Hotels, J.B. Hunt, Starbucks, McDonalds...
Actively involved in developing legislation to ensure better service dog access. Working with Representative Joyce Mason to pass "Gander's Law" which would criminalize counterfeit service dog teams that are the cause of many public disruptions and promote negative public perception of SDs.

Please visit: www.operationfetch.org

Total War on PTSD

by Courtenay Nold

Southern Arizona Press
Sierra Vista, Arizona

Total War on PTSD

By Courtenay Nold

First PaperbackEdition

Content Copyright © 2023 by Courtenay Nold

Author: Courtenay Nold
Editor: Paul Gilliland
Formatting: Southern Arizona Press
Cover Artwork: Image by Anja from Pixabay
All other photographs in text provided by each contributor

Published by Southern Arizona Press
Sierra Vista, Arizona 85635
www.SouthernArizonaPress.com

ISBN: 978-1-960038-41-8

Dedication

In Memory Of My Father - Richard Henry Haynes, Jr.

Preface

I arrived at Kandahar Airfield outside Kabul and survived the first of many rocket (missile) and ground attacks. But my innocent newbie face changed. It eroded with each race for shelter as Taliban ordnance pounded our 'secure' base. Each round of incoming added to what was becoming the foundation of the Post-Traumatic Stress Disorder (PTSD) that stalks me to this very day. A dark creature was clinging to my back and raising the hair-like hackles on the back of a dog, but that damned creature is no longer there.

It is gone because I am winning my personal fight in the Total War on PTSD. I am winning the war through mindfulness of body and soul. I am walking this path and rediscovering my passion, my emotions, and my joy in life through writing, creative and artistic expression.

Last but not least, I live my life to help others...without fail...my mission in life is to help others to fight their war and find their own path to recovery.

A Letter to My Readers

Dear Reader:

When you picked up this book you joined the fight against Post-Traumatic Stress Disorder (PTSD) and in support of its victims in and out of uniform. For me this is highly personal. PTSD invades your life with claws and teeth. It can hit you in a war zone like Afghanistan where it grabbed me, or it can pounce on you in the civilian world anywhere that repeated, life-threatening trauma tears into your body, mind, and spirit. PTSD is a potentially lethal enemy. We must fully understand it and then defeat it. We can do it. Especially if we take it on together. By this I mean all of us with all of America's diverse resources. That kind of commitment is necessary if we're going to defeat this invader. And that is why this book is titled TOTAL WAR ON PTSD.

Got PTSD or know someone with PTSD? I do too...it's me. I've been dealing with it since 2010. Please take my hand, at least long enough to read this letter, if nothing else. I think you will find that together we can get through this and create a better tomorrow.

While I refer to PTSD in the title of this book with the 'D' at the end, it can and is referenced both as PTSD and PTS throughout the chapters within. No negative connotation is meant by referring to this as PTSD...only as a common vernacular used by the general public, and the community of Veterans especially, at large.

The book in your hands was born out of my personal frustrations about the lack of a single resource for military, Veterans and civilians confronted by issues centered on PTSD in all of its forms. Please don't get me wrong...there's plenty of information out there, but it's very widely scattered and tends to be stove piped like so much uncoordinated intelligence. If you have PTSD, or if someone you care about has PTSD, you need access to all kinds of intel about every kind of therapy out there in order to facilitate recovery. You can't leave it up to just therapy or medications...that just isn't always the answer...that's not always for everyone and it also doesn't provide you with what you need to find your own path towards healing in your own way. No one heals from PTSD the same way, and in the same timeframe. That's why I set out to create this book, for myself, and for so many others who need the very same thing. I was very motivated given my own personal circumstances. My guess is that you are too, or you wouldn't be reading this right now.

Total War on PTSD contains a wealth of information on options for standard as well as alternative therapies and options ranging from Yoga, to Psychiatry, to Floatation Therapy, and so much more.

Every single contributor to this book was a volunteer, and provided their chapters, contributions and stories with no expectations other than to help those dealing with PTSD towards recovery in any way possible. My deepest possible thanks go out to each and every one of them for such an extraordinary and wonderful gesture on behalf of all PTSD sufferers.

My first mission is to gain your trust so here I am, reaching out my hand. With my own PTSD, that was, and still is, not an easy thing to do. I recall digging my well-worn Mariners Cross out of hiding from under my uniform while glancing up at the night sky for the possible glare of a rocket and furtively kissing it before quickly tucking it back out of sight while heading out to the bunkers...and how I thought seriously about kissing the good earth of America after coming home from my Afghanistan deployment.

First thing I need to say, I always loved the Navy...and I still very much do. I felt at home there. I belonged. What I didn't love is some of the antiquated beliefs, and some well-scattered pieces of the administration that tended to be left in place due to the tendency to cling to history in administrative war efforts. There was no high ground...no safe place for anyone there in Afghanistan. You did absolutely everything with your weapon at your side and you...I...was always prepared to use that weapon at a moment's notice. That is the reason I can't go anywhere now without scanning every single room I go into. That is the very reason I have to keep my back to the wall. I think I would be much more comfortable if I have my constant companion back on my hip again.

Let me share with you how it felt for me to be there.

I imagine myself standing outside at night with my head tilted up to accept the rain pouring down on my face. I don't notice, nor even feel, the tears running down my face alongside the raindrops. My emotions left me long ago, stolen by a thief in a night streaked by rockets glare, shaken by their thudding impacts, and pierced by the rapid-fire response of marine guns defending our perimeter. It doesn't matter that I am soaked to the bone, that my clothes cling to me while the rain tries to wash away my pain. I see it all and hear it. But I feel nothing but that deep dread that carries one question: does that incoming have my name on it?

Every day, and at any time of day, when I hear any sort of unexpected noise, I may go into barely controlled panic mode. My reaction includes immediately looking around for escape routes and examining everyone and everything around me as a potential threat, my anxiety and heart rate rising by the second. That's my PTSD. I returned from my Afghanistan deployment back in 2011 but, for part of me, it might as well have been just an hour ago.

I was ordered to Afghanistan in 2010 to work with the Third Naval Construction Regiment (3NCR), an outstanding Seabee regiment that has since been decommissioned, and was deployed for seven months. 3NCRs job was to support Operation Enduring Freedom and, under the direction of Captain Donald Hedrick, was in charge of four Naval Mobile Construction Battalions (NMCBs), one Air Force Engineering Command, two Army Combat Engineer Battalions, one Army Engineering Command, and three Army support units. 3NCR was responsible for construction engineering and engineering support in the Afghanistan theater and played an essential role in international security for coalition forces. Those of us who remained on the base (Forward Operating Base or FOB) never 'officially' saw combat. That is unless of course, like me, you lost count of how many rocket attacks and other attempts there were to penetrate the base perimeter and kill us there really were.

The issues I have dealt with since then really haven't let up as much as I have hoped they would. Please don't get me wrong. There are many things that have helped me along the way, and there are things that continue to help me. This is not the way I used to be. I was very laid-back and self-confident before my deployment into the outer rim of hell known in some of our military circles as Afcrapistan (a.k.a. Afghanistan), as commonly referred to by my friend, Navy Journalist (now referred to officially as Mass Communication Specialists) and Chief Petty Officer Brian Naranjo.

The thing is that it, at least for me, my journey continues to be a work in progress, and my writing is a huge part of that journey, as is my ability and my drive to help others towards their own recovery; whatever it takes.

Kandahar Airfield was supposed to be relatively secure but, in my opinion, that was bullshit. Screaming rockets and mortar rounds are unimpressed by perimeter fences and K9 patrols. Truth is it was a war zone where I and hundreds of thousands of other U.S. service personnel and civilian contractors experienced daily shocks that created PTSD, especially for the uninitiated. I was one of those, as I deployed after the main body of 3NCR did, being a late asset, as they were in need of an Administrative Officer and I didn't have the time to go through the same training they did.

I'm no battle-hardened hero. I ran an administrative team. Let me take you back there. It's been a pretty nice day — as long as you stay inside and don't inhale too much of the dust that seeps into every crevice. My three to four team members (depending on timeframe) and I are wading through piles of sometimes repetitive but still vitally important paperwork when the obnoxiously loud siren on the pole just outside our building roars to life issuing a warning that forces us to do what has become almost automatic. We then hear the booming, pre-recorded, suspiciously calm and somewhat irritating (given the number of times I heard it during my deployment) female British voice saying declaring "Rocket Attack" three times over. After dropping to the floor for the requisite five minutes...give or take...we quickly secure our computers and exit the small office building, heading out to the bunkers that dot the sprawling airbase. We pack into the bunkers much like sardines, something that has made me claustrophobic to this very day, waiting until the all-clear announcement came from the same British lady and we were allowed to exit the bunker and return to work. Then it was business as usual...as if nothing happened...more nonsense...at least to me. We didn't get killed or wounded this time but our nervous systems were assaulted by fear doing subtle damage to physical and emotional systems that are routinely ignored by military physicians as a matter of policy. It was kind of like chipping away at mortar between bricks in a wall, just a little at a time, not expecting anything to happen...and then being surprised when a brick falls out. Eventually the wall is going to fall apart. Such is PTSD.

Early in the deployment I felt comfortable in my job, my position, as a leader of my small 'department' and the job itself, working in a war zone. It gave me more purpose than anything I'd ever done. Actually, if I was able, I would go back and do it again in a heartbeat. But after many life-or-death trips from the office to the bunkers with enemy rockets closing in, that comfort started peeling away like the skin of an onion, leaving me with the raw interior that is my PTSD. Sometimes I've felt like I've become the onion.

Other military Veterans will nod their heads as they read the next paragraphs. For any family members and civilians reading this, I hope the next words provide some help in understanding what your warfighter is going through because, while there is no single cookie-cutter 'case' of PTSD, what I go through is unfortunately typical for many of us.

Months after the official welcome home ceremony and returning to civilian life in the U.S., I began to feel betrayed — by the Navy, by my friends and co-workers who 'weren't there' for me when I started experiencing worsening PTSD. I even felt that way in my civilian job environment. The main reason for this is that I felt that they just didn't understand. They didn't understand the environment I was in...the brother and sisterhood I experienced in the military and...especially so...in a joint service, war zone environment. They didn't know what the symptoms were that I was experiencing. They didn't understand my triggers...or why I couldn't sleep at night...or why I was always shaky. And, at the time, I was so lost I didn't understand that I was part of the problem...because I wouldn't let them in... because I had trouble with both trust and communication. That caused me to create an environment where I isolated myself, both at work and at home, in order to control not only my environment, but my triggers. I resented the situation I was in but couldn't help it...this was necessary to survive.

That kind of deep disappointment and resentment may not be founded in fact, but it's generated by the increments of battle related shocks that don't leave an outer scar but surely do create our ongoing, reality which can include seemingly unmotivated anger, hyper-vigilance and nightmares, among a myriad of other issues. An even more prevalent, if not new, issue, is the epidemic of suicides — something that must be addressed and changed, from the homeless Veteran living on the street to the highest governmental seat, as our lives literally depend on it. This is baseline knowledge about PTSD. I hope that it helps with understanding, between Veterans and family members, between the general public and Veterans, and even between one Veteran and another, how we also have to deal with PTSD, anxiety, fight-or-flight, panic attacks, insomnia, and even trust related issues.

The ability to trust people outside of the military, and even some people inside the military, can be very challenging after serving in a war zone, especially after surviving combat. There are many Veterans whose PTSD has been present since their service time, but that didn't get worse until they retired from the workforce. Finding themselves with nothing to occupy their time, PTSD symptoms can suddenly rise up and march forward, making daily living difficult without the distractions and satisfactions of working to fill their time and distract them from their troubled minds.

I have felt out of control. I know how it is to feel like your brain might explode. To feel like everything is stuck in overdrive and there is no escape. Like there is no corner where you can escape to that can possibly lessen your feeling of dread...your fight-or-flight...your inability to trust...and to stop your hands from shaking when you are being triggered. I know because I have been there so many times...and have been able to find my own path towards fighting against those triggers...those demons...and I know in my heart that you can too!

I have made a ton of progress since I began my own personal quest for answers...for solutions...to the beast that is PTSD. My own threat assessment — maybe I should call my 'bomb' damage assessment — is that I am 85% home. That last 15% is a bitch. The truth is that writing this book has taken a bit more time than it might otherwise have taken because there is construction work being done next to my house and every now and then some form of equipment or another will shatter the sense of peace that is my home, triggering the memories of the war zone I was stationed in, and the next thing I know I literally feel like my skeleton wants to crawl right out of my body, leaving my skin behind on the floor...while my psyche runs screaming from the house.

But enough of the extremes, that was just a temporary feeling...albeit a very real one for me...but I am getting there and you can to. This is just the unalloyed, unvarnished, unseen truth about where I stand in my own personal recovery. Maybe you and I can do this together with the help of the pages of expert insights that I have accumulated over the last two years.

Where once, when drinking or occasional drugs may have filled the gaps, or rather numbed the senses in between work and family life, there is now an opening that needs to be filled...an opening where jarring thoughts about combat seep in...seeing a rocket go right overhead and hit the building right next to you...experiencing military sexual trauma or even rape...crawling through holes as a tunnel rat with no flashlight...climbing into a crashed plane to realize you are removing the body of a fallen friend...parachuting in darkness and then watching your plane go down into German territory; all of this can all come flooding back and overwhelm your senses, your mind and your body.

I felt betrayed...just like I felt betrayed when the Navy, my friends and coworkers who I felt just 'weren't there' for me when I started experiencing worsening PTSD issues after my return from Afghanistan. I felt betrayed because no one ever told me what had happened to me at that time, after I was brought back from the dead. I experienced Traumatic Brain Injuries caused not by the concussive efforts of Improvised Explosive Devices but rather by Electroconvulsive Therapy (ECT) sessions that came about from a Navy doctor's hands while I was still in the Navy. I coded during an ECT session and had to be resuscitated with a crash cart. My heart literally stopped beating. The worst part of it all was that I was not informed of what happened, and that I only found out about it later (a year later) when my attorney was reviewing my military medical records. Because of all this I will deal with brain lesions, and trust related issues, for the rest of my life.

The ability to trust people outside of the military, and even some people inside the military, can be difficult after serving in a war zone, especially after extreme circumstances. My own spouse's PTSD didn't act up until he retired from his full-time job with the phone company. This isn't the case for everyone. Some may have had to deal with PTSD and its related issues all along including heightened anxiety and panic attacks, flashbacks, nightmares, insomnia, short-fused anger, and many other issues. Some turn to drugs and alcohol in the process.

Many Veterans I have spoken to told me that despite their issues with PTSD, they would not hesitate to return to service, or even to a war zone, to serve all over again. It is a place where those who have served are comfortable; where we worked alongside our brothers and sisters in service; where we all knew that others 'had our six'. It was a place we all felt we could trust one another despite often extreme circumstances.

"For many people, managing pain involves using prescription medicine in combination with complementary techniques like physical therapy, acupuncture, yoga and massage. I appreciate this because I truly believe medical care should address the person as a whole - their mind, body, and spirit." - Naomi Judd

Even though the Total War on PTSD is focused on Veterans, its concepts can be applied to anyone experiencing issues relating to PTSD from any sort of trauma at all, not just combat or military related experiences. It can be related to sexual trauma of any sort, rape, sexual abuse, physical abuse, mental abuse, traumatic experiences; really pretty much any event that had enough of an impact on your life that it alone, or even an accumulation of events that caused your PTSD to surface and effect your life...causing you to seek help in any way possible.

Just because someone might be scared doesn't mean they can't overcome fear.

No matter the circumstances of when you served or where, please know that there are still people out there who 'have your six' and I would be so proud to be able to call myself one of them.

You deserve to live.
Your life was lived in flight and shadow...
But now you can come out into the light...
And live the life you were meant to live...
Free from your hearts fire and shaken plight.

Please do take my hand and come with me to find a way to heal, and a path to recovery. I have learned how to minimize the impact of PTSD on my life. It can be done. I am convinced that this book can help anyone to improve the quality of their life despite their PTSD.

Endorsements

"Here, finally, is a comprehensive guide to healing from the devastating effects of PTSD. This compassionate and detailed guide could only have been written by a Veteran with front line experience who has researched a myriad of potentially helpful treatments. If you know or love someone suffering from PTSD, give them this book, because it has the potential to change lives and even save them."
-- Donna Thomson, author of *The Four Walls of My Freedom* and *The Unexpected Journey of Caring*. Caregiver activist and blogger at *The Caregivers' Living Room* (www.donnathomson.com).

"A moving collection of alternate perspectives that every service member, Veteran, and civilian can learn from."
-- Marjorie K. Eastman, Veteran and Award-winning Author, *The Frontline Generation*

"What begins as a shout of joyful gratitude evolves into a deep exploration of all cutting-edge treatments for PTSD. In the same way that Veterans and their disabilities come in all shapes and sizes, so do their paths toward healing. Courtenay Nold beautifully and comprehensively demonstrates this in *Total War on PTSD*. This is a 'must read' for every veteran, family member, and friend who can use a dose of hope."
-- Laura Westley, U.S. Army Veteran, West Point Graduate, Author of *War Virgin*

"For many Veterans, a new battle begins upon returning home from active duty. PTSD, post-concussion syndrome, and brain injuries are often poorly managed by the traditional medical establishment. Courtenay Nold presents revolutionary therapies that every Veteran and family member should know about."
-- Mickey Mitchell, Founder, BIPRI

Table of Contents

PTSD Reality Check

by Jeff Kamen
Award-winning reporter, co-author of *Final Warning: Averting Disaster in the New Age of Terrorism* (Doubleday) and author of *Warrior Pups: True Stories of America's K9 Heroes* (Lyons)

Photo Source – Leslie Stone-Kamen

Everything you need to know about Post-Traumatic Stress Disorder (PTSD) is right here in your hands. No other book is nearly as comprehensive. Courtenay Nold, the book's author/editor, has done a huge service by bringing together all this knowledge. She has done it with a fierce passion for finding the truth. Here is what you need to know as you begin the healing journey this book offers. First, the basics:

Military and civilian, heroes and victims. Any race. Any gender. Any age. Anyone can suffer from PTSD. It is not a sign of weakness, anyone who has been in danger and feared for their lives is a candidate for PTSD.

At any given moment, an estimated eight million Americans are doing their best to survive PTSD's repeated inner assaults. Too often, the patient's condition is misdiagnosed, and the patient is disrespected, adding deep insult to awful injury.

PTSD is a complex disorder created by exposure to shocking trauma and stress. It breaks into the brains of warriors who have seen too much horror. PTSD is the second brutalization of victims of rape. PTSD burns its way into the souls of children who survive school shootings and sexual abuse at the hands of relatives, family friends, ministers, teachers, and strangers. PTSD impacts someone you know or someone who you soon will meet.

The largest single group of Americans with PTSD — our military Veterans. No foreign enemy has ever so successfully invaded America as has PTSD. It sneaked onto every troop ship and U.S. Air Force transport plane bringing our brave warfighters home from Korea, Vietnam, Cambodia, Thailand, Iraq, Syria, and Afghanistan. For decades, our nation's military and political leaders made believe there was no invasion. They turned their backs on millions of Veterans whose courageous service left them tormented by the terrible invisible wounds of PTSD.

The words "Homeless Veteran," and "Veteran who committed suicide," tear at my heart and fill me with anger. Every single case is traceable to PTSD that was untreated or treated ineffectively. No American military Veteran should ever be homeless, and none of our people should ever feel so alone and disrespected that they eat their gun or overdose on opioids or alcohol.

Untreated PTSD can easily destroy the patient, his or her relationships with family, friends, and co-workers and in rare cases, the lives of complete strangers who accidentally interact with the patient during an episode of extreme hyper-vigilance.

I'm about to share with you two stories of untreated PTSD, one institutional and the other highly personal involving a good friend who gave his country pretty much everything only to be abandoned when he needed help the most.

Until recently, a Marine suffering PTSD who dared to quietly complain to his Gunnery Sergeant of a distracting emotional problem would face severe ridicule and disrespect. The standard though unofficial response to the appeal for help was the Gunnery Sgt. handing the troubled Marine a straw and then saying these words, "Here you go, sweetheart, suck it up!", and with that the upset Marine would have his masculinity attacked. He would also be made to feel that if he pursued treatment, he would be branded a failure and become an outcast. Well, it turns out that mindless, "Traditional" response to a plea for help only served to create even more troubled and less reliable Marines, not tougher ones. Marines aren't stupid. Many of their top bosses are brilliant as well as tough. But they still were caught up in the macho culture of shaming troubled Marines instead of getting them the help they needed. Finally, the Marine Corps is changing and leathernecks with PTSD can now get treatment without ridicule. Now they can get back to work being the serious bad-asses we need them to be.

The Army used to be just as bad as the Marines. That's how I lost my friend to untreated PTSD. Identifying him would only serve to open old wounds for his family and friends so I will not name him but I will describe him for you. Like most of my other friends in the U.S. military whose first name is Joseph, my buddy was called G.I. Joe. Of course, that suggests a kind of average guy who steps up when everything goes wrong. This G.I. Joe was anything but ordinary. He graduated a famous college with a degree in science and a second lieutenant's bar on his shoulders. By 1984, this G.I. Joe was a Colonel. He'd earned rapid promotions the old-fashioned way—in combat. He saw a lot of it in Southeast Asia and enough of it was absolutely so horrific that it began to hollow him out, to grind down his most human of instincts—empathy.

By the time you get to be a 1st Lieutenant in the infantry, you've already begun being management—making decisions sending other men into combat knowing that some of them won't come back in one piece and some of them will go home only in body bags.

When he got to Vietnam, intelligence said the enemy had been cutting off the arms of some villagers to terrify others into silence and non-cooperation with the Americans. My pal Joe like the rest of our troops had been told they were coming to save 'Nam from communism and to give the local people a chance to enjoy freedom and peace. Enough stories of severed limbs and enough of the kids who he commanded being killed in extremely ugly ways and Joe became cold and hard.

"Back then," he told me, "Business was killing. And business was good."

When my first marriage finally fell apart after eighteen years, I took refuge in the spare bedroom of Joe's condo in northern Virginia near the Pentagon where he was the number two boss of a high-profile unit.

At one point, Joe began drinking heavily when he came home from work. When I called it to his attention, he became uncharacteristically angry toward me. Next morning, I found a note taped to the bathroom mirror. "Sorry, Jeff. See you tonight."

But the drinking just got worse. I wanted to be of help but I'm a nondrinker and at the time I wasn't smart enough to suggest we both attend a nearby meeting of Alcoholics Anonymous. Maybe it wouldn't have mattered if I had. The stories of his repeated exposure to danger, death, and unspeakable horror that Joe told me in between drinks painted an invisible picture of what I now know to have been severe untreated PTSD. The gunfire. The screams. The growing sense of personal isolation that came home with him from Vietnam were all haunting Joe. I felt powerless to help. I was ignorant and back then there was little in print that could have guided me to help Joe.

I thanked him the night before I moved out of his spare bedroom and into my new apartment on Capitol Hill only four blocks from the U.S. Senate. After that, Joe never returned my calls. I figured he was deployed or otherwise engaged and maybe he'd had enough of me whining about my marriage. Gradually, I stopped calling him and leaving messages.

Less than three months after I said goodbye to Joe, I received a phone call from a mutual friend. "Sorry, Jeff. I gotta tell you our pal ate his gun last night. The poor maid found him this morning when she came to do her monthly clean. I showed up to get him a little while after she did because he didn't show up for work and wasn't answering his phone. Cops were already there when I arrived. Place was trashed. Lots of empties and cigarette butts. Joe left a note. All it said was, "Fuck it.'"

I now know that what it should have read was, "Score another one for untreated PTSD."

If this book had been in my hands back then with all of its tools and resources, I would have had a chance to help Joe save his own life. Now the book is here. It's going to help so many people do just that. Military and civilians. I am so proud of this book's author, Courtenay Nold, a former U.S. Naval officer whose experiences in Afghanistan left her in long-term pain but eventually empowered her to find her way out of her own PTSD and to create this very important book.

Armed with it, you can help save a life.

DEDICATIONS

The loss of even a single Veteran, of any single person, to PTSD is one too many. The loss of anyone to PTSD is one too many. My deepest possible hope is that this book is able to change these statistics for the better, and that my brother and sister Veterans, their families, their friends, and their caregivers can find some measure of peace and hope, in their fight of their own personal war on PTSD. It's no longer time to fight for who I was...it's time to fight for who I am. I hope that you all feel the same way...either now, or after reading this book, from the library, from a bookstore shelf or even from the hands of a friend. I want to be able to finally say, "I got your six" and actually save your life in the process.

Command Master Chief Ronald O. Beard, Task Force Keystone, Kandahar, Afghanistan:

"I want to dedicate this short story about a couple of my experiences while serving in Operation Enduring Freedom to all of the men and women of our armed forces.

Our experiences have touched all of us in some way. Most of us, who have been forward deployed, carry good memories of the things we've done, the places we've seen, and the camaraderie that we have experienced along the way. Still, some of us have memories of stress and fear and sadness and trauma that visit us in our sleep or at unexpected moments. For years I have kept those memories suppressed as much as possible and tried to shift my thoughts to more pleasant things. But that strategy never seemed to work for very long.

Sharing my stories, mainly writing about them, has helped a great deal in alleviating the sadness. On several occasions, I have had the honor of interviewing men and women who served in combat or field hospitals in Vietnam. I never press them for details, yet I have been surprised at how often these soldiers voluntarily share their stories of combat, trauma, and stress with me.

Their stories usually start with brief details about their war. And then, when they see that I am genuinely interested and that I am listening with sincere interest, their stories often come gushing out with all of the emotions that they felt at the time of the story's happening. Along with those details almost always come tears – theirs and mine. It is not unusual after one of those interviews for the soldier to confide that that is the first time that they have ever shared that story with anyone since the war.

On every occasion that has happened, it seems that the soldier, even though he or she may be crying as they tell their story, begins to sit a little higher in their seat during the interview. It is as if some imaginary weight is being lifted from their shoulders. And, as I sit there listening, my mind relives my own experiences, which often seem to pale when compared to the stories that are being shared. I can feel myself sitting a little taller in my seat as well.

If you are one of those men and women who still carry the war with you, then I believe this book will help you to deal with your memories better and will cause you to sit a little taller and sleep a little better. And I hope it will inspire you to reach out to others who can't seem to leave their war behind. You may be surprised to find that when you begin to help others with their struggles that your sadness will start to disappear too. That adage that, You never stand taller than when you stoop to lift someone else up is true."

The Expectant Soldier I Never Knew

A couple of weeks before Christmas, 2010, one of our subordinate units had a Mine-Resistant Ambush Protected (MRAP) vehicle strike an Improvised Explosive Devise (IED) during route clearing operations. Two soldiers in the vehicle were killed, and two others were injured, one with life-threatening injuries. One of our Navy Battalion doctors, a renowned orthopedic surgeon from Seattle Washington, who spent most of his time at the Role III hospital in Kandahar, spent nine hours in surgery in the operating room, beginning the moment that the soldier arrived, trying to save his arms and what remained of his hands. The patient would be airlifted to Germany later that night for additional surgery and treatment.

The base commanding officer, General Hodges, contacted our command requesting that our CO, Commodore Donald Hedrick, and I, as Command Master Chief of the Task Force, assist him in presenting our soldier with a Purple Heart as soon as the patient had recovered from surgery and before his flight to Germany was scheduled to depart. Captain Hedrick was in Kabul, Afghanistan, and would not be back for two days, so I represented the command alone.

General Hodges had a standing policy that every wounded soldier within his theater of command was to be presented with a Purple Heart Medal as soon as possible following their injury and that no injured soldier was to leave the theater for further care without his or her Purple Heart medal. He was determined that no Soldier was going to be subjected to bureaucratic snafus that might hold up or deny them a medal that they deserved. The level of medical care and life benefits were more significant for these soldiers than for those who were not wounded in combat—benefits that they would need down the road.

The General asked me to stand beside him as he presented the award. There were a lot of people there that evening, including a nurse that I recognized who usually accompanied me to the rooms of our wounded and injured soldiers whenever I visited the Role III Hospital.

After the presentation of the award, the contingent moved on to present the Purple Heart to another wounded soldier in a nearby ward. The nurse came up to me at that point and asked if she could talk with me a minute. I said, "Sure."

"Would you mind visiting with an 'expectant' soldier in the Special Care Unit a couple of sections over," she asked. "Maybe you could talk to him like you usually do with the other troops when you visit one of your injured soldiers. I think it would mean a lot to him." "I don't mind at all," I said. "I'll be glad to."

As we walked, she added that he was a triple-amputee and that nobody, not even anyone from his own unit, had been to see him and that no one probably would.

"The patient is heavily sedated and might not be able to talk with you," she confessed. "But I'm sure that he will hear you and will know that you're there."

She then led me down the center of an adjacent ward with soldiers lying in elevated beds along both sides of the aisle. Some were asleep. Most were in some form of traction. Nurses in blue scrubs were attending to others. There was a heavy curtain at the far end of the corridor separating us from the section on the other side – the Special Care Unit.

As we walked toward the curtain, I began to remember the words of that same nurse on my first visit to the Role III six-months earlier as she was explaining the level of injuries that came into the hospital. "Single limb amputations are common," she had said. "There are a lot of double amputees. Some Soldiers don't make it. Triple amputees rarely survive."

It was then that I realized what the term 'expectant' meant – it was a triage term for a patient who wasn't expected to live.

As we neared the wall of fabric, tears started running down my cheeks. About fifteen feet from the curtain, my legs stopped moving, and I just stood there staring ahead into space – the curtain was a blur. The nurse stepped closer and cupped her right hand around the bicep of my left arm.

I don't know how long we stood there, probably just a few seconds, but it seemed like minutes. Without taking my eyes off of that watery curtain, I said, "Ma'am, I can't do it. I'm sorry; I just can't do it." She pulled me closer to her, turned me around, and led me back the way we had come. Leaning in closer, and in a soft muted voice, she said, "It's ok Master Chief, it's ok. I understand. It's all right."

But it wasn't all right at all!

It wasn't that I had seen all that many injuries or deaths — goodness knows other units had suffered far worse causalities — but at that moment, one more was one more too many.

We walked all the way to the other end of the ward with her holding my arm and guiding my steps as I silently sobbed — a grown man crying unashamedly. I couldn't help it. As we stepped out into the hall, she released my arm and handed me a Kleenex. I dried my eyes; she dried her's too. Then she led me to the room where the General and his entourage were.

I stood at the back of the gaggle of officers; they didn't even notice that I was there. It was as if I was on the other side of a two-way mirror looking on but not part of the scene.

When the General was finished, the group broke up, and I left the hospital alone. Instead of walking toward command headquarters, I began to walk the other way. I wasn't headed anywhere in particular, just walking and thinking. I needed some time to myself.

After a while, I realized that I was about to walk into the Canadian section of the base. I had been there several times before with my boss as a guest of the Canadian General.

There was a Tim Horton's Donut Shop in the center of the compound. I went there, bought a cup of coffee, and sat outside at a small table under the shade of a scraggly palm tree to think.

I was ashamed of what I had done, or rather I should say, what I hadn't done. I wished that I had gone beyond that curtain when I had had the chance and spoken to that young man. To this day, that still bothers me. Talking to him was the least I could have done. I didn't even know his name!

The following day, as soon as I could, I went back to the Role III Hospital and found the nurse from the day before. I asked her if I could visit with the young soldier in the Special Care Unit.

She just stared at me for a few seconds before she answered. I immediately knew that something was wrong. "He's not here Master Chief," she said. "He expired late last night, and his body was placed on a plane early this morning before dawn. There wasn't even time for a Ramp Ceremony. I'm sorry."

Sometimes, at distinctive moments in your life, you only get one chance to do the right thing. I had missed my chance to make a difference in that 'expectant soldier's' life.

Chapter 1 - The Effect of Coronavirus on PTSD in Global Populations

Anita Penn Daswani, LMHC – Community Counselor Working with Substance Abuse, Anxiety, Depression, Relationships and Eating Disorders

Doctors around the globe are reporting both new anxieties among existing patients, and relapses among former ones. As a mental health counselor, I have observed many individuals who do not have access to adequate social situations or have family members who are not accommodating toward them. This results in more anxiety which forces them to relapse and turn to drugs and alcohol to self-medicate during this time of need. While normally, these individuals would turn to social interaction and meetup groups to help alleviate their symptoms, they are relegated to Zoom and Skype sessions. I have found that Skype and Zoom counseling sessions only exacerbate their already heightened anxiety or nervousness in social situations.

Additionally, COVID-19 has increased Generalized Anxiety Disorder (GAD), which was already on a rise before this pandemic. GAD involves an abnormally preeminent response to everyday challenges like qualms over money, work goals, and child-rearing or lack of child-care. Not everyone can work from home and those who can't are worrying about whether they can pay the bills, or if they are losing their jobs for good. For people with GAD, those common woes produce incapacitating anguish, and coronavirus is surely having a larger impact on such individuals. The worry becomes, 'How do I pay my bills? What if I lose my job? What if I lose my car or home?' (Kluger, 2020). Because many anxiety disorders are based on hypotheticals, as this is a time of extreme uncertainty these disorders are already elevated additionally by the "worst-case scenario" thinking our brains can formulate under extreme duress.

Experts warn that but it may be too early in the coronavirus plague to know the exact extent to which anxiety disorders are on the rise, because the clinical cases are lost in the sense of global panic in the media.

There is also a huge sector of the population that is very at risk for developing trauma and anxiety from this pandemic. This sector of the population is one that we have been forced to expect considerable effort from and not consider the repercussions of these needs due to the severity of the situation. In large-scale catastrophes, such as the coronavirus outbreak, first responders, including nurses, ambulance and social workers, are at a higher risk of developing anxiety, depression and post-traumatic stress disorder. First responders endure significantly increased assignments, wear protective gear for extended periods, while meticulously following contagion control procedures, which puts them at risk for stress, anxiety and PTSD.

Although there has been much concern on the mental health crisis that is occurring related to the coronavirus pandemic, much of this information has fixated on the anxiety, panic, and fear that many are facing. While this is important something that has not been discussed is the psychologically traumatic nature of what our nation, and our world in general is now experiencing. This pandemic is very rapidly causing a psychological trauma crisis. Healthcare workers who are on the front lines of this situation are the most at risk. These individuals who go into work every day and are faced with making life and death decisions about the patients they interact with are the most at risk for some type of anxiety or PTSD. They are increasingly faced with the life-or-death decision of going to work each day, for fear of exposing themselves or their family to this virus.

Many of these healthcare workers are working long hours while facing something they have never seen before on a global scale. The experience is one that requires an immense amount of support for these individuals. They are soldiers in a war on life itself. Many of these individuals will come out of this pandemic with intense post-trauma symptoms.

For the general public, including those who never actually obtain the virus, the general lifestyle alteration and the fear that is felt will lead to a trauma response. Some people will lose their jobs, homes, cars, and this is a trauma. Not only are many facing that possibility, but they are also facing it without knowing when things will ever return to "normal". Additionally, some of this population are Veterans already suffering pre-existing PTSD.

According to psychologist Elyssa Barbash, "Not everyone who experiences a trauma, or even the exact same situation, will perceive or respond to it the same. Likewise, not everyone will experience post-trauma symptoms or go on to develop PTSD. But for those do experience post-trauma symptoms, know that it is normal to feel and display the symptoms of PTSD in the first month that follows". This is called acute stress disorder and can often go away after a month.

However, medical research shows that long term over the last 40 years forced quarantine can have long-lasting effects that can lead to PTSD symptoms and severe depression. Studies in Toronto analyzing the psychological consequences of previous SARS outbreaks found that "29 percent of those quarantined showed PTSD symptoms while a further 31 percent had symptoms of depression. It's not only the uncertainty and isolation" (Abdou & Leila, 1970). Individuals lost their daily routines, work or study environments and stability. In the previous study, many individuals were forced to stay in hostile family environments during quarantine that also damaged their needed stability and mental health.

The effects of COVID-19 are still being studied around the world; therefore, we don't know what the consequences of this pandemic will be long term. However, looking at previous outbreaks will give us the tools to revise how we deal with these mental health effects. Luckily, we have technology and virtual counseling available to us now, whereas 40 years ago this was impossible.

Because the U.S. has still not reached its peak for COVID-19, we must look to China for studies on how the pandemic has changed life as they know it in the short term. A recent Chinese Psychology Society survey found that "42.6% of 18,000 Chinese citizens who are still free of coronavirus have clinically significant levels of anxiety related to the coronavirus epidemic" (Dorfman & Dorfman, 2020). Clinically significant depression was identified in "16.6% of surveyed individuals. Up to 40% of SARS survivors suffered from depression and Post-Traumatic Stress Disorder (PTSD) 30 months later, which is higher than the 20-30% PTSD rate after natural disasters" (Dorfman & Dorfman, 2020). Healthcare providers in the most highly affected regions are also at higher risk of mental distress.

Additionally, as the world progressively deals with the COVID-19 epidemic, other natural catastrophes (earthquakes, floods, fires, and tornadoes) or public health emergencies (influenza in the U.S.) have simultaneously occurred. These events pose serious threats to people and have resulted in a great loss of people's lives and property. By March 21, 2020, "15 earthquakes had occurred in China during the COVID-19 outbreak, increasing the fears, concerns, and anxiety of more than 1.4 billion Chinese people about natural disasters and public health emergencies" (China Earthquake Administration, 2020). "Flash floods, bushfires, and dust storms have occurred in Australia, killing at least 33 people and more than a billion animals, and destroying nearly 11 million hectares of land and thousands of homes" (British Broadcasting Corporation, 2020). In America, "more than 19 million people contracted severe flu, resulting in more than 10,000 deaths and 180,000 hospitalizations" (Bursztynsky, 2020).

There are many recommendations we can take for dealing with the consequences that will ensue due to COVID-19. Essential trauma maintenance should be applied for people exposed to multiple traumatic events during the COVID-19 outbreak. The WHO's guidelines for essential trauma care states that "to minimize the negative effects of trauma on survivors, essential aspects must be considered in the treatment process" (World Health Organization (WHO), 2004).

The WHO breaks down these processes into very practical steps. "First, to minimize the mortality rate, life-threatening injuries should be properly and promptly treated as a priority. Second, potentially disabling injuries should be rapidly detected and treated to reduce impairment and ensure a quick return to normal life. Third, experienced health professionals should be assigned to provide trauma health care for people in need, Lastly, the management models of disaster or public health emergencies should be developed focusing on the phases of mitigation and preparedness, which would better ensure assistance to victims" (World Health Organization (WHO), 2004).

According to the U.S. Department of Veterans Affairs, "The COVID-19 (coronavirus) outbreak has the potential to increase stress and anxiety, both because of the fear of catching the virus and because of uncertainty about how the outbreak will affect us socially and economically". Around the globe, many people are fearful and anxious. Medical research shows that forced quarantine can have long-lasting effects which can lead to PTSD and severe depression.

As the physical coronavirus pandemic began to spread, experts have noticed an emotional pandemic is subsequently developing. Many doctors around the globe are reporting the spread of "despair, worry and depression among their patients, especially those already suffering from some form of anxiety disorder" (Kluger, 2020).

Military Veterans themselves are comparing the situation healthcare workers are facing on the front lines with the war some of them have endured. Rates of PTSD among military Veterans have risen as the phenomenon is just becoming better understood.

Because PTSD symptoms include and mimic some of the symptoms that already exist in people who are being quarantined for long periods of time, this can aggravate PTSD in Veterans. Symptoms such as being constantly anxious, unable to relax, vividly re-experiencing traumatic events, avoiding triggers, memories or feelings and becoming socially isolated, are all effects that people are becoming all too familiar with.

Although, in some cases this knowledge is helping military Veterans to team up with healthcare workers and come up with solutions, it's generally not a beneficial phenomenon for people to become more socially isolated when they already have PTSD. PTSD can lead to problems in relationships and at work, which could affect all global populations who are being forced into quarantine or forced to work essential jobs for 12 plus hours. These symptoms include irritability, anger and substance misuse, particularly alcohol dependency. "While some symptoms, such as nightmares, are normal in the weeks following a traumatic event, symptoms that last longer than this can indicate a problem. It's being harder to diagnose and treat such long-lasting symptoms the longer the quarantine gets drawn out" (Mcfarlane, Jetly, Castro, Greenberg, & Vermetten, 2020). However, Mcfarlane et. al also describe that "the ongoing COVID-19 coronavirus pandemic would, by most definitions, be considered a "crisis" and while crises can be overwhelming, and often expose vulnerabilities and gaps in our preparedness, they can also be seen as opportunities to quickly adapt, innovate and learn".

Those already identified as being at-risk may need further support in the context of the COVID-19 pandemic. "For instance, Veterans who live on meagre ill-health pensions or benefits may be less able to sustain themselves during a period of self-isolation. Consideration for how best to support such individuals should be treated as a special issue during coronavirus risk response" (Mcfarlane, Jetly, Castro, Greenberg, & Vermetten, 2020). Mcfarlane et. al also highlight the importance of the development of a program for "managing anxiety through exercise and relaxation strategies for those in isolation. In addition, technology must be leveraged to disseminate these programs and, ideally, tailored to the Veteran milieu".

However, according to Dan Sabbagh from The Guardian journal, there are some Military Veterans who are hopeful that they can help this situation. Military Veterans "who served in Afghanistan and Iraq who have drawn up a package of guidance and support to help NHS workers cope with the traumatic stress from treating patients on the frontline of the coronavirus crisis" (Sabbagh, 2020).

According to an interview with Sabbagh, "Carole Betteridge, a former Navy nurse who ran a field hospital at Camp Bastion in Afghanistan, said the understanding of traumatic stress had changed dramatically over the past 20 years and lessons could be shared". She spent 26 years in the Navy as a nurse and medical planner and is now head of welfare and clinical services at Help for Heroes. Betteridge goes on to say that "there are so many parallels I can see between the military experience and what NHS workers are having to deal with. This is a conflict situation, and we have to make sure we care for the care workers". "Medical staff are being faced with daily life-or-death situations just in the same way as in Iraq or Afghanistan", Betteridge claims.

There are also recommendations for those individuals or Veterans already experiencing PTSD, which may be elevated additionally during the pandemic. According to Barbash, "the answer is working with a trained, experienced, and licensed trauma specialist. Not just a general therapist who happens to have also been trained in EMDR. Trauma psychology is very specialized area of mental health treatment".

Even before COVID-19 made its way to the U.S., the U.S. was a clinically anxious nation. According to the National Institute of Mental Health, just over "19% of American adults will experience at least one anxiety disorder over any 12-month period. Many of these disorders are ones that are already social or compulsive in nature". For example, people with COVID-19 pandemic, but a number are, especially obsessive-compulsive disorder (OCD), generalized anxiety disorder, social anxiety disorder, agoraphobia, acute stress disorder and separation anxiety disorder will react differently to information on COVID-19 than those without these disorders. Globally, we are being told by public health and political officials not to come within six feet of one another, so separation and anxiety disorders could hit these individuals particularly hard.

Self-isolation can worsen the mental health status of people who are prone to anxiety and social phobias. Cutting social bonds and isolation in general can have a negative impact on mental health. Maintaining consistent routines and interaction with people, as well as in person counseling sessions, are essential for people with social anxieties.

Following general mental health advice from the experts is helpful for most individuals dealing with anxiety and depression during this pandemic. One of the best coping strategies when it comes to trauma is "making media consumption a choice," Bedard-Gilligan says. If the news is making you feel bad or negative, stop and ask yourself if the news is helping or hurting you. Be intentional about what you allow yourself to be immersed in, as to limit anxiety and depression.

Crisis is both a challenge and an opportunity to transform and acclimate. There are lessons to be learned from the past and Veterans must be the experts we look to for hope and solutions. Veterans (although a vulnerable population) provide clues and principles that may be pertinent to many groups globally during this pandemic. Taking care to understand our Veterans has always been a goal in mental health counseling. It is even more important now that we take care of each other. By following the recommendations of the VA, the WHO and psychologists, we will be able to ensure that we help traumatized individuals around the globe. Veterans can help us come up with solutions and tips that are tried and true, so that we can heal as a world after the pandemic has passed.

References:

Abdou, H., & Leila. (1970, January 1). Us versus them?: Covid-19 and its effects. Retrieved from https://cadmus.eui.eu/handle/1814/66680

Au A, Chan I, Li P, Chan J, Chan YH, Ng F Correlates of psychological distress in discharged patients recovering from acute respiratory syndrome in Hong Kong. *The International Journal of Psychosocial Rehabilitation.* 2004;8:41–51

Barbash, E. (2020, March 24). *Coronavirus: The Psychological Trauma and PTSD Event.* Retrieved from https://www.psychologytoday.com/us/blog/trauma-and-hope/202003/coronavirus-the-psychological-trauma-and-ptsd-event

Dorfman, R., & Dorfman, R. D. R. (2020, March 4). Coronavirus outbreak: managing anxiety and depression among your workforce. Retrieved from https://www.pillcheck.ca/2020/03/04/coronavirus-outbreak-managing-anxiety-and-depression-among-your-workforce/

Hawryluck L, Gold WL, Robinson S, Pogorski S, Galea S, Styra R SARS control and psychological effects of quarantine, Toronto, Canada.Emerg Infect Dis. 2004;10:1206–12

Kluger, J. (2020, March 26). The Coronavirus Pandemic May Be Causing an Anxiety Pandemic. Retrieved April 18, 2020, from https://time.com/5808278/coronavirus-anxiety/

McFarlane, A., Jetly, R., Castro, C. A., Greenberg, N., & Vermetten, E. (2020). Impact of COVID-19 on mental health care for Veterans: Improvise, adapt and overcome. Journal of Military, Veteran and Family Health, COVID-19. doi: 10.3138/jmvfh.co19-001

Sabbagh, D. (2020, April 20). Military veterans help draft PTSD guidance for NHS workers. Retrieved from https://www.theguardian.com/society/2020/apr/20/military-veterans-help-draft-ptsd-guidance-for-nhs-workers

VA.gov: Veterans Affairs. (2020, March 9). Retrieved April 18, 2020, from https://www.ptsd.va.gov/covid/

CHAPTER 2 - SIGNS, SYMPTOMS AND TREATMENT OF PTSD

Dr. Heidi Knock, Clinical Psychologist, Department of Veterans Affairs

Post-Traumatic Stress Disorder (PTSD) can result from a variety of traumatic experiences, affecting children and adults alike. Most lay people understand that individuals exposed to war can develop PTSD, however, any trauma, whether it was witnessed by or being directly threatening to, the individual can result in PTSD. Some examples of traumatic events include childhood abuse, car accidents, natural disasters, physical or sexual assault, being the victim of a crime, etc. According to the Diagnostic and Statistical Manual of Mental Disorder-Fifth Edition (DSM-5), the prevalence rate of PTSD among adults is approximately 3.5%, with women having a higher occurrence rate than men. PTSD can be diagnosed anytime throughout the lifespan, however, 6-years-old is the minimum age requirement for an individual to be diagnosed with this disorder.

Signs and Symptoms of PTSD:

PTSD can be diagnosed in individuals who either witness or are directly threatened with death or serious injury either to themselves or another person. The child who witnesses their mother being physically beat by their father is just as likely to develop PTSD as the combat Veteran who is attacked in an ambush or a mortar attack. Not everyone who is exposed to a trauma will develop PTSD, however, combat Veterans are more susceptible to this disorder due to their often repetitive and prolonged exposure to trauma in war zones, which can include mortar attacks, suicide bombers, snipers, improvised explosive devices (IEDs), vehicle borne IEDs (VBIEDS), ambushes, etc. Besides being in potential danger 24/7, combat Veterans often bear witness to fellow service members and local nationals being severely or mortally injured. The level of fear, horror, and helplessness that can occur with both these direct and indirect threats can be equally impactful.

PTSD is considered an anxiety disorder and there are very specific criteria that need to be met for an individual to be diagnosed with this disorder. First, we will go over the formal criteria according to the DSM-5 and afterward look at the symptoms may manifest in the combat Veteran's actual life upon returning home. According to the DSM-5, there are eight clusters of symptoms that must be present for an individual to be diagnosed with PTSD. For the purpose of this book, we will primarily focus on PTSD in adults. The criteria is as follows:

A. "Exposure to actual or threatened death, serious injury, or sexual violence in one (or more) of the following ways:
   1) Directly experiencing the traumatic event(s)

2) Witnessing, in person, the event(s) as it occurred to others

3) Learning that the traumatic event(s) occurred to a close family member or close friend. In cases of actual or threatened death of a family member or friend, the event(s) must have been violent or accidental

4) Experiencing repeated or extreme exposure to aversive details of the traumatic event(s) i.e., first responders such as police officers and firemen

B. Presence of one (or more) of the following intrusion symptoms associated with the traumatic event(s), beginning after the traumatic event(s) occurred:

1) Recurrent, involuntary and intrusive distressing memories of the traumatic event(s)

2) Recurrent distressing dreams in which the content and/or effect of the dream are related to the traumatic event(s)

3) Dissociative reactions (e.g. flashbacks) in which the individual feels or acts as if the traumatic event(s) were recurring

4) Intense or prolonged psychological distress at exposure to internal or external cues that symbolize or resemble an aspect of the traumatic event(s)

5) Marked physiological reactions to the internal or external cues that symbolize or resemble an aspect of the traumatic event(s)

C. Persistent avoidance of stimuli associated with the traumatic event(s), beginning after the traumatic event(s) occurred, as evidenced by one or both of the following:

1) Avoidance of or efforts to avoid distressing memories, thoughts, or feelings about or closely associated with the traumatic event(s)

2) Avoidance of or efforts to avoid external reminders (people, places, conversations, activities, objects, situations) that arouse distressing memories, thoughts, or feelings about or closely associated with the traumatic event(s)

D. Negative alterations in cognitions and mood associated with the traumatic event(s), beginning, or worsening after the traumatic event(s) occurred, as evidenced by two (or more) of the following:

1) Inability to remember an important aspect of the traumatic event(s) typically due to dissociative amnesia and not to other factors such as head injury, alcohol, or drugs.

2) Persistent and exaggerated negative beliefs or expectations about oneself, others, or the world (i.e., "I am bad," "No one can be trusted," "The world is completely dangerous").

3) Persistent, distorted cognitions about the cause or consequences of the traumatic event(s) that lead the individual to blame himself/herself or others

4) Persistent negative emotional states (fear, horror, anger, guilt, shame, etc.)

5) Markedly diminished interest or participation in significant activities

6) Feelings of detachment or estrangement from others

7) Persistent inability to experience positive emotions (i.e., inability to experiences happiness, satisfaction, or loving feelings)

E. Marked alterations in arousal and reactivity associated with the traumatic event(s), beginning or worsening after the traumatic event(s) occurred, as evidenced by two (or more) of the following:

  1) Irritable behavior and angry outbursts (with little or no provocation) typically expressed as verbal or physical aggression toward people or objects
  2) Reckless and self-destructive behavior
  3) Hyper-vigilance
  4) Exaggerated startle response
  5) Problems with concentration
  6) Sleep disturbance
F. Duration of the disturbance is more than one month

G. The disturbance causes clinically significant distress or impairment in social, occupational, or other important areas of functioning

H. The disturbance is not attributable to the physiological effects of a substance (i.e., medication, alcohol) or another medical condition"

Source Cited: (2013). Diagnostic and Statistical Manual of Mental Disorders: DSM-5. Arlington, VA: American Psychiatric Association.

Many combat Veterans will present in my office with trauma symptoms, but do not endorse enough of them to actually meet the criteria for PTSD. As noted above, individuals can have multiple symptoms, but if they do not have symptoms under each of these specific criteria, they will be given a different diagnosis based on the symptoms they do endorse. This is by no means minimizing their distress or level of symptomatology they do experience, instead, these individuals are given a diagnosis related to the disorder for which they meet criteria. These diagnoses may include an acute distress disorder (PTSD symptoms with a duration of three days to 30 days), generalized anxiety disorder, an adjustment disorder, a panic disorder, etc., just to name a few. Individuals with PTSD often have co-morbid conditions, such as depression and substance abuse, as their PTSD often leads to considerable community, word, social, and family adjustment issues.

**The following description of symptom presentation is based on my clinical experience of treating combat Veterans for over a decade. It is broadly generalized, and it should be remembered that combat Veterans may present with only a few of the symptoms listed below or the majority of them, based on the individual. Please keep this in mind as you read the following summary, as it will not be descriptive of everyone.

Community and Family Reintegration:

When combat Veterans are in a war zone, their families and hope of returning home, as well as camaraderie with their combat peers, are lifelines for enduring their experiences. However, during the reintegration process, they often encounter struggles they do not anticipate while overseas. While they were deployed, their families, who also serve, have gone through significant adjustment issues to live without their combat Veteran while he/she was away. The military spouse has suddenly become a single parent, taking on the role of both parents in the family. This phenomenon is called role shifting. The family, including the Veteran's children, may have endured a significant sense of loss and abandonment while the combat Veteran was deployed, even with the understanding that it is the combat Veteran's job and responsibility to be deployed and serve our country.

The military spouse takes on new roles and rules of the house may shift to accommodate the loss and absence of the combat Veteran. The discipline and decisions in the home are left to the military spouse and commonly by the time the end of deployment occurs, the combat family has forged a new routine and rhythm to adjust to the absence of the combat Veteran. It is not hard to anticipate that although the family happily awaits the return of their combat Veteran, reintegrating him/her back into the family system is not always an easy task. The combat Veteran upon returning home, may feel like an outsider in the newly established system, not only due to shifting roles, but because they have endured trauma, they often cannot reconcile within themselves and begin to have symptoms for which they cannot cope. The family or spouse of the combat Veteran may experience a profound sense of loss related to the return of the Veteran, as the individual who left months earlier truly did not return home.

When combat Veterans return to their communities, they are often isolated from their military peers and the men and women with whom they were deployed. They feel alone in their experience and feel those around them do not understand what they have been through, as well as start to view civilians as oblivious to the truth of the evilness of human nature and what people really are capable of doing. They continue to feel protective of those around them and believe that if they are "complacent" something bad will happen. Because of their trauma and their need for control over their environment, they are chronically vigilant wherever they go. Combat Veterans will keep their backs to the wall, watch entrances/exits, size up everyone in their environment, trust no one, and will always develop a mental plan of how to escape an environment or how they would respond if something dangerous were to occur. They have difficulties being present in the moment and enjoying their experiences. They chronically run "What if" scenarios in their heads, often anticipating the worst-case scenario. In some sense, this gives a sense of preparedness related to their environment. On a whole different level, however, it actually keeps them in a very negative mindset and perpetuates their anxiety and negative beliefs about people and the world in general. Combat Veterans will often go to businesses during off hours to avoid people. They will steer away from crowded areas or environments that they view as "soft targets." They will often leave environments when triggering occurs and their anxiety peaks. Some Veterans rarely leave their home at all and become isolated from the world they perceive as unpredictable and dangerous. Even in their homes, they will can have new combat related behaviors and routines, such as always keeping the blinds closed to avoid being seen or targeted, needing everything in their homes in a designated spot (to maintain predictability), "Clearing the house" and repeatedly checking the doors, windows and perimeter for intruders. These, along with many other combat related behaviors, start to affect the Veteran's quality of life and that of their family members. The family can often start to take on the behaviors of the combat Veteran to accommodate the Veteran's PTSD and can lead the family into isolation.

Triggers and Re-experiencing Symptoms:

When combat Veterans are in public places, their anxiety is frequently triggered by stimuli that remind them of their combat experience, either on a conscious or unconscious level, which creates a significant fight/flight physical reaction in them and/or anxiety response. At times the triggers in the environment are clear, such as loud noises, crowds, and people being aggressive towards one another. At other times, however, the triggers are very subtle to the point the combat Veteran is not even aware they are being triggered. For Veterans who have been deployed related to Operation Enduring Freedom (Afghanistan) or Operation Iraqi Freedom (OIF), common triggers can include heat, sewer smells, debris, driving, animal carcasses, and even Middle Eastern individuals. Environments that are unplanned, over-stimulating, or ambiguous are also commonly stressful for Veterans. To give an example of triggering, a combat Veteran who was involved in an IED/bombing was eating Sunchips at the time of the incident. When he returned home from his deployment, he would become highly anxious whenever he went to Subway to get a sandwich, as the smell of Sunchips would instantly trigger his anxiety.

When he came into treatment, he did not understand that that this seemingly benign sensory trigger in his environment was creating a fight/flight response in him related to what had occurred while he was in danger overseas. Like most Veterans who are exposed to triggers, he would become instantly anxious and almost automatically his anxiety would be channeled into irritability and anger, causing him/her to want to flee the environment or lash out. Again and again in my office, I have witnessed the phenomenon of Veterans focusing on things that annoy them or make them angry to pull back from their anxiety or vulnerable feelings such as fear, helplessness, or uncomfortable primary emotions. I have long surmised that this is an attempt to have some sense of empowerment and escape emotions that they feel are intolerable. Most Veterans will eventually present at my office due to either their overwhelming level of anxiety or anger issues that impact their families, jobs, or functioning in the community.

When fight or flight symptoms occur, they can feel overwhelming to the combat Veteran. Of course, different individuals can experience different levels of symptomatology. Common fight or flight symptoms may include:

A full feeling in the head due to elevated blood pressure, which can lead to headaches

Visual changes that can include tunnel vision or narrowing of the visual field

Heightening or dampening of their hearing

Increased ringing or pitch heightening of tinnitus for those who already have this ailment

Dry mouth

Muscle tension

Feeling hot or sweaty

Increased heart rate

Increased or shallow breathing patterns

An increased urge to urinate

A feeling of a surge of adrenalin

In a combat zone, this cascade of symptoms is usually related to something bad happen and the individual being in a dangerous situation. When they symptoms occur in the combat Veteran's daily life stateside, they often will become more vigilant, believe something bad is about to happen, and will often leave the environment out of fear and anticipation that something dangerous is about to occur. They have relied on this "Spidey sense" as a survival in the combat zone and continue to be reactive to it when they return home. At the beginning of treatment, I almost always ensure that the Veteran understands the role of combat triggers in their response to their environment and try to help them recognize how these subtle and now benign experiences are no longer danger indicators.

Many individuals do not understand how physically ingrained PTSD is for the individual who is experiencing it. The combat Veteran cannot simply "forget about their experience" or "let it go" and it will take considerable work and processing for them to reduce their symptoms over time. Re-experiencing symptoms can occur day or night and often feel like they have a life of their own, haunting the individual who has been through traumatic experiences. The combat Veteran struggles to cope with both their internal and external world upon returning from a combat zone. Beyond the fight or flight symptoms mentioned above, combat Veterans can experience nightmares, flashbacks, intrusive memories, and even dissociation when emotions or triggers become too intense to handle. Combat Veterans will often have nightmares about their most traumatic experiences. When these occur, because the body believes it is actually in that traumatic experience, the Veteran will experience fight/flight symptoms in their sleep. This can lead to them yelling out in their sleep, thrashing around in their beds, and even punching or swinging at people who share their beds, as they act out their dreams without awareness. Veterans will often wake up with their heart racing and feel frightened, disoriented, and soaked in sweat.

It is also not unusual for the combat Veteran to experience nausea and bed wetting with these fight/flight symptoms as well. When they awaken, due to the anxiety level the dream created, they will often get up and check their homes to ensure they are secure and even "clear the house" at times due to safety concerns. During the daytime, combat Veterans may have what seems almost like "short video clips" or pictures running through their mind uncontrollably of traumatic events. To those around them, their family and friends may notice the combat Veteran often stares off or seems inattentive when these images are occurring. When triggers are intense or unexpected, they can cause flashbacks, where the combat Veteran actually loses orientation to the environment and believes they are back in the traumatic event...they smell it, feel it, experience it...they are there for seconds to minutes or even longer in some instances. In extreme cases, Veterans can black out and have for longer periods of time and have no recollection of their actions. The Veteran is unaware this is happening at the time and often only recognizes this has occurred due to missing chunks of time or when other people inform them of behavior they do not remember doing. This is the brain's way of protecting them from intolerable emotional states or triggers. Many Veterans will dissociate while discussing their trauma in my office and will need assistance grounding back to their current environment. Trauma congruent visual, auditory, and sensory hallucinations are not uncommon with PTSD and individuals who have been in war may experience hearing people screaming, gunfire, mortars, etc. They may also see images of people who they have lost or harmed. It is not unusual for sensory experiences to occur when memories replay, such as physical pain when a memory of a personal injury replays or smelling blood when a scene where someone is hurt replays.

Altered Sense of Self:

Combat Veterans are often placed in situations where they are forced to be aggressive as a means for survival either for themselves or their peers. They may have taken the lives of individuals, including women and children, in order to save the lives. The combat zone often leads to numbness and their actions, which are certainly warranted, are often not looked at through an emotional scope until they return home and start viewing their actions outside of the context they occurred. The combat Veteran will often struggle with their own sense of violating their core values and beliefs, especially the belief "thou shall not kill," leading to moral injury. They keep their actions secret from their family and those around them, suffering silently and often believing those they love would judge them or look at them like a "monster" if they knew what they had done. They often have a fear of destroying their family members' sense of innocence or naiveté should they learn of the realities of war and what has actually happened. Combat Veterans often shoulder a crushing sense of guilt over not being able to prevent negative events from occurring, especially if they involve the injury or loss of one of their peers. Their helplessness and sense of vulnerability over these events is commonly replaced with self-blame, guilt, and self-loathing.

Combat Veterans can also be self-judgmental over their reaction to events in the combat zone. It is not uncommon for them to experience morbid humor, dehumanizing, escalating aggression across the course of their deployment, and numbing in the combat zone. They can experience a sense of elation and empowerment during the kill cycle, which they later find shameful and disturbing when they start to process their trauma. These reactions to combat are considered normal and actually can be adaptive in helping the Veteran survive and cope while in a chronically dangerous environment where he/she is targeted and hunted. Again, a combat Veteran's actions must always be viewed in the context they occurred to come to terms with them.

There is no safe zone in a war. Even on bases, there is constant mortaring, suicide bombers, VBIEDS, and snipers. Also, in order to "win the hearts and minds" of the country, local nationals are often allowed on bases as interpreters, for training purposes, and to assist with maintenance of the bases. Most combat Veterans have a distrust of these individuals, as they can never really know who may be giving intelligence to insurgents and who may be conspiring against them. There are no enemy uniforms overseas and everyone is a potential enemy. It is not hard to fathom why trusting people in the community upon returning home is difficult for Veterans to do, as they continue to distrust everyone and see others as a potential enemy.

Treatment of PTSD:

The following summary is given as an overview of aspects of treatment of PTSD but is not considered a training in the treatment of PTSD for providers or lay people. Be cautioned that common presenting issues are broadly generalized, and Veterans may range from having a few of these issues to most of them, depending on their personal experiences.

Combat Veterans are trained to be Warriors. The battlefield is not considered a place for emotions and most Veterans will convey that they believe emotions in a combat situation will cause them to lose focus and endanger themselves and/or their peers. They often convey feeling "weak" when they are emotional and tend to be highly uncomfortable with their internal experience of their feelings. Because they have consciously and unconsciously suppressed their feelings to function in the combat zone, as the mission must always come first, many of them return home numb, unable to access their emotions even at times when they would like to do so. When emotions do arise, they will often cause the Veteran to feel anxious and uncomfortable. These feelings can be channeled into irritability and anger to escape more vulnerable feelings. Combat Veterans are often resistant to seeking treatment, as they believe this indicates they are "weak" or "broken." There is a stigma in the military surrounding being diagnosed with PTSD or a mental health diagnosis, as well as Veterans fearing that it will jeopardize their careers if it is discovered they are struggling with symptoms. Combat Veterans will almost always have a preference to see a counselor who has a history of being in the military themselves, as they believe civilians will not understand or relate to what they have been through. Because there are limited mental health counselors who have a military background, it will often take considerable time for civilian clinicians to gain rapport with combat Veterans who do seek treatment.

Despite these barriers and multitude of symptoms combat Veterans experience, in general they tend to be a very resilient and motivated group of individuals when they do seek treatment. There are several evidence-based treatment protocols for PTSD, including therapies such as Prolonged Exposure Therapy (PE), Cognitive Processing Therapy (CPT), and Eye Movement Desensitization and Reprocessing Therapy (EMDR), just to name a few. If you read even a basic book on the treatment of PTSD, you will readily learn that the avoidance of feeling anxious or of distressing memories only perpetuates PTSD and leaves the combat Veteran stuck in their symptoms. Many combat Veterans will leave environments or situations when anxiety arises, as associated emotional and physical symptoms have previously been a danger indicator overseas and arose when life-threatening events were occurred. Although the Veteran may now be in a safe environment, this overwhelming flood of anxiety and fight/flight (increased heart rate, feeling hot/flushed, adrenal drop, increased breathing patterns, muscle tension, visual/hearing changes, etc.) symptoms can feel intolerable and cause the individual to leave relatively benign situations.

When a combat Veteran first presents for treatment, it is imperative that they, along with their family members, are educated regarding their symptoms of PTSD and that these symptoms are normalized as a natural reaction to experiences that outside the typical range of human experience. Educating them on the nuances of how trauma can impact them emotionally and physically cannot only help them understand that what they are experiencing will not harm them, despite being distressing, but it can also help build rapport, as it gives structure to initial sessions and is not as anxiety provoking for the Veteran who may already feel resistant to therapy. Early treatment sessions should include education regarding how triggers form, breathing exercises to bring fight/flight symptoms under control, grounding exercises to pull back from anxious states, education regarding primary vs. secondary emotions, layers of PTSD (primary emotions-anxiety-anger) and mindfulness exercises to help them regain their ability to be present in the moment.

Breathing training is especially important as a concrete tool to teach Veterans when they first present for treatment. Techniques may include a breathe-and-hold technique to quickly reduce physical anxiety and panic-like symptoms, as well as a diaphragmatic breathing technique coupled with stress ball for less distressing moments. Breathing to control anxiety and fight/flight symptoms at times is a hard sell to combat Veterans who feel this may be a bit too "feminine" of a coping skill, however, often being reminded that the military teaches breathing as part of weapons training to help calm the shooter and give them the most proficient performance helps in their acceptance of these techniques. Combat Veterans often feel more anxious when they slow down and their minds are not preoccupied, so breathing skills may initially evoke some anxiety in them. Again, this should be normalized and practicing sitting with their experiences can reduce this over time.

Many Veterans will present for psychotherapy, not due to their nightmares or even their anxiety, but due to anger issues and their spouses or loved ones insisting they get help. The triggering and agitation that are experienced secondary to the Veteran's anxiety will often lead them to be reactive and snappy, as well as possibly have significant anger management issues. Although this is not true for all combat Veterans, it is a fairly common occurrence. Basic anger management skills, such as the ABCs of thinking, weighing stressors on a 1-10 scale to help keep them in proportion, and basic time-out skills will help at least keep damage in their relationships to a minimum until some of the underlying issues can be addressed.

Combat Veterans have ongoing safety beliefs they have developed related to their trauma, including a significant distrust of people, believing everyone is a potential enemy, and fearing that negative events can occur at any moment, especially in undefined or ambiguous situations. In treatment, time is spent exploring these belief patterns and helping the Veteran understand why their perspective has shifted due to their trauma. In trauma work, the "overgeneralization" occurs when aspects of the individual's experience of the traumatic event negatively shift their beliefs of the world and they start to view all environments through that newly formed trauma-based belief system. For example, if a combat Veteran suffers a VBIED (vehicle born improvised explosive device/bomb) attack by a red vehicle, the combat Veteran may be fearful and leery of all red vehicles upon returning home. Because combat Veterans are immersed in an ongoingly dangerous environment for months and sometimes even years at a time, these belief systems become very ingrained. Their vigilance in the community, anticipatory thinking patterns that involve worrying about potentially harmful events occurring in their environment, and their distrust related to the unpredictability of people only perpetuates their isolation and intolerance of being outside of their home. Combat Veterans are often resistant to letting go of this distrust and guarded perspective, as they believe if they are complacent, something bad will happen. As a therapist, they may often view you as naïve to the true evils of the world and will often state that their experiences in the war zone have opened their eyes to the true potential of humans. These beliefs are challenged and actions, including the Veteran's actions in the combat zone must be viewed in the context they occurred. Reflecting to combat Veterans that they have not taken lives since returning home and that their actions, as well as the actions of their enemies, happened in specific and isolated environments can help with letting go of these generalizations.

No matter what form of trauma treatment the Veteran attends, it will involve elements of exposure to both environments/feared situations and their trauma memories. This exposure is essential to help the combat Veteran learn to sit with their anxiety and not be avoidant of it, as well as help them gain a sense of competency in handling feared situations. Through exposure, the Veteran learns that their memories cannot hurt them, as well as the negative events they were fearing when going out are not actually happening or occurring. Underlying their agitation and anxiety are primary emotions with which they are uncomfortable and that have remained unresolved. By processing their trauma, they learn to sit with these emotions, become tolerant to them, and eventually reintegrate them into their experience. The core to healing PTSD is to help the Veteran to reintegrate their emotions and learn to be comfortable with them. Over time, this helps breaks numbing, reduce dissociative symptoms, helps them feel more connected to their world and people, as well as reduces their anxiety and anger. Until combat Veterans reintegrate their emotions, they will convey that they feel like they are just "going through the motions" day-to-day and they do not actually enjoy their lives or feel connected to them.

It is human nature for a combat Veteran to harbor guilt over their peers being injured or killed, even if events were unpredictable or not within their control. Throughout their military career, the combat Veteran has been inculcated with the belief that if they follow their training, they can overcome any obstacle and defeat their enemy. Although this mentality and training certainly helps them persevere in aversive situations, no one can ever have complete control over events in a combat zone no matter how great of a warrior they may be. Inevitably, individuals will at times get hurt and be killed. This leaves the combat Veteran with the sense that in some way them must have failed or done something wrong. Consistently the combat Veteran will hold onto their belief they should have been able to change the situation to prevent the trauma from occurring. By carefully processing events as they actually occurred, the combat Veteran can gain clarity that choices were made in a reasonable manner with the information they had at the time of the incident. It is helpful to remind combat Veterans that they cannot control what they cannot predict.

Combat Veterans also struggle with violating their core values and beliefs. An unavoidable truth is that war always involves killing and the taking of lives. Although the Veteran cognitively understands this going into combat, actually being placed in a situation where killing is necessary, especially if it involves women or children, can be devastating for the Veteran. In treatment, we discussed the difference between murder and killing; one which occurs out of lust and the other out of necessity. The combat Veteran will need to come to terms with their actions in the context they occurred, as well as work through aspects of self-forgiveness. It is always important for them to recognize that children can be lethal in a combat zone and are often used to stop convoys for ambushes, as vested suicide bombers, and often carry guns and throw grenades. The combat Veteran may be conflicted over believing the child did not fully understand what they were doing and will see the minor as innocent and/or forced to engage in the behavior they are doing. The combat Veteran may struggle with guilt over having their own children when returning home and the crying of their own children can then become a significant trigger for them stateside.

Over the course of a deployment, combat Veterans often become more numb and more aggressive. They will dehumanize people and see them as objects, targets, or "Haji," the slang and derogatory term given to Middle Eastern individuals in the combat zone. The combat Veteran often will use morbid humor to cope with aversive events, as well as may feel empowered or even elated during the kill cycle and the taking of lives due to adrenaline highs. All of these reactions to the combat zone can be considered adaptive and a way to minimize the emotional impact on the Veteran at the time of the trauma. As one can well imagine, the combat Veteran will often come home and in hindsight start to question their morals and values that they could act in such a cold and callous manner, often labeling themselves "monsters." Again, these adaptive behaviors must be looked at in the context they occurred and viewed as necessary to function. Often these numbing and chemically driven reactions are not driving the Veterans behavior. The situation and context, typically the need to survive and protect their peers, almost always are the deciding factors in the Veteran's actions and behaviors. To be aggressive and angry in the combat zone are viewed by peers as much more favorable attributes than being emotional or breaking down, which are viewed as weak or "combat ineffective." When a combat Veteran comes into treatment, it is important to give them a space that is judgement free and where their actions can be viewed contextually. In treatment, we discuss the natural progression of aggression over the course of deployment, suppression of the fear that stalks the Veteran and is replaced by numbing, and the necessity of these adaptive behaviors to survive horrific and overwhelming circumstances.

Combat Veterans can go beyond what situations dictate as far as aggression and the harming of others. They are often deeply ashamed by their actions and question their values and morals that would allow them to act in such a cold and seemingly sociopathic manner. These individuals are typically not sociopaths. I have repeatedly seen this phenomenon in God-fearing men who, in general, have very good values. Whether it is the group mentality, mid-brain/animalistic functioning in dangerous situations, the low level of chemical shock they experience related to repeated trauma exposure, dissociative symptoms, or simply vengeful behavior, there has to be some normalcy to a phenomenon that occurs in greater frequency over the course of deployments, particularly in individuals who have had multiple deployments. Commonly, a combat Veteran will have to be in treatment a long time and have a great deal of trust and rapport with an individual before they disclose these incidents to a clinician. Over the years I have come to truly believe that there is nothing a person can do that is not human on some level. It is imperative to always provide a supportive, judge free zone for the combat Veteran. No one will condemn them more than they condemn themselves. For individuals who do cross the line of necessity with aggression, forgiveness, and the belief they can be forgiven will be essential for their healing. I often refer individuals to our chaplaincy services for adjunct counseling if they are spiritually conflicted over their combat experience.

The traumatic events combat Veterans have survived will replay through intrusive memories, flashbacks, nightmares, and physical reactiveness to reminders of their trauma in their current environment. When combat Veterans present for treatment, they discuss their distress over not being able to lessen these symptoms or get them to stop. The treatment of these symptoms is complex and often takes time to work through, especially in individuals who have experienced multiple traumatic events. Directly processing these events and helping combat Veterans sit fully with their experience, especially emotional aspects with which they have not dealt, is paramount to recovery. Veterans are often skeptical of repeatedly processing these events, as they play daily already without their desire or consent. This repetition of trauma playing is often the body's way of trying to purge the trauma, although quite unsuccessfully, as only the most intense parts tend to play and emotions that arise are avoided. The primary therapies used to treat PTSD (PE, CPT, and EMDR) all repeatedly visit the trauma to help the Veteran sit with their experience more fully, as well as work on helping them view their experience through a different lens. Although these therapies use different modalities to process the trauma, the goal is to help resolve the Veteran's inner conflict over their trauma, challenge negatively held trauma beliefs about themselves and the world, and to come to an acceptance of events as they occurred.

Combat Veterans are often avoidant of the community. They are commonly triggered by benign aspects of their environment that remind them consciously or unconsciously of the combat zone. For Veterans who have been to Iraq or Afghanistan, for instance, common triggers can include loud noises, sewer smells, diesel fuel, heat, crowds, driving, potholes, debris, and even Middle Eastern Individuals, just to name a few. Ambiguous situations, environments that are overstimulating, or unplanned events can also be quite anxiety provoking for combat Veterans. It is essential in treatment that combat Veterans understand and come to recognize triggers in their environment, so they can learn to modulate their anxiety response. Combat Veterans often externalize their reaction to the environment, believing others are causing them to be angry or anxious. They may also focus on negative aspects of their environment when they are anxious, causing them to feel irritated and more empowered. Although this is not a healthy cycle, feeling angry is a much more familiar feeling to the combat Veteran and comparatively, they will feel more comfortable in an angry state than when they feel anxious or vulnerable. Until the Veteran starts to learn it is not others causing their discomfort or irritability, they will not gain an internal sense of control over their emotional reaction.

In treatment, combat Veterans are assigned to go to avoided or feared environments that should include social scenarios, places that have specific triggers identified by the Veteran, and public places that are busy or crowded. The Veteran should work on learning to be in the moment and focusing on "what is" happening, as opposed to "what if" scenarios that fuel their anxiety. They need to work on disengaging from safety behaviors, such as having their back to the wall, sizing up people, and watching exits. Ultimately, they need to be willing to give up their basic need for a sense of control and to recognize they can still be safe even If they are not constantly vigilant or "battle-ready." They will need to place effort into learning to refocus on positive aspects of their environment, as opposed to looking for potential threats or negative aspects. Throughout the course of treatment, we explore how combat Veteran walked around in the world prior to their deployment vs. after returning from combat, focusing on helping the combat Veteran see how their perspective was changed due to these experiences and whether they can safely give up their sense of control slowly over time. Again, the combat Veteran can feel highly uncomfortable with letting go of control, as they will feel they are being complacent and have been inculcated with the belief "complacency kills." Veterans will need to recognize the cost of their vigilance, including never actually enjoying environments, how their negative anticipatory thinking patterns actually feed their anxiety, not being truly mentally present with their family at the events, and recognizing that being on guard all of the time steals precious moments from them and their family that they cannot get back. There is a saying that goes, "The nature of anxiety is drowning in the past or worrying about the future, while the moment is lost." Part of the goal of going to environments is to stay through the anxiety peak and tolerate it, teaching them that avoidance only perpetuates their anxiety, while pushing through it can help them to feel more efficacious and competent to handle their own emotions. Until they confront their anxiety, it will most likely will dictate "if they go, when they go, where they go, and how long they go." Through the course of treatment, hopefully the combat Veteran can gain insight that they are not controlling their anxiety through their behaviors, but actually it has a great deal of control over them.

Even in this brief treatment summary, it is clear that PTSD is a highly complex disorder that can be challenging to treat. Despite its challenges, PTSD is highly treatable, and symptoms do progressively improve over the course of recovery, to the point they resolve and the Veteran no longer meets criteria for PTSD. The journey can clearly be arduous, and it takes a great deal of commitment on the part of the Veteran to overcome these symptoms and to regain equilibrium. These pages are considered an overview of some of the key elements of treatment in traditional therapy but are clearly not exhaustive in nature. There are many excellent adjunct treatments that can also help reduce the symptoms of PTSD, many of which that are covered throughout this book.

To access the VA Treatment Decision Aid please access it here: https://www.ptsd.va.gov/apps/Decisionaid/

CHAPTER 3 - ACUPUNCTURE FOR PTSD

Acupuncturists Without Borders - Carla Cassler, DAOM, L.Ac. (VP)

Acupuncture is obviously a very old therapy, but it is relatively new in western culture. If you look at its history in relation of how it came to the West, it's kind of interesting. Chinese medicine and Acupuncture dates back between 4,000-5,000 years. Dr. Paul Nogier is the 'father' of scientifically researched acupuncture and modern Auricular Acupuncture is based on work by Dr. Paul Nogier of France in the 1960s. Battlefield Acupuncture is an Auricular Acupuncture protocol invented by Dr. Richard Niemtzow, MD, consisting of treating the patient by placing five needles at five specific points on each ear.

It didn't come to the West as a pain treatment, it was more of a treatment that came through Canada into the United States and it was first used relatively officially as a treatment for drug addiction...and primarily for opiate and heroin addictions as a replacement for Methadone treatment. It is kind of interesting because now we have more of an opioid crisis now and that's how Auricular Acupuncture came into the United States. It was more fully developed at Lincoln Hospital in the South Bronx where they had a big detoxification program. That is where the National Association of Detoxification Acupuncture (NADA) Program, which is what we use for our work, was developed. NADA, as an ear acupuncture treatment, was developed as a drug treatment initially and we refer to it as the NADA 5-Needle Protocol (or 5-NP).

The other piece is that when, in 1972, Richard Nixon was President, and he did an astonishing thing. He actually went to China and that was a big deal in those days. He was accompanied by James Reston, who was the editor of the New York Times. During the trip James Reston ended up having to have an appendectomy which they were there because of an emergency case of appendicitis. Well, after the surgery he received body acupuncture as part of his treatment for rehabilitation and pain control instead of using drugs. Once they had returned from the trip and James Reston wrote about it, and it was kind of like a door opening, not only to China on a political level but also that this ancient therapy was being practiced widely in China and that the treatment had some validity. There was a whole bunch of history about acupuncture in China itself but in 1972 it kind of came on the scene through this drug treatment approach that was being developed by some creative practitioners in the South Bronx; but also due to Nixon and James Reston coming back from China.

The person who really worked with this at Lincoln Hospital was Dr. Michael Smith. He was an MD, and he worked with other practitioners in the drug rehabilitation unit of Lincoln Hospital. It was really a team approach of numerous practitioners who kind of distilled the NADA 5-NP into what we use today. This protocol has been used for

30 years now. Again, it was initially used as a drug rehabilitation treatment, then as a pain treatment, and more recently (maybe the last 15 years or so) as a trauma treatment. The reason acupuncture in general is useful for PTSD as well for pain and drug addiction is that it works with the brain's chemistry...it works to regulate the system...and when I say regulate, I mean that very physiologically. This is because, in trauma, the nervous system and the whole body is dis-regulated. And so you can't process the experience of trauma when you're in a dis-regulated state. Literally, you can't process something if the frontal cortex of your brain isn't getting any blood. When you are in a trauma state, that part of your brain is not getting any blood. The blood is going to the part of your brain that is involved with emotional development, emotional memory formation, and survival (the limbic system part of your brain). When you have a traumatic experience or cumulative traumatic experiences you tend to be in a dis-regulated state and things like acupuncture have a regulatory effect and help you to reset the body...using the body's own chemistry to do so. As a result, you don't have to use drugs. With this kind of somatic (or physical) treatment, you have to do some sort of somatic or physical intervention in trauma treatment so that then, the brain as well as the rest of the body, regulates and can actually function normally enough to process the experience.

We don't, for example, just advocate the use of acupuncture. Ideally, you would have acupuncture and then you'd have a really good psychological counselor so that you can actually process some of what you have experienced. We like to use acupuncture as an immediate intervention, often in concert with other therapies. There are other kinds of somatic treatments that you can use like somatic experiencing, certain types of meditation, craniosacral work, some of the Yoga practices including Qigong. These are all physically based practices that help re-regulate the system when it's dis-regulated. Then you have a better chance of being able to process your trauma emotionally. So, that's our role, as an organization.

We started in earnest as Acupuncturists Without Borders (AWB) after Hurricane Katrina, then, after we started doing the work in New Orleans, for a couple years it was kind of the high point of the Iraq/Afghanistan conflicts, and we were seeing a lot of people coming back from those places with a lot of PTSD. That has always been the case with war, if you go back and look at historical writings you can see that there's always been PTSD. Emergency and military medicine has been better and better at saving people's lives through the years. But then you are left with military personnel and Veterans with a lot of damage, including things like Traumatic Brain Injury (TBI) and PTSD. So, you see a lot of people who lived through very difficult situations but can end up very challenged. The use of drugs to try to manage the symptomatology was obviously compounding the problem for many of the Veterans. This is because a lot of the drugs we do have available for mental health treatment have very limited effect on PTSD.

Often PTSD doesn't exist by itself. You will have other things...pain...TBI...substance dependence. It just becomes a more complicated situation. What's good about acupuncture is, like I said, it started as a drug treatment, and it works well for pain. A lot of it has to do with the fact that the things that create pain in the body, as well as addiction and trauma; a lot of those system pathways are the same or shared. With acupuncture you have one treatment that works with all of those things together. That's part of why it's very useful. It's because it's one treatment that works on the entire system to re-regulate it. That's our goal with acupuncture...to re-regulate and balance the brain chemistry so that then people can think more clearly, and can be in a better mood, and reduce pain and sleep better, etc. Helping to reduce trauma helps with pain, and vice versa. PTSD is not the event; it is the way we process it. If you can intervene with some sort of somatic treatment like acupuncture right away, then you can actually re-regulate the system so that the cascade of chemically based events and metabolic events don't happen. Then the trauma imprint isn't developed in the first place. People will often ask if a single treatment is enough, and the answer is yes. If you can treat a person shortly after something bad happens to them then you can change the direction of the body's response. I have treated numerous Vietnam Veterans, and they have dealt with their PTSD for, on average, 45 years. If you're consistent, and especially if you combine acupuncture with other kinds of treatments, after a couple of years you can really see huge differences...so for longer-term or chronic PTSD, consistent treatment is what matters the most.

You can use certain drugs in certain situations, like anti-psychotics and anti-depressants and all these other kinds of drugs and they may only be useful for a certain amount of time. The data is just not supportive of pharmacological approaches to PTSD being very effective. That's why we started a project that would help spread the use of simple ear acupuncture for trauma given that so many people were coming back with issues, and they weren't getting any treatment that was working. Meanwhile, in around 2004, some people working in the VA system started looking at options for alternative medical treatments. Cognitive Behavioral Therapy (CBT) was somewhat successful but was difficult to deliver in the way that it was needed. To be effective with CBT, you have to do a lot of therapy and you have to do it quite often...and there generally weren't enough therapists or time available to make that work. So, we started trying to educate the VA about the benefits of acupuncture and other somatic therapies for Veterans. Because the VA is a big bureaucracy and it's also controlled by Congress, it meant that the hoops that we had to jump through to even be considered...for acupuncture to even be considered as a valid therapy...were nearly impossible to overcome.

It wasn't until 2017 that acupuncture really started to be introduced into the VA medical system as a whole. It is also only within the last year that professional, credentialed acupuncturists have been hired to work for the VA. It took 14-15 years for that to finally happen. In the regular military it was faster because the Department of Defense is in charge rather than Congress. One of the limitations hindering acupuncture within the VA is a lack of physical space to conduct the treatment. Meanwhile, because there was no acupuncture being offered on site until recently, and a lot of Veterans were getting their treatments through private practitioners. The Veterans often had to advocate for their own care. They had to tell their doctors that the drugs weren't working, and they had to ask for a referral to an acupuncturist outside the VA if one wasn't available internally. That is why we have trained our acupuncturists, since 2006, to set up all volunteer community clinics in different parts of the country that are dedicated to benefit Veterans and military personnel and their families. As of August of 2018, we have 40 such clinics. Some are daily, some weekly, some bi-weekly, depending on the need and the capabilities of the volunteer staff. Across the entire United States, we do an average of 50,000 individual treatments a year for our Veterans alone.

Military Stress Recovery Clinics (MSRC)

All of the MSRCs listed are independent entities run by local acupuncture volunteers and have no legal affiliation with AWB. We collaborate as part of AWB's national Military Stress Recovery Project. AWB makes no guarantees about the services provided and is not legally responsible for those services.

Navigate to this link to view locations where clinics are currently operating: https://www.acuwithoutborders.org/military-stress-recovery-project/

The Military Stress Recovery Project (MSRP) provides free acupuncture treatments for Veterans, active military personnel, reservists, and their families. This work is part of AWB's Community Service Clinic Program which serves all types of communities affected by traumatic events. The MSRP began in 2006 with a pilot clinic in Albuquerque, New Mexico. As AWB trains more practitioners through its "Healing Community Trauma" educational program, additional clinics are being established.

AWB created the MSRP program during the wars in Iraq and Afghanistan because so many soldiers and Veterans were suffering the effects of trauma without effective treatment within the military medical system. Pharmacological treatments for post-traumatic stress (PTS) have been shown to be relatively ineffective and can create chemical dependence with devastating side effects, including increased suicide rates. AWB pioneered the use of acupuncture as a safe, effective, non-pharmacological therapy for returning soldiers that fills this trauma treatment gap.

Currently, the Department of Defense, National Institutes of Health and the Veterans Affairs Administration are supporting research on the efficacy of acupuncture for treatment of combat-related pain and trauma. Increasingly, acupuncture is being integrated into health services provided on military bases and in VA hospitals. AWB's work over the past decade has helped make this happen.

Treatments offered in the **MSRP** program are based on the National Acupuncture Detoxification Association (**NADA**) ear protocol, which has proven to be extremely powerful in alleviating symptoms of stress and trauma. During treatment, people sit fully clothed in a room together, often in a circle of chairs, and a licensed acupuncturist places five tiny needles in each ear. Recipients are invited to close their eyes and rest for 30-45 minutes as the acupuncture does its work. In many **MSRP** clinics, the **NADA** protocol is supplemented with additional ear, scalp, or body points.

Clients at **MSRP** clinics experience benefits such as a full night's sleep for the first time in years and fewer bad dreams. They experience improved mental clarity, less anxiety and depression and a renewed interest in social relationships and community. Many subsequently report that they are able to reduce medication dosages for a wide variety of symptoms that are co-morbid with stress and post-traumatic stress, including pain and insomnia.

The potential of this program is enormous. History has shown that the long-term impact of war takes a tremendous toll for decades. By providing free acupuncture to Veterans who have recently returned from war, we can play a part in preventing history from repeating itself. By offering treatment for Veterans from previous wars and conflicts, we take part in helping mend the psychological wounds of the past.

The beauty of acupuncture is that it is a simple, low-cost modality offering immediate, effective, easily accessible support for large numbers of people. It can also work harmoniously with other more conventional treatment modalities such as counseling and medication.

CHAPTER 4 - ALEXANDER TECHNIQUE AND PTSD

Andrea Pollinger Bruno, Alexander Technique, Gestalt Certified, Reiki and Chios Master

Each of us has a way that we move that is recognizable to those who know us. Friends or family may be able to discern who we are by the echo of our footsteps before we are visible. They may also recognize us from afar by our gait despite the fact they are not close enough to identify our faces. The way we move is as ingrained in who we are as our likes and dislikes. Or is it?

"I feel like myself for the first time in ages." This is the experience of a Veteran during an Alexander Technique (AT) lesson. It's a movement re-education that teaches you to include yourself and your environment in your thinking before and while you move. Over time we take on a different or less mindful way of "using" our body. A combination of age, injury and cultural demands creates interference in our natural movement. The technique uses gently guiding touch that allows you to experience a way of moving that does not include the interferences you have learned and taken on with time. Tightening of your musculature is a common reaction to fear and pain that prevents you from sensing yourself in your environment. One Veteran expressed his experience in a lesson, stating, "I feel more connected to the ground with my feet."

How we move is more complex than the mechanics our joints allow. Our entire being, the combination of mind and body, are responsible for the patterns of movement each of us uniquely displays. The discovery of why we move the way we do becomes a large part of the work to be done when studying the Alexander Technique. It occurs when the different movement experiences you have in a lesson awakens something about yourself. Our movement patterns and our emotional state are closely tied together. For example, a person who feels pressured to get as many things done as possible in their day might move in a rushed fashion. Their breath might become shallow, their footsteps and hand movements quick, their musculature tight or held, and their vision narrowed. A depressed or sad person may move slowly; they may carry themselves in a collapsed posture, sigh frequently and not want to make eye contact with their environment. Someone fearful might be hesitant in their interaction with others, hold their musculature rigidly, strain their eyes to see, and function in a constant state of caution. An overexcited individual might have quick, short movements, a high-pitched voice, and rapid speech. Another Veteran told me that the things he learned about himself in his lessons helped him become more aware of himself and then everything started to change. Are you aware of unnecessary tensions that you hold in your body?

Most of us are unaware of how we move. Fredrick Matthias Alexander, the founder of the Alexander Technique, tells us that our sensory perception is "debauched," or faulty. This was one of Alexander's first discoveries. Alexander was born in Australia in 1869. His passion was acting, yet he frequently struggled with the loss of his voice while on stage. He sought medical attention and was advised to rest; however, shortly after returning to the stage he would again lose his voice. His determination to continue acting led him to begin a process of self-observation. His doctors agreed with his thinking that he must be "doing" something to cause the loss of his voice, yet they were not able to tell him what it was. Using a three-way mirror, he observed himself astutely and noticed several things. When he took a breath, he sucked his air in loudly and lifted his chest. Having been instructed to grasp the floor while acting, he tightened his feet. Until he took the time to see himself in the mirror, he had been unaware that he was creating muscular interference (tension), in his body. But if he tried to move in the opposite direction from the way he was positioning himself in an attempt to reverse or undo what he was doing it did not provide a solution. He concluded that he needed to "not-do" what he was doing.

"Non-doing" is another basic premise of the Alexander Technique. Alexander realized that he needed to not suck in air, not lift his chest and not tighten his feet to grasp the ground. These interfering activities that he thought would improve his acting were, in fact, contributing to muscular constriction in his neck and around his vocal cords. This muscular tension was interfering with his voice. He later realized these habits were present all the time, while acting. These are two of the guiding principles of the Alexander Technique. One, we are unaware of what we do and two, the concept of "non-doing" — we need to "not do" that which is interfering with our natural movement.

Alexander thought he was preventing these interfering habits. He noticed, however, that when he began to speak, his old movement habits would reappear. The act, even the thought of speaking, was a stimulus for his old habits. He had to relearn how to use his voice, so it did not require him to perform his customary interfering movements. How he thought about his movement even before he spoke became crucial. His continued observations led him to discover a third important concept that has to do with the relationship between the head, neck, and back. Downward compression or over-extension of the head and neck determines how well we move. The tension Alexander created in his neck affected his entire coordination. If and when he would "leave himself alone" (not engage muscles not required to speak), he found he was successful in retaining his voice.

Alexander shared his discoveries with actors in his native Australia, where he became known as "The Breathing Man." He soon realized that so much more than the breath was affected by the changes he was able to make in his habitual movements. In the early 1900s, he relocated to London, England, where he began to gain greater recognition for his discoveries. He found supporters in the medical and scientific community and began to publish. He was sought out by many in need and by those who wanted to learn and teach the work. He found he was able to teach his process of "non-doing," and was successful in helping people who stuttered, those who suffered the results of polio, athletes, and many more.

Today there are different lineages of Alexander teachers working with groups and individuals throughout the world. Teacher training programs are also available worldwide. Two generations removed from Alexander, the work has grown and expanded while the key principles remain. You may find specialists in Alexander Technique for golf, skiing, acting, tennis, horseback riding, musicians, pain relief, mindfulness, business, motivation, personal development, and more, yet all will teach and apply Alexander's same principles. The Alexander Technique has become known as a technique you can apply to any discipline to accomplish more with less effort. Alexander had been known to say, "Give me a thief and I will make him a better thief."

Medical acceptance of the Alexander Technique is growing as awareness increases, and scientific research continues to find funding. Scientific endeavors began with Frank Pierce Jones and a group of professionals from major universities in the Massachusetts area in the 1960s and 1970s. Techniques like multiple image photography, electromyography (a rough way to measure changes in the electrical potential of muscle), and X-ray photography helped document movement with and without the technique. It also confirmed the head, neck, and back relationship, demonstrating that the brain stem is where tension initiates when individuals experience "startle." The startle reflex is, "A reflex seen in normal infants in response to loud noise. The infant makes a sudden body movement, bringing the legs and arms toward the chest." (MedicineNet).

The British Medical Journal first published a study on the Alexander Technique and its success in treating back pain in 2008. Dr. David Garlick, University of New South Wales, had done studies on the physiological mechanisms of the technique. Aside from the science behind this work and the specific studies being done to confirm its efficacy, there continues to be a challenge in describing and understanding the Alexander Technique and how it works from the layman's perspective. Consider that our emotional state is easily felt and transferable. We connect energetically with each other. Walk into a room where everyone is tense, and you are not welcome; chances are you will feel this tension. Walk into a room full of loving people happy to see you, and that too will be tangible. The scientific work to describe this phenomenon that we all know is still young. Science is still catching up with the Alexander Technique.

An Alexander teacher's thinking is shared with their student. You connect with your teacher through your senses. The teacher must think in their body in a way they want their student to feel in theirs. The work is experiential, much like learning to ride a bicycle. Few can read a book on how to ride a bike and be successful in their first endeavor. Instead, repeated tries are more likely to lead you to success. Once you've experienced the sense of balance required to ride, it will likely stay with you.

Similarly, once you've experienced the delicate balance of your head on top of your spine (often with the well-trained guiding hands of an Alexander Teacher), and the movement that results, you are likely to gain insight into the potential of this work to help you make a positive change in your life. You may experience lightness in your body, and a sense of overall calm; you may feel more present in the room, experience less pain in your body and become less reactive to the stimuli in your environment that cause anxiety; "I feel more stable when I walk" (Veteran). These experiences will remain as long as you can maintain or continually renew the thinking of "non-doing," the stopping of the interference you are creating and holding. With time, the changes you experience will become the norm. The chatter in your head may quiet, and solutions you are struggling to find may become apparent. "Because of this work I can do all the things I'm learning to help my Post-Traumatic Stress Disorder (PTSD) better." "In the AT classroom I've learned practical things like how to get off my bed and how to get in and out of a car more easily" (Veteran's comments paraphrased).

Repeated experience is necessary to learn this work for your habits to change. Walk the same pathway on the grass, and you will wear away the grass. Change your pathway, and you will create a new path leaving the old one to regrow.

With movement and the Alexander Technique, you are creating new "neurological" pathways and allowing old ones to fade. The former pathway is still in your memory; however, you can make a choice to use and reinforce the new one, thus allowing the old pathway to fade. You learn to bring intention to your movement in the same way a baby is motivated by their environment to roll over and crawl. Babies become curious about something they see and want to touch, which motivates them to move in that direction. Their desire to move has a purpose and a motivation.

Even without purposeful practice, research tells us the experience from lessons will find their way into your thinking, and you are likely to experience change. "After one year the results of this work remain effective. Six lessons followed by exercise prescription were as effective as 24 lessons." You may think of the process of learning the Alexander Technique as noticing how you think in your body. If you think, "I'm in a rush, hurry up," you will move differently than if you invite in the thought of "ease," "connectivity," "fluidity," and, "I have all the time in the world." The change in your thinking may slow you down slightly, and it will increase your efficiency and reduce your tension. You will find you achieve more with less effort. The Alexander Technique allows you to respond to your environment without the baggage of old muscular memories. You see, hear and respond to the situation as it is happening in real time, without the judgmental thoughts that are a result of past experience. Is there a person in your life you do not care for? Are you on your guard when you see them?

Will you respond to their requests with caution because of your past experience when dealing with them? Are you able to hear what they are saying or are you anticipating that they will annoy you as they have in the past? What if you could interact with them without having to be on-guard, without judgment? Your response and how you feel when interacting with them may change. This is what the practice of the Alexander Technique provides. A Veteran expressed his discomfort with being touched prior to coming to Alexander lessons. "If someone bumped into me I would get angry and want to yell at them. Now, I just let it go. It's no big deal."

How one teaches the Alexander Technique may vary, although the principals of what we teach remain the same. Barbara and William Conable developed "Body Mapping." It is based on the theory that if you don't know how you are put together, you won't know how to move. Instead, you will move the way you think you are designed. For example, understanding the location of the atlanto-occipital joint where the head and neck connect and how it functions changes the way your head balances and moves on your spine. Knowing that your hip socket is near your groin and not on the outside of your upper leg allows your legs to move more freely from the joint, changing the way you walk. Experiencing that your shoulder blades do not connect to each other in your back and that the clavicle (the horizontal bone you can feel beginning below your throat and follow out towards your shoulder), connects at the sternum (the cartilage connecting your ribs in front), will grant you freedom of movement in your arms, shoulders, and fingers.

There have been new developments in how this work is presented. Recently the Alexander Technique has even been taught over the Internet and without physical touch. With or without touch, the teacher is not actually doing something to you. You must allow the release of your tense musculature and your joints will free. You work with the teacher; one is guiding, and one is allowing. For this reason, the Alexander Technique is a unique process. It is different from massage, yoga, Tai Chi, acupuncture and other "doing" (exercise), or "being done to you" disciplines. You are the doer, or "non-doer." Only you can change your thinking. It cannot be forced. The teacher awaits your release and guides you through a new movement pattern. Your ability to move with less effort as a result of releasing the interference you have created in your body over time is a personal journey. The teacher and student are engaged in a learning experiment together. "I don't know why I always looked at the ground when I walked. I can look ahead and still see the ground". (Veteran)

The interferences in your musculature, once released, allow you to become more present and intentional about your life. You become more stable and less fearful. A Veteran experienced less severity in his vertigo. He stopped trying to hold himself "still." You discover the "stimuli" that causes your "startle response" just as Alexander discovered that the act of speaking was a stimulus to suck in his air loudly, lift his chest and tighten his feet. Another Veteran realized in a lesson how he held onto his anger from a recent minor car accident. He had become preoccupied and unmotivated to do the self-care he usually provided for himself. While practicing sitting in a kayak (in preparation for an upcoming vacation), in a way that required less effort and tension he shared his frustration about the accident. Becoming more comfortable in this position required him to release the tension he was holding onto as a result of this accident. The following week he told me he was less preoccupied and able to return to his healthy regime.

Many of the symptoms occurring with PTSD are addressed indirectly with this work. The plasticity of the brain makes it possible to re-educate the body to prevent overreacting to what are now non-threatening situations and to move with ease and intention. This learned process serves as an antidote to the habit of fear and anxiety expressed in our demeanor and our reactions. When experiencing trauma of any sort we move into a mode of survival. In this mode, we experience many of the symptoms of PTSD including dissociation, a split in the conscious process in which a group of mental activities breaks away from the mainstream of consciousness and functions as a separate unit, as if belonging to another person (Webster). Over time, the Alexander Technique lessens the impact of the survival mode.

A feeling of safety and a lack of judgment in the Alexander classroom are critical. For this work to be done, the student needs to be able to trust their teacher. Changing the thinking that maintains the posture of fear to a mentality that involves a more fluid whole-body movement will allow the release that will result in better self-awareness, better proprioception, more connectivity of body and emotion and a reduction of the dissociative personality experienced with PTSD. Emotions can be felt and your inner calm retained. Positive experiences that are calming, centering, and grounding become more present with time. The body/mind connection is relearned.

The impact of how we posture ourselves and how we move has an indirect effect on our physical and mental health. By becoming aware of our habits and patterns we can make a different choice about how and what we do. While medical research continues to explore this process, those who have learned the Alexander Technique over the last hundred plus years have voiced the benefits they've experienced and the changes they've made for the better. With the help of this practice self-discovery is unending. "When I take the time to think about what I've experienced in class I'm able to walk further and with less pain. I could not have done this before I studied the Alexander Technique" (Veteran). Your experiences in the classroom are just the beginning. Becoming aware of your tension and posturing, in your everyday life, grants you the opportunity to respond authentically and not automatically? Are you supported by the ground, seeing what's around you and connecting with your whole body before your move? The ability for you to make change for the better exists and can be learned.

For additional information on the Alexander Technique, Reiki, and Chios Energy Healing, please feel free to visit my website at www.empoweringdirections.com.

Biography: I have a BA from George Washington University. I graduated from the Philadelphia School for the Alexander Technique in 2007. I began exploring alternative health during college in 1973 first with Trancendental Meditation and then Yoga. Later my explorations led to the Alexander Technique, assorted disciplines in energy work and the Gestalt Process. I continue to explore movement through sport and exercise, music by playing the flute, art through the mediums of ceramics, watercolor and fabric and the study of Hebrew through prayer. I began my employment as an Alexander Technique teacher at an VA flagship center for alternative health care in 2016.

CHAPTER 5 - AROMATHERAPY, THE OLFACTORY SYSTEM AND ESSENTIAL OILS

Rehne Burge, C.A.

PTSD, once referred to as "shell shock" or battle fatigue, was first brought to attention by war Veterans, and is a result of a direct traumatic, tragic or a terrifying event that one has witnessed or experienced in their lives. This not only effects Veterans but also people that have experienced a tragic or traumatic event. Being frightened under these circumstances is normal.

Fear triggers many split-second changes in the body to help defend against danger or to avoid it. This "fight-or-flight" response is a typical reaction meant to protect a person from harm. Nearly everyone will experience a range of responses after trauma, yet most people recover from initial symptoms naturally. Those who continue to experience problems may be diagnosed with PTSD. People who have PTSD may feel stressed or frightened whether danger is present or not. From my personal experience, this can occur at any given time, without notice. There are usually persistent frightening thoughts and memories of their ordeal and feel emotionally numb, especially with people they were once close to.

Some people, unaware, will block the trauma and have their memory come back at a later time in life, leaving them even further traumatized. Most people with PTSD repeatedly re-live the trauma in the form of nightmares, panic attacks, anxiety and disturbing recollections during the day. The nightmares or recollections may come and go, and a person may be free of them for weeks at a time, and then experience them daily for no particular reason. This can occur whether the person remembers the trauma or not. It can sit idly by with no memory yet the symptoms can still take place.

A person with PTSD may experience sleep problems, depression, substance abuse, feeling detached or numb, or being easily startled. So how can we combat or deal with the responses of PTSD? Because the olfactory receptors are extremely sensitive, they can be easily stimulated by very subtle and sometimes subliminal scents.

A technique was developed called Hypnotherapeutic Olfactory Conditioning (HOC), for exploiting the ability of scents to arouse potent emotional reactions. During hypnosis, the patient learns to associate pleasant scents with a sense of security and self-control. The patient can subsequently use this newfound association to overcome phobias and prevent panic attacks. This may be especially effective for PTSD with episodes of anxiety, flashbacks, and dissociation triggered by smells. The authors presented three cases, patients with needle phobia, panic disorder, and combat-induced PTSD who were successfully treated with the HOC technique.

Many combat Veterans with PTSD have an olfactory component to their traumatic memories that might be utilized by HOC therapy. Thirty-six outpatients with chronic PTSD, featuring resistant olfactory-induced flashbacks, were treated with six 1.5-hour sessions using hypnosis. Significant reductions in symptomatology were recorded by the end of the 6-week treatment period, as well as for the Beck Depression Inventory and the Dissociative Experiences Scale; 21 (58%) of the subjects responded to treatment by a reduction of 50% or more. Improvement was maintained at 6-month and 1-year follow-ups. HOC showed potential for providing benefit to individuals suffering from PTSD with olfactory components.

Abstract: Silexan, a lavender oil preparation for oral use, had been authorized in Germany for the treatment of states of restlessness during anxious mood. An open-label, exploratory trial was performed to assess the potential of the medicinal product in the treatment of restlessness caused by anxiety as related to several disorders. The results of this trial justified further investigations on Silexan in disorders with accompanying restlessness caused by sub-threshold anxiety.

Considering that so many illnesses are stress related, Lavender holds a special place in both preventative health care and in the treatment of tension-related illnesses. It offers a soothing and antispasmodic effect. Lavender not only offers anti-inflammatory, skin-healing properties but also is loved for its effectiveness on stress related symptoms. It's calming, tension releasing and sedative properties are a big benefit to PTSD and other stress related symptoms.

There is growing evidence suggesting that Lavender oil may be an effective in treatment of several neurological disorders. Several animal and human investigations suggest anxiolytic, mood stabilizer, sedative, analgesic, and anti-convulsive and neuroprotective properties for Lavender. These studies raised the possibility of revival of lavender therapeutic efficacy in neurological disorders.

Lavendula Angustifolia (Lavender) inhalation has been used in folk medicine for the treatment of anxiety, and clinical and animal studies have corroborated its anxiolytic effect, although its mechanism of action is still not fully understood. The results indicate an important role for the serotonergic system in the anxiolytic-like effect of lavender essential oil.

The next oil that is showing promise in many research documents is Citrus Bergamia, also known as "Bergamot," which is a plant belonging to the Rutaceae family and is defined as a hybrid of bitter orange and lemon. It is an endemic plant of the Calabria region (Italy). Bergamot fruit is primarily used for the extraction of its essential oil. Clinical studies on the therapeutic applications of Bergamot essential oil (BEO) exclusively focuses on the field of aromatherapy, suggesting that its use can be useful for reducing anxiety and stress.

Abstract: BEO is used widely in aromatherapy to reduce stress and anxiety despite limited scientific evidence. A previous study showed that BEO significantly increased gamma-aminobutyric acid levels in rat hippocampus, suggesting potential anxiolytic properties.

Basil plays another important role. Amongst other properties, Basil is anti-spasmodic and a cephalic (in Aromatherapy, pertaining to remedies for the head). It has the ability to clear our minds and help to relieve voluntary or involuntary muscle spasms. Looking at case study on a 37-year-old male with panic attacks and agoraphobia was taking venlafaxine 225 mg, alprazolam two mg, and risperidone two mg daily, after three months of olfactory conditioning with Basil, he was able to go without his presently used drugs.

At his one-year follow-up, he was smelling Basil only once or twice a month and no longer suffered from panic attacks or agoraphobia.

During a single-blind randomized clinical trial, a comparison was made of the effects of massage therapy utilizing aromatherapy for anxiety and pain on burn victims, it was found that the aromatherapy reduced the anxiety and pain exponentially. Anxiety and pain are recognized as major problems of burn patients; because pharmaceutical treatments for controlling anxiety and pain symptoms lead to complications and an increase in health costs, non-pharmacological nursing interventions were considered for this group of patients. This led to the present study aimed at comparing the effect of aromatherapy massage with inhalation aromatherapy for anxiety and pain in burn patients. The study results showed the positive effect of aromatherapy massage and inhalation aromatherapy compared with the control group in reducing both anxiety and pain of burn patients. Therefore, both interventions, which are inexpensive, and noninvasive nursing tasks can be proposed for alleviating anxiety and pain of burn patients.

We've heard about the oils but what makes them so effective? The major chemical components that assist with the symptoms discussed is listed below. Linalool and Linalyl acetate are big contributors.

All oils mentioned offer emotional support as well as clinical support. Basil offers energetic support, self-confidence, motivation as well as clears the mind. Ho Wood is calming to the mind, Roman Chamomile calms, soothes, sedates, lessens anxiety and stress, and harmonizes thoughts. Clary Sage reduces anxiety, calms the mind and is emotionally uplifting. Sweet Marjoram calms obsessive thinking, supports self-care, comforts and warms and has a calming effect to the heart and is known to assist with high blood pressure. Bergamot is relaxing, restorative, calming, emotionally uplifting, supports the release of repressed emotion and helps to reduce insomnia and anxiety. Lavender is calming, soothing and nurtures. It encourages balance in all the body systems. It has a strong ability to reduce anxiety and fear. Lavender helps to calm and control panic attacks.

As you can see, Aromatic treatment can offer a great deal of support to those with PTSD and those who live with loved ones with PTSD.

CHAPTER 6 - ATEASE THERAPY GLASSES

Steve Clute

More than 40 million Americans suffer with anxiety? AtEase Glasses LLC has created a drug-free, scientific therapy for that anxiety and in our specific case, Post-Traumatic Stress Disorder (PTSD). The new answer is in the form of amazing therapeutic glasses patented to relax your mind and relieve your brain from anxiety, stress, panic attacks and PTSD. AtEase blocks distractions and makes you relax. The new, patented glasses give more focus and concentration.

The inventor, Kenneth Finochiaro, has always been passionate about helping others. Believing that focus and concentration would improve performance led Ken to experiment and design glasses to enhance those abilities. The first glasses Ken designed were for his son and grandson to improve their golf game and while the product was being used as a sports training tool, Ken received feedback from a golfer who suffered from PTSD. He thanked Ken for helping him golf, but he was more excited about the impact on his health. By wearing the PTSD glasses, he gained confidence to do everyday things normal people take for granted but he struggled to manage with PTSD. He also appreciated the overall "calming effect" the glasses provided without the use of prescription drugs. As a result, Ken started providing glasses to people with PTSD and waited for feedback. It turns out that the unsolicited feedback was very positive.

The causes of PTSD are many, from childhood abuse, to rape to war. The emotional scars run deep. Traumatic experiences hurt more than our physical selves, they harm our psyche as well. Hiding deep within our brains, and in some cases actually changing its structure.

• Neuroimaging studies show that hippocampus can shrink. This is the part of the brain where memory is stored, making it harder for someone with PTSD to tell the difference between present and past.

• The prefrontal cortex can shrink as well. This is the part of our brain that controls our negative emotions, like fear.

• The amygdala, which helps process our emotions goes into overdrive.

Put this all together and it's no wonder a war movie can trigger a memory of a bad battle with a Veteran or a rape victim can break into a sweat in a parking ramp that resembles where they were attacked.

Ken had been working with Dr. Wes Sime, a PHD and Psychologist, to refine the golf glasses and asked Dr. Sime what he thought about use of the glasses for PTSD. Dr. Sime had done in-depth studies of trauma reduction in first responders with PTSD and conducted brain scans of PTSD patients using the glasses. The results proved the glasses helped quiet the brain, reduce stress, anxiety and even panic attacks. Dr. Sime asked Dr. Jim Nedrow, OD, MS., FAAO, DIPL, NBEO, to conduct VEP testing (visual evoked potential) on PTSD patients. Again, positive results. The investigations proved the PTSD Relief Glasses to have high value in quieting the symptoms of PTSD. The inventor continued to do research and development and now holds the Patents for this technology invention. Mr. Finochiaro brought together a group of consultants to evaluate the glasses and prove their effectiveness. The consulting group is as follows:

• Dr. Wes Sime, Ph.D., Psychologist: Dr. Sime has done extensive research on trauma reduction working with first responders.

• Dr. Jim Nedrow, Ph.D., Optometrist: Dr. Nedrow is one of the top 10 prism experts in the country.

• Dr. Summers at U of M: Helped with research on horizontal line. Tested vision strips at depth. Evaluated Multiple uses — multiple product lines.

• Dr. Debbie Crews (Arizona) Founder of Optiband. Conducted brain scans to prove the reduction in elevated anxiety while using the glasses. Completed formal testing and is currently finishing a new study at Arizona State University.

• Former Surgeon General James Tuorila: Dr. Tuorila has a medical practice in Saint Cloud, MN and over 30 years of experience in the field of medicine. Dr. Tuorila served three terms as the National Surgeon General for the Veterans of Foreign Wars and Post-Traumatic Stress Disorder. Dr. Tuorila has been active in testing and study of the positive results of AtEase Glasses for PTSD.

The results of all studies have proven to be very positive. We have learned that the Delta and Theta waves are the lowest frequency brain waves and are typically only experienced during deep sleep. These are the waves that become active during the production of dreams. Alpha waves are typically prominent in an adult who is awake but relaxed with their eyes closed. In general, amplitudes diminish when subjects open their eyes and are attentive to external stimuli. Unfortunately for victims of PTSD, Delta, Theta, and Alpha waves can increase activity during wake time, leading to vivid flashbacks and intense emotional reactions that cannot be differentiated from the present.

AtEase products have been designed to provide therapeutic relief for illnesses that can be treated using visual tools rather than pharmaceutical products. AtEase is accomplishing this every day using the scientific technology delivered through the highly specialized, patented and FDA approved glasses. The glasses use a precisely manufactured lens with unique color coating and modified visual field. Having our mission to improve the lives of people impacted by chronic conditions and those seeking enhanced performance through a drug-free and non-invasive approach, that calms, soothes and focuses the brain drives us to evolve and deliver the best products and services that we can. To the world, this product looks like the coolest sunglasses of the season. To the wearer, these lenses calm and focus the brain, resulting in improved performance in life, work and play.

Optometry is normally concerned with ocular health and correction of eye problems such as vision and visual systems that can hinder the sight in humans. In the optometry industry, the demand is governed by changing healthcare practices, eyewear fashion trends and demographics. There is significant demand for leading edge technical solutions to fill the need for productive treatment in this field. The total vision care market in the United States generated about 34.54 billion U.S. dollars, with annual services expenditures growing toward $40 billion annually. With the development of areas like Behavioral Optometry and Vision Therapy the industry needs resources to deliver efficiency, effectiveness and most important, help and healing. Thinking in terms of Behavioral Optometry which is described as how the brain uses the eyes to gather information and how the brain processes that information to form a response AtEase is on track to provide a valuable tool for treatment in specific cases.

The industry needs resources to deliver efficiency, effectiveness and healing.

- 28 Million adults suffer from PTSD during their lifetime.
- 37 Million people suffer from migraine headaches in their lifetime.
- 6.4 Million ADHD patients treated annually.
- 3.8 Million sports related concussions annually.

AtEase provides the scientific technology that delivers therapy through highly specialized and patented glasses. This solution is a unique combination of optical relief and focus, which eliminates distraction, calms the brain from noise and activity that inhibits neurological function and performance. This solution is effective, drug free and low cost.

- AtEase glasses are precision manufactured to exacting standards.

- The construction quality is excellent and the horizontal gold vision fields become opaque.

• Many people will have multiple uses, i.e., PTSD, CTE, migraines and athletic training.

Chronic conditions can last over a lifetime and require far greater health care needs and in many cases ongoing, long term drug therapies. In addition, it's not easy for those experiencing problems to ask for help. The conditions are invisible and in many cases are viewed as a sign of weakness (PTSD), bad parenting (ADHD) or a problem that impacts a far greater circle of people than the person experiencing the challenge (health care costs, missing work, stress on family and friends). Nearly $200 Billion is spent each year on four chronic conditions, PTSD, ADHD, Migraines and Concussion treatments, and still people are suffering from issues related to these conditions. Access, cost and the stigma for admitting that you need help in the first place create significant barriers for help. We have talked to many people who are spending thousands of dollars every year to find relief from their challenges. The AtEase Glasses are distributed at a **MSRP** of $149.95 at https://ateaseglasses.com. The effort to make these glasses available to everyone who seeks relief is real and will not go away.

There are several different products and CTE, ADD and Migraine specific products are in development. We manufacture glasses in children's, women's, and men's sizes with slip over glasses for those who need to use their specific corrective lenses. There have been thousands of users with thousands of positive responses and the glasses have even been used successfully during dental treatments, diagnostic imaging and dialysis. Children with ADD and ADHD have had positive outcomes and testing is currently being done in a major school district in Minnesota. We will continue to test and develop as fast as possible to find as many ways to provide relief as this invention will allow us to find.

The company leadership team is composed of a diverse group of inventors, military, scientists, technology, medical, sports, health and wellness, optometric, engineering, marketing and research professionals with decades of extensive experience, deep with talent and proven capable of designing and building innovative and effective solutions. The organization is assembling an extremely bright, diverse and capable advisory board that will include well-recognized, industry-connected and highly successful professionals.

A unique combination of medicine, research, analytics, manufacturing and engineering capabilities enables our company to do good for the world we live in. The company has aligned itself with major researchers, optical experts, companies, doctors and scientists to continue developing and delivering this product to a market that really is in need of the outcomes the company expects to deliver. There have been hundreds of users and loads of positive feedback from those same people.

Readers can visit the AtEase website (https://ateaseglasses.com) to do further evaluation, read and see testimonials, as well as follow the AtEase Facebook page (https://www.facebook.com/ateaseglasses) or YouTube Channel (https://www.youtube.com/channel/UCTvvAN3XYyPjDeerb8yeG_g) to keep up with all of the ongoing process.

Kendra: "I suffer from anxiety and depression from PTSD from my time in the military. I have found very little relief from tried-and-true methods. However, when I wear the AtEase Glasses, they help me calm down and bring me back to reality. After the initial time getting used to the way the glasses work, I am able to put them on and breathe through my anxiety attacks. Being a mom with two small children I don't have a lot of time to suffer through panic and anxiety attacks, the AtEase glasses start working within a few minutes!"

Eric: "I am a veteran of Iraq and Afghanistan and have PTSD with agoraphobia and generalized anxiety disorder. Heavy things that affect me daily and things I've sought and continue to seek treatment for four years now. One major challenge is trying to find a way to be calm without meds, though that's a certain option that is useful I wanted to find an alternative. I checked out AtEase glasses for a while and admit I was definitely skeptical. After explaining my story and posing my questions AtEase was kind enough to send me a pair to try. I've tried them now for a month and these things a great. They take a little to get used to and a little time to see the effect but after about 5-10 minutes of wearing them I began to have a sense of calm come over me. I use them typically in the later part of the day or before I go out when I feel it will be difficult for me and they have a lasting effect. I use them for about 15-20 minutes, and they are just calming, I notice that my breathing lets up and eases, my mind feels free of as much worry and stress begins to relax away. These glasses are an exceptional tool in the arsenal of reducing anxiety and relieving stress, even in someone like me who it is severe for. I hope you will try them because they work and are usable for anyone and as much as you want. I experienced no side effects."

Visit AtEase at https://ateaseglasses.com for more information.

CHAPTER 7 - BEING PRESENT IN CHAOS AND PEACE: TRAUMA CONSCIOUS YOGA

Judy Weaver, C-IAYT, E-RYT500, YACEP

In 2007 I met Beau MacVane, an Army Ranger recently returned home from his fourth tour of duty in the Middle East. Beau had just been diagnosed with Amyotrophic Lateral Sclerosis – also known as "ALS" or Lou Gehrig's disease. Over the next few years Beau incorporated the teachings of Yoga to both battle and ultimately make peace with his body's inevitable decline. When Beau passed away surrounded by friends and family, he left this world with an indomitable inner strength and peace-of-mind more powerful than any mere physical malady.

Using my 30 years of learning and teaching, I founded Connected Warriors, a non-profit delivering Trauma-Conscious yoga programs to Veterans and their families around the world and Body-Mind Recalibration™ a multi-discipline practice building cognitive and somatic body-mind relationships. I also developed protocols for three clinical studies used by Connected Warriors and other health care practitioners. Connected Warriors empowers service members, Veterans and their Families worldwide through evidence-based Trauma-Conscious Yoga with a vision of helping the world feel better — one breath at a time. Today Beau's legacy is a burning torch Connected Warriors holds high to light the way for others to find the path of inner peace.

I am also a Yoga Alliance On-line Presenter, part of Core Curriculum Working Group, participate in one of their advisory boards and was a contributor to the Yoga Service Council (YSC) book "Best Practices for Yoga for Veterans."
What is Yoga?

Yoga is an ancient system of physical postures (asana), breath (pranayama), meditation and self-awareness. Synchronization of the mind, conscious breath and movement regulates the nervous system increasing resiliency. Yoga postures and breathing techniques build the body-mind connection by strengthening self-awareness, aiding the ability to observe and to stay with inner thoughts and feelings. This practice can help regain a sense of control and ownership over your body and experiences. Practicing yoga is a tool to learn to listen to your body and make choices to take care of yourself. This is mindfulness.

The objective of this practice is to sit quietly with yourself without employing a strategy to hide from yourself. This evolution of your higher consciousness or enlightenment happens when the physical, emotional and spiritual energies connect.
Physical Energy – The body can be quiet and still without effort for a duration of time.

Emotional Energy – The mental body can let go.
Spiritual Energy – The spiritual body can focus inside.

"My name is Melody Jackman and I will always think of myself as a beginning yogi. I started Yoga in college but couldn't find the right class or instructor to hold my interest for more than a couple of classes here and there throughout the years. When I joined the Army I hadn't been practicing for several years and I volunteered for a unit that is more physically demanding than most. Pain that I had been able to ignore in the past was quickly beginning to affect the way I performed on runs, and I was unwilling to go on profile. Yoga at that point was still so far back in my mind that I never even considered it for pain management or correction, and so started going to a Chiropractor. Being in a male dominated profession I was willing to do what I had to keep myself pieced together enough to stay off profile and physically keep up with them, and at that time it meant going to the Chiropractor five times a week.

I went on like that for close to a month before a new program became available to the unit, Connected Warriors. I didn't go right away, Yoga isn't considered something that the "guys" would do, and I was very careful to keep my image of being one of the guys. When I started to hear about attendance increasing I figured that was my chance to give it a try. I was still only thinking at that time of changing up my physical fitness routine, and not wellness. When I did finally drag myself in there I discovered something wonderful, here finally was an instructor who "got it." I had never before gone to a Yoga class and sweated as much as I did that day, I was sore, the kind of sore you get when you push yourself to your limit, and the pain that was threatening to put me on profile was going away. One Connected Warrior class a week brought my Chiropractor visits from five times a week to three, then once a month.

After a while I began to notice that the Yoga was also good for quieting the mind, for an hour I could let go and just breathe, not process, not worry, not stress. I could deal with the days issues without getting angry, my resilience improved, and stress management became easier. I began sleeping better, and relationships improved because I was a happier person.

Today I am no longer in that unit, but I now fly helicopters and that can be physically demanding on a whole other level. On a recent deployment we were lucky enough to have access to a Connected Warriors class, and I can tell you I really depended on that class. The wellness of the mind is just as important as wellness of the body and in a hostile environment those things can get off kilter very quickly.
 In closing, go and do Yoga, just do it. What do you have to lose? Who cares what everyone else is doing, or what they think? It's your body, and you have to live in it. Why wouldn't you want to be the best, happiest you that you could possibly be?" –
Melody Jackman — Aviation Chief Warrant Officer Two

Classical Definition

"Yoga is derived from the Sanskrit (ancient Indian language) root yuj meaning to bind, join, attach and yoke, direct and concentrate one's attention on, to use and apply, also means union or communion. Yoga is a timeless pragmatic science evolved over thousands of years dealing with the physical, moral, mental, and spiritual well-being of man as a whole." (B.K.S. Iyengar, Light on Yoga).

Yoga is one of the six orthodox systems of Indian philosophy that was systematized in 200 BC by Pantanjali, author or representative of the Yoga Sutras. The Yoga Sutras consist of more than 196 aphorisms covering the Science of Yoga. These are the four classic Yogas:

Karma Yoga – right acts, selfless actions
Bhakti Yoga – loving devotion
Raja Yoga – meditation
Jnana Yoga – inner wisdom/contemplation/enlightenment

The Sutras clearly delineate; its aim, the necessary practices, the obstacles you may meet along the path, their removal, and precise description of the results that will be obtained from such practices. These selected Sutras are examples of the scope of this practice:

Yogas Chitta Vrtti Nirodhah – Sutra 1.2
The restraint of the modifications of the mind-stuff is yoga.
The entire science of yoga is based on this. Patanjali has given the definition of yoga and at the same time, the practice. "If you can control the rising of the mind into ripples, you will experience Yoga."

8 Limbs of Ashtanga Yoga – Sutra 2.29
Steps to quiet one's mind and merge with the infinite
Yama – Social Ethics, "restraints" – Karma Yoga
Ahimsa – nonviolence, reducing harm
Satya – truth
Asteya – non stealing
Brahmacarya – appropriate use of one's vital energy
Aparigraha – non possessiveness
Niyama – Personal ethics, "internal restraints", self-observation – Bhakti Yoga
Sauca – purity, cleanliness
Santosa – contentment
Tapas – practice causing change, "heat"
Svadhyaya – self-study/observation (especially mantra)

Ishvara Pranidhana - devotion, surrender to a higher force
Asana - Posture, sitting - Raja Yoga
Sutras 2.46 - The posture is firm and soft.
Pranayama - Breath regulation - Raja Yoga
Sutras 2.49, 2.50 and 2.51
Pratyahara - Internalization of the senses, "drawing back" - Raja Yoga
Sutras 2.54 and 2.55
Dharana - Focus, concentration - Raja Yoga
Sutras 2.53, 3.1 and 3.7
Dhyana - Maintaining focus, meditation - Raja Yoga
Sutras 3.2 and 3.7
Samadhi - Complete absorption, a state of joy and peace - Jnana Yoga
Sutras 3.3 and 3.7

Yoga and the Military

The Bhagavad Gita is a beloved Hindu narrative about moral and ethical dilemmas and the violence and death of war. The concept of dharma or life's purpose discusses how warriors are to be their very best to achieve their dharma. In India, there is a long history of the practice of Yoga and the military — maharajas retained yogis to train their troops because of their strength, flexibility and powers of concentration.
The Eight Limb Path correlates yoga and the military:

Yama: Social Ethics - Standard Operating Practices (SOPs)
Niyama: Personal Ethics - SOPs
Asana: Postures - Physical Training
Pranayama: Breath Control - BRASS - Breathe, Relax, Aim, Slack, Squeeze
Pratyahara: Withdrawal/Control of senses - Stealth Maneuvers
Dharana: Single pointed focus - Mission Purpose
Dhyana: Meditation - Sustained Mission
Samadhi: Enlightenment/Awareness of higher consciousness - Mission Achieved

The Practice of Yoga

Hatha Yoga introduced in 15 AD by Yogi Swatmarama, a yogic sage, is a system of postures. Hatha comes from the Sanskrit language — "ha" meaning "sun" and "tha" meaning "Moon" united pairs of opposites. Yoga is a mindfulness practice inclusive of physical postures, breath regulation and meditation practices.
Asana and Pranayama Practice

The physical practice is a controlled environment to notice the condensed energy in the body and habitual ways of reacting to confrontations and to learn to use tools or strategies to transform an outcome. As you manipulate the body to find the tension, you are developing self-awareness through conscious breath and mindfulness — synchronization of breath and movement regulates the nervous system, thereby reducing stress and anxiety and increasing resiliency.

According to Dr. Timothy McCall, Yoga as Medicine, "Breath is perhaps the most important tool in yoga practice." Pranayama practice is breath regulation to develop correct normal breathing. Prana, a Sanskrit term meaning "absolute energy" is the universal vital life force that holds all things together; it is a physical, mental, spiritual and cosmic energy. Prana is connected through the breath and is the key that connects life to the universe. Ayama means "extend, draw out, restraint or control".

Pranayama is the science of breath control and, according to Patanjali's Sutra II.49, "It is to be practiced only after perfection in asanas is attained." Dr. Krishna Raman states, "In pranayama, the mind and consciousness is withdrawn deep inside to the core of the being". The practice of Pranayama is the conscious expansion of the natural capacity for breath that ultimately allows the free and undisturbed flow of prana that quiets the mind and enables concentration or focus (dharana).

There are many different pranayama practices providing different physical, physiological and biochemical effects on the body; either stimulating or soothing cells. The main objective of practicing pranayama is to achieve "normal breathing" by the abdomen expanding on the inhale and contracting on the exhale or normalizing the levels of oxygen and carbon dioxide in the body. It is the practice of controlled inhalation, exhalation, retention and suspension of breath while moving the thoracic organs vertically, horizontally and circumferentially.

Each inhale brings in oxygen and prana; each exhale removes carbon dioxide, toxins and apana (downward and outward flow of energy) and each pause (kumbhaka) allows less oxygen absorption leaving more carbon dioxide in the blood which aids in the calming effect. This assists in quieting the mind. However, the stability of the mind is first achieved by the control of the body through the practice of asanas. The mind becomes peaceful when the health of the body occurs.

This regular practice cultivates a listening which gives space to what is, while deepening connections to who you are. Begin to ask what your body is communicating to you? What sensations are present? Where are you stiff, tense and stuck and what contributes to this state? You will find that the answers come easier the more you practice.

"I am a Connected Warrior. I have recently retired after 36 years in the military: 10 years in the United States Marines, 26 years in the United States Army. The last 19 years have been with the Special Operations community as a helicopter pilot deploying with the most elite forces that the U.S. military has executing missions in every environment that only the most elite can accomplish. I never titled myself as a warrior, but I was blessed to be around warriors of great bravery and commitment to defend and fight for the freedoms that we as Americans are so grateful for. The acts of heroism that I have witnessed go beyond the imagination where most people only see them on movie screens.

So how does this fit with being a Connected Warrior? Yoga is hard; in fact, I have been told it is a journey to finding your own position, your own breath, and your own peace. As a 54-year-old married with two grandchildren I have to rethink what life is and what is my purpose in this life. Being around great men and women who gave it all and leaving the company of heroes has been difficult for me. I don't have my brothers with me anymore. There are no missions to plan. There are no dark nights to fight in. And I miss it. But now I want to focus on how I can stay as healthy (physically, mentally, and spiritually) as I possibly can for this next phase of my life so I can honor my wife and children, to be in their lives and make great memories that will hopefully be passed down for generations to come.

Yoga physically is challenging. I have been sitting in a helicopter cockpit for over three decades and it has punished my body by not being able to have full range of motion. I have lumbar stenosis and Yoga is helping to rehabilitate me so I can enjoy my life in the act of MOVING which as I get older, is a gift to do.

Yoga mentally is helping me use my thoughts to concentrate on listening to my body, helping me to command my body and helping to fuse both thought and movement together. Honestly, I have found Yoga has a way to refresh or elevate your thoughts to a better place so I can live a fuller life.

Yoga spiritually has helped me hear my breath. Even now I write this and can't explain how wonderful that is to me. Breath is life and it is wonderful. As a Christian, Yoga reminds me how God has given me the gift of life and how grateful I am to breathe, move and think. I am a better person, fuller person with Connected Warriors. I love being around warriors who are still pursuing LIFE. Thankful for my time on the mat. NAMASTE." – CW5(R) Kenneth Poindexter — Owner of Mugsy's Coffee Company

Meditation Practice

"With an eye made quiet by the power of harmony and the deep power of joy, we see into the life of things." These words from the poet William Wordsworth quite beautifully reflect the process of meditation. For this, of course, is what we want: to see into the life of things, to be in touch, to be connected, to feel at home in our own lives.

We don't want to live out our days mechanically, unaware, disconnected, and lost in the shadow of our conditioning.

According to Dr. Joan Borysenko, a pioneer in the field of mind/body medicine, "Meditation is anything that brings us to the present and keeps us there". This mental discipline moves us beyond the conditioned "thinking" mind into self-awareness and a deeper state of relaxation. Meditation is being prescribed as an adjunct to improve many dysfunctions and diseases. Practicing meditation is equally important as the core goal of Quieting the mind.

Meditation may take on many forms but its foundation basically lies on these principles:
Focus on one thing or object.
Focus using one of your senses.
When thoughts occur or wander, bring them back to your focus.

To concentrate, bring your focus on one thing or object. The object of focus may be your breathing, a word that you repeat either verbally or mentally, or the sensations that we feel in our body. Meditation usually involves the senses of which we smell, feel, see or listen. "Quieting" the mind is not easy so whenever you find yourself thinking of some other thoughts, don't fight them but rather acknowledge them and let them pass. Meditation is the practice of maintaining complete awareness of one's experiences on a moment-to-moment basis. This gives us the ability to respond to situations, as well as to our thoughts and emotions, with full awareness.

"I am from Arkansas. I am a husband and father. I joined the Army in 1996 as a helicopter repairer. I have been on numerous combat deployments. I am a leader and I lead by example. I started Connected Warriors Yoga to enhance my fitness performance and to deal with some nagging aches and pains. Through my own practice, I recognized the value a consistent Yoga program would bring to my Soldiers physical and mental well-being. I plan on incorporating Connected Warriors Yoga into my current aviation unit's physical fitness program." – Mark B. Baker, Command Sergeant Major, U.S. Army

One meditation technique is to use a mantra or a Focus Phrase which is a positive word or short phrase that you can use to help bring your mind back to the present and intercept negative thoughts. You use your Focus Phrase by silently repeating the words to yourself. Repeating the phrase is like pushing a pause button on your mind. The repetition intercepts or slows down the distracting thoughts, increasing your level of mindfulness and redirecting your stream of consciousness toward a more beneficial and calmer space. A Focus Phrase can also be used when you feel stressed or unmotivated.

Choose a phrase that is comfortable and natural to you. Examples – Breathe. Be still and trust. All is well. Just be. This will pass.

Another technique is to focus on the breath – either counting the inhales or exhales or noticing the feel of the breath on the upper lip or counting the breath to a selected number and repeating,

Plan to meditate about the same time every day – whatever time of day or night you can be consistent. Establish a place you can use every day where you can be relatively undisturbed during your practice. Sit as long as you can every day, it will help you cultivate and maintain your awareness as you continue through your day. A daily practice of as little as five minutes or more is beneficial.

Begin by taking a few deep breaths and soften and lower your gaze or close your eyes. As distractions come continue to gently bring your attention back to your Focus. As long as there are no emergency sirens blaring in the background, there is no need to acknowledge outside noises or your thoughts – let them come and go without engaging them.

Remember the whole point in meditation is not to stop the thoughts in the mind, but to notice the thoughts and without engaging them, let them pass through your mind. When you focus your mind on something, you are less likely to get caught in your thoughts. And when the mind does wander, which it will inevitably do, coming back to your Focus is a way to bring your mind back to the present and on your intention to meditate.

Benefits of a Yoga Practice

Multiple research projects have demonstrated the significant benefit of Yoga as an adjunct to treatment modalities to include substance abuse, anxiety, depression, and Post-Traumatic Stress (PTS). "Yoga treats the biology and psychology of an addict" (Frederick, 2012, P-8). Addicts and those suffering from stress, anxiety, and Post-Traumatic Stress Disorder have shown a low level of gamma-aminobutyric acid (GABA), an inhibitory neurotransmitter calms the neuronal pathways in adults. "Yoga has been proven to increase the levels of GABA in participants" (Saeed, 2010). "Exercise may be efficacious in reducing depressive symptoms, but the poor quality of much of the evidence is of concern." (Lawlor, 2001, P-767).

"Three years ago a retired Army Command Sergeant Major invited me to a Connected Warriors yoga class at Fort Campbell. Needless to say, I was apprehensive about going to an unfamiliar activity that I perceived as new age stretching for women. Walking in the room, I was surprised to find such an eclectic group of participants from all different age groups, genders, body types, and fitness levels. Many had some type of knee, shoulder, or back injury — battle wounds from a dedicated life of service. Much to my surprise, the class was an intense workout that challenged my strength, balance, and flexibility. I found myself returning each week to learn new postures and for the challenge of pushing myself to the edge. During that year, I noticed physical changes such as my knee no longer swelling after long runs and ruck marches, increased inner core strength, and an overall improvement in my level of fitness.

After that year, I changed jobs and could no longer attend the class at Fort Campbell but was fortunate to find the Yoga Mat studio in Clarksville that offered Connected Warriors classes. I started bringing my six-year old daughter to class, and she instantly fell in love with her Yoga practice. She even started conducting her own classes at home where she would teach her younger brother. Throughout the year that we practiced together, I found that the classes strengthened our father-daughter relationship. I also started noticing mental changes. I felt more calm throughout the day, was able to fall asleep faster at night, and those little annoying things that would set me off were no longer that important.

This past year everything changed. My teacher and mentor, Kathy, invited me to participate in the Elevated Warrior program and attend the 200-hour Connected Warrior Teacher Training. Having seen and experienced all the benefits of Connected Warriors Yoga, I knew I had to share those benefits with my fellow service members, our Veterans, and their Families. I've had the opportunity to teach injured Soldiers, Family members who deal with the stress of frequent deployments, and seasoned Veterans who continue to serve our nation. It's incredibly rewarding to see their practice grow as they realize the positive effects of Yoga on their mind and body. Looking back at that first class three years ago, I can't believe how much my life has changed and how many others have been able to share that same experience thanks to Connected Warriors." - Michael, SGM, U.S. Army Veteran with 20 years in service, RYT-200

A YOGA self-practice will help you learn how to handle stressful situations in a more relaxed manner by quieting and focusing your mind, which encourages positive thoughts and self-acceptance. By increasing relaxation and lowering stress, you may feel benefits in the following areas:
   Longer and deeper sleep
   Increased strength, flexibility, balance and focus
   Increased resiliency to stress
   Heightened cardiovascular conditioning, lower blood pressure and weight management
   Stronger bones, improved immune functions and increased oxygen supply to the body
   Improved mental and physical health; management of PTS and TBI symptoms

A non-pharmaceutical method to manage pain and relieve stress

Improved self-confidence, self-worth, enhanced ease, and equanimity in daily life

Some benefits of correct breathing are a flexible spine, improved posture, healthy nervous, immune, and autonomic systems, improved circulation, increased oxygenated blood and improved metabolism.

Some symptoms of incorrect breathing are bad posture, restricted movements, nervous tension, anxiety, poor circulation, lung/breathing conditions, fatigue and depression.

Trauma-Conscious Yoga

Trauma-Conscious Yoga is based on the understanding that trauma is held in the cells of the body and mind — it is physiological rather than psychological and that reconnecting the body and mind with the synchronization of conscious breath, movement and concentration in a safe, secure, and predictable environment supports health and wellness. The evidence-based protocol manages and eases trauma's negative consequences occurring in the body and mind by reducing potential triggers of stress and providing choices which is the opposite of trauma. Practitioners learn techniques to reconnect and develop awareness of the body-mind needs in that moment.

Connected Warriors classes serve as therapeutic community engagements providing benefits to both the veteran/military and civilian communities. A large part of the physical benefits is the release of calming and positive thought producing chemicals which occur when in social gatherings with like-minded individuals. Handing out the first Connected Warriors T-shirts in 2011 our warriors immediately took off their branch of service T-shirts, put on their Connected Warriors T-shirt and started talking to one another — something that was missing previously. They became a new tribe with a new uniform.

In a landmark study published July 25th, 2017 in the *American Journal of Preventive Medicine*, Dr. Erik J. Groessl and researchers from the VA San Diego Healthcare System found that Veterans who completed a 12-week Connected Warriors Yoga program reported improved behavioral-based pain management, demonstrating a significant decline in opiate use (Veterans Affairs Research Communications). Additionally, a Connected Warriors-partnered scientific study from 2015 operated in conjunction with the Department of Veterans Affairs found that 62% of participants reported a positive reduction in pain, 70% an increased level of flexibility and balance, and 100% reported an increased level of social interaction and stress management behaviors.

A Nova Southeastern University multi-year study completed in 2015 researching the effectiveness of trauma-conscious Yoga instruction clearly demonstrates the physiological and psychological benefits: participants report that one of the most meaningful outcomes of their time spent in Connected Warriors sessions is the camaraderie they experience as a result of belonging to a group of "brothers and sisters" who are also embracing Yoga to improve their lives. That is, engagement in Connected Warriors sessions helped participants to no longer feel isolated. Social isolation is recognized as a primary contributing factor to suicide. As such, through work with trauma-conscious Yoga instruction, Connected Warriors is directly battling our current suicide epidemic.

"My military story begins in May 2011 where I graduated as a Distinguished Military Graduate (DMG) from The Citadel: The Military College of South Carolina (DMG-top 10% in the entire Nation for Army officers commissioning into service). I served in the Army from October 2011 to November 2016 as a Medical Service Officer. I was a medical platoon leader for 3-187 IN BN, 3rd BCT, 101st Airborne Division (AASLT) where I deployed to East Afghanistan and received a Combat Medic Badge and two Army Commendation Medals. I then was given the position as the 3rd Brigade Combat Team-Medical Operations Officer where I was in charge of six of my peers, 212 medics and responsible for the medical readiness of over 4,500 Soldiers.

My transition back into society was one of the hardest things I have ever went through and still go through today. My story is filled with trauma and suicide (13 close friends/peers/Soldiers) because they could not find solutions to the mental health difficulties that combat Veterans face. My own solution was to drink and use pharmaceutical drugs in order to escape the realities of mental torture that I was experiencing on a daily basis. The constant feeling of loneliness and depression (which would transition into stints of adrenaline-fueled anxiety) was driving me crazy. Coming back from deployment I did not have my support system (my platoon) anymore. They were transferred to other bases or had their own lives and families to tend to. And by 2014, I started to think about suicide myself. I even attempted suicide on multiple occasions.

After the last failed attempt (while in the military) I decided that I needed to get out of my current environment and start all over. I transferred to Ft. Knox, KY to become a medical recruiting officer. The geographical change did not make things better, it only made things worse. My loneliness and depression intensified, and my alcohol and drug use took off. I was drinking and using just to get through the day (not just to go to bed at night). This is where my "solution" soon became a bigger problem than my emotional distress. Luckily, I was admitted into a 30-day program at Ft. Knox-Lincoln Trail Behavioral Health facility. This is when I truly knew I needed help, but I also knew that mood stabilizers and sleep meds were just another short-term fix (just like my previous misuse of alcohol and drugs). I was discharged from the Army under Honorable conditions in November of 2016. And shortly after, I was back to using and abusing drugs and alcohol because by that time it was my solution to everything.

I was truly ready to die, and I welcomed it. Luckily a friend reached out and got me into a treatment facility located out of Fort Lauderdale, Florida and this is when I first found Yoga and meditation. I knew that I had found a new passion and a new solution. My new goal in life was to help other Veterans who were struggling. After treatment, I was homeless/living in a halfway house, with no bank account and desperate for someone to take a chance on me! That is when I reached out to Judy Weaver and Connected Warriors. Judy and this program truly changed my life on every aspect. Without Judy, I know in my heart I would be dead today-through suicide or overdose. This program did not only give me a career purpose. It led me down a path of contentment, community, and spiritual growth that most men/women never get to experience in their entire lives. Today, because of Connected Warriors, I am enjoying life drug, alcohol free and medication free (mood stabilizers and sleeping medications). I wake up every morning and make it my mission to help a Veteran. I volunteer on my off time as a Veteran Liaison for the Amiri King Foundation and Save a Life: U.S.. I volunteer to help Veterans find affordable sober living housing through a company called "Sober Living by Tiffany" in Fort Lauderdale. I truly have an understanding of myself and how I can be most useful to my community and the world around me and I owe it all to Judy Weaver and Connected Warriors". - Brian Thornsberry, Director of Operations, Connected Warriors

General Asana Practice Guidelines – Getting ready for a physical practice

When you practice either at a Connected Warriors led Trauma-Conscious Yoga class or on your own, please practice with these guidelines in mind:

Wear loose comfortable clothing that allows movement.

Refrain from eating anything heavy two hours prior to practicing.

Stay hydrated before and after you practice.

Use the blocks and/or strap to support the posture to meet your physical abilities.

Listen to your body's rhythm and adjust your practice accordingly in regard to duration, difficulty and intensity considering any injuries, illness, and mental stress.

Acknowledge the ability to balance the various levels of the body and the mind into an alignment that is effortless. Do not force the body into any "expected" alignment.

If self-practicing, review the Connected Warrior's Asana Guide – You can complete the practice in 30-75 minutes, depending on the length of time in each posture (shape). Suggested hold is three to five full breaths.

Breathe – Typically maintaining conscious breath control throughout your asana practice.

Equal length inhales, exhales, and intensity — preferably through nose

Inhale during upward movements — opening front of the body

Exhale during downward movements — opening back of the body

Link movements — transitioning in/out of postures to inhale/exhale

Engage – Using bandhas (bodylocks) to protect your spine and strengthen your inner core

Mula Bandha – Lift and engage your pelvic floor (perineum muscle)

Uddiyana Bandha – Draw the abdominals below your naval in towards the spine and lift them up underneath the ribcage.

Connect – Noticing a physical connection to the ground, your body, and your mind.

Be mindful of the placement of hands and feet

Be mindful of direction of pelvis in relationship to the spine

Be mindful of direction and rotation of extremities

Be mindful of a clear, steady focus and a quiet mind

Cultivating an ease of effort regardless of difficulty of posture

Types of Asanas – This informs the relationship of the spine and pelvis

Standing	Forward Bends	Inversions
Seated	Twists	Supine
Back Bends	Arm Balances	Neutral

Check-in with yourself – Opportunities to notice your breath as you consider

Awareness – Can you acknowledge and observe your body's physical abilities and limitations?

Intention – Can you direct your mental energy to control physical action?

Effort – Can you balance intensity of action with release of strain with no attachment to outcome?

Mindfulness – Can you actively observe and control the direction of your thoughts?

Concentration – Can you focus on synchronizing breath and movement?

Words from a Connected Warriors teacher and Veteran below best summarizes how Trauma-Conscious Yoga is an intervention for physical, mental and spiritual health and wellness.

"I'm a damn Marine and haven't cried in a hundred years."
MSgt "Lee" Beckler, USMC (RET), 20 Years
RYT-200, Owner Sage Yoga Studios, Fallbrook, CA

"Have you ever noticed that when two people look at a piece of art that they usually focus on something different? Abstract art is a great example, you probably see a man in uniform sitting on a yoga mat in an art studio with a dusty floor. Well, I am that man. Let me tell you what I see."

I see a child that was beaten by his alcoholic father. "I probably deserved it." [scrape away some clay]

He beat my mother in front of me and my brothers. "She DIDN'T deserve it." [scrape away]

Finally, after all these years she is leaving him. [more dust on the floor]

Why am I getting tossed back and forth? [dust]

My best friend killed himself. We're just kids! [scrape, press, dust]

I have to move out on my own, get a job, pay my bills and finish high school on my own. [more dust]

I am trying hard to make dad proud but nothing is working. I'll try harder. [scrape]

I have to get away from here but how? I'll join the military, that'll make him proud. No. [squeeze]

Going to war. I want to go. I need to go. [press]

My best friend was burned so badly that I didn't recognize him when he asked for help. [take more off]

Back from war. He'll be proud. No. [dust]

He died. Damn it! Why? Just once! Why didn't you say those words? PROUD. [fuck]

Regroup. My family. My career. Focus. [dust]

Failed marriage. Kids won't speak to me. I'm alone. [mud, dust, scrape]

Career. New love. New life. Hope. [dust]

Another war, deployments, will she put up with it? Will she put up with me? [scrape away]

Dave...my friend, my mentor, my Marine brother. Why? Why did you do it? [hell, fuck, dust]

She did it. She stayed with me. How? [dust]

She shared her breath, her life, her Yoga. I can sleep! I can breathe. I can rest. [dust]

This is what I see coming from the clay. "Namaste." – MSgt Beckler

Connected Warriors is deeply committed to helping the world feel better one breath at a time.

Address: 4950 Communication Avenue, Suite 115, Boca Raton, Florida 33431

Phone: 954-278-3764

Website: http://www.connectedwarriors.org

CHAPTER 8 - BIOWAVE

Bradford Siff, Founder and President, BioWave

BioWave is technology that blocks pain at the source. It's patented, proven, effective neurostimulation is changing lives every day. It leapfrogs today's current technology with its bold pain blocking approach to pain relief. Because it's designed to block pain at the source, healthcare providers and patients alike affectionately call the BioWave device the "blue box" as if it has magical properties to it.

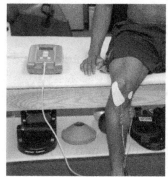

There are many differences between BioWave's neurostimulators and other devices. BioWave "blue boxes" utilize a proprietary signal mixing technology that delivers two continuously summed, high-frequency alternating current signals through skin into deep tissue where the body creates a new set of signals, one of which is in the form of a low-frequency electrical field. This field is optimized for blocking pain and providing functional improvement including a greater range of motion and a reduction in stiffness and muscle spasm for up to 72 hours with percutaneous electrodes and for up to 24 hours with noninvasive electrodes following a 30-minute treatment. In addition to providing long-lasting efficacy, these signals are significantly more comfortable leading to improved patient treatment compliance.

BioWave is a frequency conduction pain block. This mechanism of action is similar to a chemical anesthetic like Novocain, except Biowave is blocking the pain signal electrically instead of chemically. BioWave's signal technology is based on the discovery that when two high-frequency signals are added together in the device and then delivered into the body through a single electrode, the signals will pass into deep tissue and affect all polarized tissues, including nerves like pain fibers, tendons, ligaments and muscle tissue. These polarized tissues cause the two high frequency signals to multiply together resulting in an active therapeutic low frequency electrical field focused in approximately a 3.5-inch diameter hemisphere (think of the size of half of a grapefruit) beneath and surrounding each electrode, not across the surface of the skin between the electrodes like TENS. The BioWave active electrical field prevents the transmission of pain signals along these pain fibers, causes a light numbness to form five minutes into the treatment and causes an increase in blood flow in the volume of tissue beneath and surrounding each electrode. The light numbness remains at the treatment site for up to 20 minutes following a 30-minute treatment. Additionally, muscle tissue is held in tension during the treatment, so the treatment feels like a deep smooth pressure sensation.

Because the electrical field blocks the pain signal internally right at the pain nerve, the magnitude of the efficacy is much greater and the length of residual pain relief can last as long as 72 hours which is a dramatic improvement over TENS and other types of old-fashioned electrical stimulation.

All BioWave devices utilize the company's patented signal technology which includes active monitoring and control of the electrical signals to ensure the accurate and safe delivery of therapeutic energy into deep tissue. BioWave neurostimulators automatically prevent patients from receiving too much current which could lead to a burn.

All BioWave devices alternate the delivery of the two summed high-frequency signals so quickly back and forth to the two electrodes that the patient cannot distinguish that the signals have left either location. The net effect is there are two active electrodes, each of which can treat a distinct volume of tissue simultaneously and there is no noxious twitching sensation like TENS.

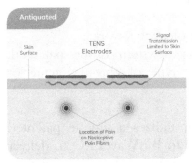

Low frequency signals (1-180Hz in frequency) are required to inhibit transmission of pain signals along nerve fibers in the body. However, electrical signals in this frequency range cannot pass through the skin because of the skin's impedance and capacitance. TENS devices deliver pulsed low-frequency signals across the surface of skin typically between two surface electrodes placed on either side of the painful area. The result is a surface effect based on Gate Control Theory and the patient feels a noxious twitching, electrical sensation between the electrodes. The TENS signals never get to the pain fibers inside the body that are conducting the pain signals. The sensation produced by TENS may act as a distraction from the pain while the device is on, however, there is little residual benefit or functional improvement once the therapy session is over.

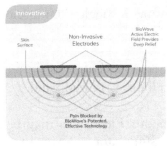

High-frequency signals can easily pass through skin, but individually do not affect pain nerves. BioWave's signal technology is based on the discovery that when two high-frequency signals are added together in the device and then delivered into the body through a single electrode, the signals will pass into deep tissue and affect all polarized tissues, including nerves like pain fibers, tendons, ligaments and muscle tissue. These polarized tissues cause the two high frequency signals to multiply together resulting in an active therapeutic low frequency electrical field focused in approximately a 3.5-inch diameter hemisphere (think of the size of half of a grapefruit) beneath and surrounding each electrode, not across the surface of the skin between the electrodes like TENS. The BioWave active electrical field prevents the transmission of pain signals along these pain fibers, causes a light numbness to form five minutes into the treatment and causes an increase in blood flow in the volume of tissue beneath and surrounding each electrode. The light numbness remains at the treatment site for up to 20 minutes following a 30-minute treatment. Additionally, muscle tissue is held in tension during the treatment, so the treatment feels like a deep smooth pressure sensation. Because the electrical field blocks the pain signal internally right at the pain nerve, the magnitude of the efficacy is much greater and the length of residual pain relief is much longer than TENS and other types of old-fashioned electrical stimulation.

Clinical studies report that 85% of patients respond to BioWave neurostimulation – it literally gets them "back in the game". BioWave neurostimulators can be used to reduce acute, chronic or post-operative pain and improve function including an increase in range of motion, decrease in stiffness and reduction of muscle spasm for up to 72 hours with BioWavePENS and for up to 24 hours with BioWavePRO or BioWaveHOME following a single 30-minute treatment.

BioWave is non-opioid, FDA cleared, pain relief technology that works.
The BioWaveHOME Neuromodulation Pain Therapy System is the patented, proven-effective prescription therapy for treating any type of chronic, acute or postoperative pain at home or while traveling.

The BioWaveHOME neurostimulator utilizes a unique patented signal-mixing technology that is identical to BioWavePRO to deliver electrical signals through the skin directly to nerves for inhibiting pain transmission and improving function. The signal technology is covered by several U.S. and international patents.

Clinical studies have shown that BioWaveHOME with noninvasive electrodes can be used to reduce pain and improve function, including an increased range of motion, decreased stiffness and reduction of muscle spasm for up to 24 hours following a single 30-minute treatment.

BioWaveHOME can be used to treat pain in numerous locations including the lower and mid back, neck, hip, groin, knee, shoulder, ankle, foot, elbow, wrist and hand.

If patients require greater pain relief, BioWave Percutaneous Electrodes may be prescribed for patients for use with a BioWaveHOME neurostimulator.

If treatment by BioWavePRO with noninvasive electrodes in your healthcare provider's office reduced your pain or increased your range of motion, then you will receive a similar response from BioWaveHOME with noninvasive electrodes.

Easy to Use

Only three buttons are used to operate BioWaveHOME and there is no programming. The signals are optimized to penetrate skin, block pain and improve function.

BioWave is patented, smarter pain relief technology that is professional athlete proven — used by and trusted by the NFL, NBA, NHL, and MLB. Imagine what the effective and wearable BioWaveGO can do for your bad back, neck, shoulder, elbow, knee or almost anywhere you have pain. Just one 30-minute treatment blocks pain for up to 24 hours, so you have nothing to lose except the pain — or your money back. Feeling is believing.

Who uses BioWave

You have found BioWave because you or someone you love suffers from acute or chronic pain and you are looking for something that actually works to relieve it. There is a reason most teams in the NFL, NHL, NBA, and MLB, as well as over 160 NCAA programs, use BioWave. It's the same reason the U.S. military and veterans at more than 90 VA's use BioWave. It really works. If it works for them, imagine what it can do for you? BioWaveGO is based on 15 years of proven RX experience and is now available in a non-prescription strength for everyone else that needs effective, fast, safe, comfortable, wearable, and 100% drug-free chronic pain relief.

What is BioWave - 100% drug-free. Smarter pain relief. More than 15 years of proven RX experience, now available in non-prescription strength. BioWave is patented, non-opioid, and effective pain relief technology. This is NOT some old-fashioned TENS or something you have wear for 30+ days. BioWave is simply the best-kept secret in pain relief and once discovered is often excitedly shared among family and friends who will thank you for changing their lives. How much would you pay for significant relief from pain? $1,000, $10,000, more? If you suffer from chronic pain, you know what we are talking about. We invite you to do the research and learn why BioWaveGO is affordable life-changing pain relief technology that is patented and different from anything else, and that actually works — or your money back. Whatever your passion, get back into the game of life — pain-free. Effective, non-opioid, proven pain relief is finally here for everyone.

Most of the treatments deal with chronic pain and I would say the majority deal with lumbar and cervical pain. That's probably the bread and butter for our device, but certainly any extremity pain in the shoulder, elbow, elbow, wrist or ankle. We can really treat almost any location on the body. Over 75% of patients respond to BioWave treatment, with a significant improvement in their pain scores, mobility and stiffness. The device can even help patients with complex conditions such as pain from arachnoiditis, which is an inflammation of one of the membranes that surrounds and protects nerves in the spinal cord. There's a handful of anecdotal data that we have where patients with pain from arachnoiditis have responded to treatment with BioWave. Similarly, patients with failed back surgery or complex regional pain syndrome (CRPS) have been treated with BioWave and it has helped them. I'm not saying it reduces their pain 100 percent, but patients may get a 30, 40, or 50 percent reduction in their pain level and the relief lasts for an extended period of time following the treatment.

Contact Information/Hyperlinks

**Be sure to visit the main BioWave page for more information: https://www.biowave.com/what-is-biowave/technology/

**Call 1-877-BIOWAVE or E-Mail info@biowave.com

**If you have any questions please go to: http://www.biowave.com/contact/

CHAPTER 9 - BLU ROOM

Mike Wright

Are you reaching your breaking point? No matter how much we train — mentally and physically — everybody has their breaking point. Whether it's physical and mental health challenges, financial woes, or what some describe as the "daunting task" of re-assimilating to civilian life, the pressure can be overwhelming.

In its first four years of use around the world, the Blu Room technology has demonstrated consistent health benefits for tens of thousands of people. This chapter presents personal stories from three Veterans as well as an introduction to the science behind the Blu Room technology to help explain how the Blu Room structure with all of its components — some obvious, some not — can account for those health benefits.

Science helps alleviate doubt in the minds of people who are unfamiliar with the technology and it will reinforce hope in those people who have not found complete relief in other medical technologies. The Blu Room augments and integrates with any conventional treatment plan. It provides a synergistic influence that helps provide balance by bringing the user to a point of stasis. A person suffering from acute or chronic health conditions need not give up the other programs that may be helping their condition. The Blu Room will compliment any other program.

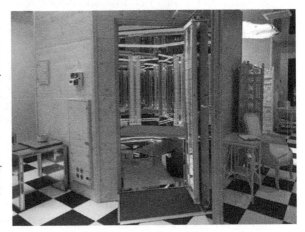

What is not covered as much in this chapter are the subtler emotional and mental health improvements that are often overlooked in the search for relief from a physical malady. Compassion, love, understanding, a state of calm in the face of adversity — these are also benefits that Blu Room users have reported. They are the renewed states of mind that deeply influence the physical state of the body.

"Far too often, we're leaving our Veterans to fight their toughest battles alone." - Senator John Walsh (D-MO) (First Iraq War combat veteran to serve in the U.S. Senate)

You are not alone. The healing journey begins with a change of perspective, a mental reset or rebirth that leads the body to a physical renewal. May the words in this chapter help restore your confidence in the journey to a greater you.

We are at wonderful place in the evolution of the Blu Room. Over 120,000 user sessions have been provided in the U.S. and 11 other countries. There are 35 operational Blu Room locations with eight additional locations under construction. Countries with Blu Room services include the U.S., Argentina, Austria, Canada, Colombia, Ecuador, Germany, Italy, Japan, Mexico, Switzerland, and Taiwan. Four locations are for private use or employee-only programs and the remaining locations are open to the public in either clinical or spa/wellness settings. You can find locations at www.bluroom.com.

The Blu Room has become so popular so quickly because it works. It's effects are not just skin deep. It works down to the cellular level. We have strong evidence of this in how the Blu Room has helped people with cancer, diabetes, blood pressure, cholesterol levels, Post-Traumatic Stress Disorder (PTSD), neurological disorders, and more.

What we have found to be the most effective is how the Blu Room stimulates the mind to change an attitude — how you look at yourself. Self-love or self-respect or self-confidence are topics we don't talk about enough in medicine. In the last hundred years, medicine has become so specialized with the body people sometimes forget to attend to the mind and spirit. The Blu Room technology supports all three — the body, the mind, and the spirit or will.

The Blu Room helps the patient move forward from their past. For example, a Soldier who has had trauma on the battlefield is finally able to move forward and find place of equilibrium or stasis.

The Blu Room technology helps a person begin to feel better, sleep better, and have renewed hope that he or she can get physically better. We know how powerfully the mind influences the body. We know that healing always begins in the mind. The Blu Room provides the user with a beautiful sense of well-being. When you feel better, you think better. When you think better, you begin to feel even better. Our Blu Room patients reach a place where they are able to see themselves well.

The Blu Room is a novel environment so the experience varies from person to person because we are each individuals. It bumps you into a different part of your brain and opens a door for a new mind perspective. Many people have described it as being deeply relaxing, lifting their mood, and bringing about a state of slightly detached calm or peace. A common side benefit of this state is a relief from aches and pains. Some people experience dynamic shifts in perspective and spiritual insights. Some people have reported profound personal healing.

Our state of mind influences everything we perceive. Our state of mind also influences our genetic expression, so mind and DNA are inextricably combined. Whatever the mind is, the body becomes, and the environment reflects. Since the mind is the greatest healer and the mind is intertwined with DNA, the Blu Room can augment a person's natural healing abilities. We have really only scratched the surface of what the Blu Room can do. The future of health technology is very exciting.

Three Stories

Dale and Dave are both Vietnam Veterans. Like many Veterans, they walled off that part of their lives when they returned to civilian life. But behind the wall, powerful issues festered and grew. They were explosives waiting to go off. This is a similar theme for those who are transitioning out today. But what do you do when pills and alcohol don't work? Lash out? End up on the street? Suicide? Most Veterans who commit suicide are over the age of 50, just like Dale and Dave.

Dale's story:

I am the younger of two boys born in 1942 to a beautiful teenager who gave me a doorway into a world of potentials. She was the oldest of a dozen sisters and a couple of brothers. I never met my biological father as he had another path to follow that did not include raising children.

My mother felt that my brother and I needed male guidance. Her occupation as a waitress did not allow time and money so she placed both us in a Catholic military school which I attended for grade levels 1st, 2nd and 4th.

Highlights of my journey include:
Great friendships and association with remarkable people who influenced my life
Becoming a middleweight boxing champion
Six years of active military service as a military policeman, dog handler, and door gunner on gunship in Vietnam
Becoming an exhibition skydiver and parachutist with 800 jumps
Running over 20 years including 13 marathons, and
Managing a nightclub in the San Francisco Bay Area that fostered the likes of Moby Grape and the Grateful Dead

After the Vietnam war, I married and had my first of two children. Working as a professional photographer for a large color processor I managed a staff that provided services for 30 or so high schools and universities. Sports photography included Skydiving, Rose Bowl, Stanford, and the 49ers. I have a degree in aviation, and I am a licensed pilot.

Plagued with PTSD and other war-related issues, I left California in the early 70's and bought a small country store in southern Oregon. Here I became the gas station, grocery store, and U.S. Postmaster, as well as a volunteer fireman. My son was born. I sold the store, kept the Postmaster position, and built a horse ranch on the edge of the Kalmiopsis Wilderness. This is when my "running" activity began. Moving to Grants Pass where I attempted to keep my PTSD under control, I became Postmaster at Murphy, OR.

Shortly after a near death experience in Red Bluff, CA, I made some radical changes in my life. I divorced my first wife and left the Postal Service just a few months before my retirement after 25 years. I felt this choice was necessary to avoid going "Postal" and getting myself in serious trouble because of harassment by my then boss in the Postal Service.

I remarried to a wonderful woman that introduced me to a video called "The Magic Brain" which introduced me to Ramtha's School of Enlightenment and the Great Work. We moved to Kauai where we lived on a 4,000-acre cattle ranch that had been private for 200 years. Using what I learned at RSE, I made a focus card on building a cabin which became a reality but was much larger than expected. I also made a focus card on fabulous wealth that also was also realized. It is my understanding that the only reason I am still in this body is directly the result of my ability to grasp what I have been taught.

About five years ago, having no insurance, I was encouraged to go see if the VA would assist me in removing a tumor that had been growing on my neck. After reviewing my Combat records, the VA did so. The VA has been treating me for Agent Orange, Prostate, Urinary, IBS, Nerve and Esophageal Issues. Concussion issues accompany daily life with noise from the brain.

At present I am 75 years old, have six wonderful children and 14 incredible grandchildren.

In the fall of 2016, I was gifted 30 sessions in the Blu Room and after 10 sessions they profoundly affected my physical and mental status to the point I am amazed on a daily basis.

My wish is to convey my story in a way that inspires movement from within those that have the ears to hear. - Dale

Dave's story:

David is a 71-year-old Vietnam Veteran with a history of PTSD who had a severe heart attack in April 2014, and subsequently a stroke in August of the same year. His heart attack was so severe, that on the way to the hospital he went into cardiac arrest — he was successfully resuscitated and required stents in two of his heart arteries. The sustained heart damage caused him to have congestive heart failure from severe ischemic cardiomyopathy with a heart pump fraction of 30%, normal being about 65%.

Only four months after this heart attack, he had a severe stroke, that left him with right sided weakness and expressive aphasia, the inability to speak — he had a vocabulary of two words — "yes" and "no". After his stroke, he was in a rehabilitation center for a month. He has been doing speech therapy for the last four years.

David started using the Blu Room in February of 2017 and has been coming twice a week for two years. He still has speech difficulties and his memory is affected but he is doing a lot better. He must pause and find his words but is able now to speak in full sentences. Sometimes he has to try several times to say what he means before it comes out with the meaning he intended. His speech therapists are amazed at his remarkable progress. He gets teary eyed when he talks about his journey with the Blu Room. He says it is not because of his PTSD, he only killed one person in the war and was able to cope with the horrible things he saw — it took him about eight years after the war to come to terms with his life. There was something else that happened.

David explains that he experienced the Blu Room as both negative and positive for several sessions. Then something happened to him in January of 2018 and since then all his sessions were positive. He says that it was not the Blu Room that was negative, it was that something in his being was out of sync. David did not realize that his body and mind were not in harmony. Then in January he felt in the Blu Room like his body, his age and everything about him caught up with himself. After that, everything was all right.

David's neighbor Helena notes that she was the one he came to when he had his heart attack in 2014 and she called 911. Having known him for many years, she describes David's transformation over the past year nothing short of miraculous. She says David used to be a grouchy, grumpy man, easy to get angry and have a temper. In the last few months she notes that he is so sweet, completely transformed, moved to tears in his emotions and able to express them with the people around him. Helena notes this is not the old David, he is completely new, completely transformed, and unrecognizable from his old self.

David explains that the Blu Room can help you heal at your own pace. If you add to it by intentionally working on healing yourself and your attitudes, it can help you speed up your healing. He says he added to his healing by looking at this "negative" in his life, his "shadow," this being out of sync with himself. He explains that if you are adding more to your healing then it will take even less time in the Blu Room, until there is a time where the negative "issue" is diminished to "nothing". The negative disappears, it just is gone one day. David says it depends on what you are doing and how you are in your own healing. That is what happened to David in the Blu Room. His negative disappeared to nothing, and what was left was love.

He cries exhausted after he explained this, and the look in his eyes speak to a much greater understanding than he has words for. David describes that after January 2018 the Blu Room helped him heal something that now is peaceful and calm, like a shadow that got lifted.

He cries because he has no words for what happened to him. How do you say that something in the depth of your being, that you felt throughout your life but could not give words to, but you could feel sitting there with every breath and that was like a nagging shadow? That is what got healed in David through the Blu Room. He can best express it in his eyes with his tears, and this thing that happened is bigger than words. And yet because it happened he is now able to speak better, and his brain is continuing to heal.

David continues to improve, and he surrenders to his journey. He is scheduled to get an implantable defibrillator put into his heart soon due to his low pump function. A few months ago, he had some chest pains, but now despite his poor heart function, he does not have any symptoms of heart failure. He is accepting his journey and is doing what he needs to support his improvement, including following up with his doctors and continuing the Blu Room treatments.

Cynthia's story:

A pilot who served in Afghanistan, Cynthia returned home from the war and was struck by a pickup truck, suffering a traumatic brain injury. After trying physical and speech therapy, she started Blu Room treatments. "The Blu Room was very peaceful and therapeutic," Cynthia said. She went three to four times per week for 20 sessions. "My short-term memory was coming back thanks to the Blu Room sessions."

A brief overview of the science

The Blu Room is a patented technology that shields the user from the outside world. It provides an environment that induces a deep state of mental and physical tranquility.

The room includes music to provide a relaxing — and for many people a therapeutic — effect on the individual within. Speaking as a former Top Gun fighter pilot, any treatment that includes music, relaxation, and soft lighting seems at first to be a bit too "touchy and feely" but there is plenty of evidence that the Blu Room's high-tech combination of all those items helps a lot of people.

The Blu Room creates a novel atmosphere that insulates the user from the daily environment. It provides the user with an uplifting environment that can augment one's state of creative focus. The room is a small octagon-shaped space about 12 feet across with a couch in the center. Highly polished mirrored stainless-steel lines the interior walls, floor, and ceiling which give the room a high-tech look reflecting into forever. Blue LED lights illuminate the interior and non-visible ultraviolet phototherapy lamps stimulate some of the metabolic effects described below. Since the brain isn't busy responding to the stimulus of the everyday environment, the mind is able to relax, free associate, or hold a relaxed state of focus without distractions (theta state).

The sun is an indispensable factor in regulating our genetic material, biological rhythms and many biological processes via the skin and the eyes[1]. However, with the emphasis on medications in the modern marketplace, the therapeutic effects of sunlight — in particular the ultraviolet B portion of the spectrum — have been overlooked. Even so, clinical studies guided by the progress in physics, chemistry and molecular biology have resulted in very effective treatment of certain conditions with ultraviolet phototherapy. We now have a greater understanding of the science behind what our ancestors knew intuitively in previous centuries with their veneration of the life-giving properties of the sun.

Frequent, brief exposures to UVB light have many bio-positive systemic effects on the human being. In many cases, these effects can be obtained from UVB lamps with very low "doses" to compensate for the shortage during the darker months of the year when there is less sun.

For example, vitamin D3 is created in the skin when it is exposed to UVB irradiation. When processed in the liver and the kidneys, the bioactive form of vitamin D3 is created. Vitamin D3 is actually a hormone. It influences cellular information, cell differentiation, endocrine regulatory systems, immune function, and heart metabolism.

The sun emits a wide spectrum of light whereas the Blu Room provides only narrowband UVB florescent light along with visible blue LED light. The amount of solar radiation in the entire UV spectrum that reaches the earth's surface varies by latitude, time of year, time of day, and atmospheric conditions. The total UV (UVA + UVB) portion of solar radiation is roughly ten percent of the total irradiance reaching the surface. The UVB portion of solar radiation is even less. Direct measurements with a UVB meter indicate an irradiance level of 0.33 mw/cm^2 at solar noon on the summer solstice at 45 degrees north latitude on a clear day. This provides a general exposure guideline that users can relate to their personal experience. Three minutes of UVB in a 20-minute Blu Room session is roughly equivalent to 10 minutes in the summer sun on a clear day at mid-latitudes, except that Blu Room users are not exposed to any UVA which is the main cause of skin cancer. A 10-year follow-up study of patients exposed to narrowband UVB showed no significantly increase in the risk of skin cancer[4].

The Blu Room Experience

The Blu Room is useful for anyone — including children and the elderly — who wants to step out of their daily environment. Users have reported a wide range of personal benefits, including:

Deep relaxation
Faster healing processes
Relief from physical pain
Relief from mental stress and anxiety including PTSD
Improved health and well-being
Deepened focus
Increased creativity
Greater self-awareness
Significant increases in Vitamin D3

Under the supervision of a physician, patients with the following conditions have found benefit from their Blu Room experiences:

Cancer: breast, meningioma, lymphoma, prostate, bladder, colon, uterine, squamous cell

Pain: back, hips, knee, neck, shoulder, headache, ankle, foot, stomach, spinal stenosis, cervix

Also:

Acid reflux	High blood pressure
Allergies	High cholesterol
Ankylosing spondylitis	Left ventricular ejection fraction
Anxiety	Multiple sclerosis
Arthritis/Arthrosis	Nasal congestion
Astigmatism	Osteoporosis bone density
Cerebral palsy	Parkinson's tremors
Chronic Fatigue Syndrome	Post-operative infection
Crohn's disease	Psoriasis
Decubitus ulcer	PTSD/Trauma disorder
Depression	Stroke
Diabetic insulin level requirements	Tachycardia
Diabetic neuropathy, foot/ankle open sores	Tendinitis/Tendinosis
Epiretinal Membrane reduction	Thyroid disorder
Erosive Osteochondrosis	Vitamin D3 serum levels
Hepatitis C viral load	

To date, all research has been informal, retrospective, and primarily anecdotal. A number of the patient benefits reported above have been documented with before and after lab work or imaging ordered by either the supervising physician or the referring physician. A selection of case studies and user testimonials[5] can be viewed at www.bluroom.com. The volume and wide range of beneficial reports have paved the way for more formal prospective clinical research that is slated to begin at a new Blu Room facility in a U.S. State that currently does not have a Blu Room service, thus bias can be reduced in both patients and providers.

Healthcare providers, scientists, and most of the public agree on the benefits of relaxation. Peer-reviewed medical studies on relaxation and meditation confirm the benefits. However, mediation takes training and relaxing can be a challenge in our busy lives. We know the healing powers of relaxation such as increased attention span, improved memory, relieving anxiety and depression, pain relief, and spurring creativity. The deep relaxation induced by the Blu Room promotes vasodilatation, facilitating blood flow throughout the body and especially the brain. A 20-minute session provides a natural "high" that creates a whole-body healing effect. Relief from nagging discomforts is commonly reported by Blu Room users.

The Blu Room also provides a lifting of mood. Mood is a residual attitude we carry with us between emotional storms. When mood is lifted, the storms can abate. In addition to a vitamin D boost, the Blu Room triggers the brain to release endorphins. Among other effects, the secretion of endorphins induces a sense of euphoria and enhances the immune response. With higher endorphin levels, you feel less pain and are less affected by stress. Many users report a sense of detachment, a sense of no time passing, and a state of joy, all of which are normal states.

There is a great deal of research on the benefits of a short nap during the day. A 20-minute nap provides significant benefit for improved alertness and performance without leaving you feeling groggy or interfering with nighttime sleep. A 20-minute Blu Room session will give you an extra boost over a regular nap. Shift your brainwaves from beta (the day-to-day reactive state) to the deeper – more creative — frequencies of alpha or theta.

The theta brain state is a slower rate of brainwaves that occurs during deep focus or during dream sleep. The theta state can be accompanied by vivid imagery, creative thoughts, insights, and inspiration. Many Blu Room users report experiences similar to the theta state, including temporary loss of awareness of time, a sense of detachment, even mild euphoria.

In our daily waking state of consciousness, we are polarized in our thoughts and emotions, self and other, positive and negative, good and bad, morality and karma. To move in consciousness to the alpha or theta brain state provides a period of stasis, calm, peace, and even joy in the absence of polarized thought. Imagine a little slice of heaven on earth. The Blu Room is based upon the metaphysical science of elsewhere — "on earth as it is in heaven."

All pathologies begin as polarized attitudes that chemically stress the body. When you remove the polarity, you make room for deep relaxation, a sense of tranquility, and the opportunity for the greater mind to be present and observe a greater reality to be experienced in the body.

In addition to clinical locations, the Blu Room can be found at spas and wellness services. Most spa/wellness programs treat the body. When we think "spa," we often think of massage, facials, manicures, etc. When we think "wellness program," we conjure up weight loss, fitness, supplements, and more. With the Blu Room, relaxation and beauty starts with the mind. True beauty is a radiance from within, where one feels calm, open, light, and inspired! It is hard to be radiant when you are stressed out, in pain, in fear, or lacking sleep. That is where the Blu Room comes in. The Blu Room was specifically designed to give you peace in your mind, helping you to explore unknown vistas that were there all along.

The Blu Room experience is designed to be safe. With any experience in a new environment, it takes a while for the individual to adapt. For example, in learning to SCUBA dive or fly an airplane, the training starts slow and simple. We do advise people about the cautions related to UVB exposure which are minimized by the structure and duration of the Blu Room sessions. As described above, short but frequent exposure to UVB light has many positive systemic effects on the human body.

The Blu Room offers a door to a new future through a synergistic environmental experience for the occupant. It provides a safe tool to foster a wide range of subjective and objective improvements. When it is also used in an integrated health management practice under the supervision of a healthcare provider, it may provide a valuable adjunct for prevention, rehabilitation, and innovation thru synergistic medicine.

Visit https://www.bluroom.com/ for more information.

End notes
1. Koninklijke Philips Electronics N.V. Medical treatment with phototherapy. 2013.
2. Figure retrieved August 24, 2016 from
http://www.solarcsystems.com/us_narrowband_uvb.html
3. Gorham E, Garland C, Mohr S, Garland F. UV: The original Source! How to use it. Diagnosis and Treatment of Vitamin D Deficiency Workshop. April 9, 2010. UCSD Department of Family and Preventative Medicine. [6/2010] [Health and Medicine] [Professional Medical Education] [Show ID: 18717]
4. Weischer M, Blum A, Eberhard F, Roecken M, Berneburg M. No evidence for increased skin cancer risk in psoriasis patients treated with broadband or Narrowband UVB phototherapy: a first retrospective study. Acta Derm Venereol 2004; 84: 370-374.
5. Disclaimer: Testimonials are based on the real-life experiences of a few people, recorded in their own words regarding their own personal experiences of the Blu Room, and you are not likely, nor should you expect, to have similar results. Testimonials are not intended to make claims or even imply that the Blu Room can be used to diagnose, treat, cure, mitigate or prevent disease. Testimonials have not been evaluated by the FDA or any other regulatory entity. Blu Room Enterprises, LLC makes no representations or warranties as to results.

Blu Room® is an internationally registered trademark and service mark of JZ Knight. Used with permission. U.S. Patent 9,919,162.

CHAPTER 10 - CAMP 4 HEROES

John Woodall

My father is the President and Founder for Camp 4 Heroes. His name is John A. Woodall and I am John T. Woodall. I am known as John T. and everyone calls my dad Captain Woody. So, 17 years ago, when the towers fell in New York, I was standing on the riverbanks in New Jersey and I watched the buildings fall. My father ended up becoming a liaison from North Carolina to New York (he's a retired North Carolina/Raleigh Fireman) to support the Firemen who lost 343 brothers in the World Trade Center. So, we made those connections and began to help him to build relationships with the New York Firemen, and helped support them to raise millions of dollars; helped them by buying vans, supporting families who had lost loved ones.

We began to go from New York down to Walter Reed Hospital once the war started and people were starting to come back injured. We started going there and we would work with Gary Sinise or John Voight or any of these celebrities that supported the Warriors. There were a lot of these guys around at the time and we'd go in with them and they'd sign autographs and I'd bring my guitar and would take requests. I would play and sing and John Voight or somebody would talk to them. My dad would be there in his uniform and he would tell them that, "We were sorry that they were injured but we were all there to support them...and that their service wasn't for no reason...that we were, and are, all here behind them."

This became this very special thing, and even now to this day, there are at least two such events each year if not more. We put on a big Christmas Party and a big Super Bowl Party every year for service members and Veterans coming through Walter Reed each year. A lot of the men and women we have supported before come back and volunteer to help with these special events as well, making them even more special, and more like a family, in the process.

Fast forward a few years, I began opening up and doing shows with Gary Sinise & The Lieutenant Dan Band in South Carolina we played at: the Citidel; Beaufort, S. Carolina; North Charleston Coliseum. We did several shows together down there and at the Lieutenant Dan Weekends (LDW) One through Five we did four shows. One weekend was down at a place called Palm Key, and it was just a special weekend where we had art, crafts, classes, camping, campfires, etc.

Around a campfire one night we realized that the guys were like hugging each other and telling these stories...and their Caregivers were saying that they never heard them mention these stories before...or open up the way they were. And so, at that moment, it was like a lightbulb lit up. We thought what if we created a place where Veterans could come and sit around a campfire, in an organic non-sterile environment, and be able to just talk to each other and really relate their experiences? What if we get rid of the doctors and the white walls where they are all asked the same things as other Veterans? There is a time and place for everything, but we know that Veterans don't always relate that well in such an environment so why not try something we found that works?

Veterans have no problems trusting others who have been in battle with them, or who have relatable experiences; the people who were there supporting them, directly or not, throughout their years in the military. My dad and I have worked in that community for 17 years now and some of them have extreme trust for what we are trying to do. We are all volunteer based. The program is year-round and is located in Fairmont, North Carolina, which is pretty much in the middle of nowhere.

Our main mission is to lower the suicide rate in the Veteran and First Responder community. Everyone knows about the 20-25 number in the Veteran community and 10-15 for the First Responder community each day. We are trying to lower that rate and make a real difference by providing a place where, once enough people have heard about it, that will be a household name and a reference so that, if you are a Veteran or First Responder and are feeling that low, you can go talk to these guys and get away for at least a weekend. We want to offer a place of tranquility and sanctuary where individuals can come to and that will help them with their transition from service life into civilian life.

That's pretty much our mission statement. We'll offer classes and alternative 'therapies'...everything from art to music, recording, blacksmithing, welding, resume building, yoga, acupuncture, just all kinds of things. This is on top of athletics. We have a gym where we already have handicapped basketball. We have an equestrian center and two horses (and are planning on getting more horses), we have four goats who think they are dogs and a pig named Otis, we have a bathhouse, we have cabins, and we have fire pits. Everyone who comes out there says it's such a unique place...and that it's so peaceful.

Everything we offer at the camp is at no cost for our Veterans. We are also in the process of making the entire 'camp' ADA compliant. It's wonderful seeing our vision coming to life.

John T.: Bobby has a great sense of humor and is one of the greatest guys I have ever had the honor of being friends with and hanging out with.

Bobby H.: I served when I was nineteen and after 9/11 I went back for three more tours. On my third deployment my Humvee was hit by an IED and I was the only one to survive. I suffered the loss of my left hand and sustained burns over 38% of my body. I now go around the world and use my situation to help others. Now I speak at events and do comedy shows.

Below is a song I wrote:

Not a Day Goes By

First verse:
  We lined up our vehicles getting ready for war
  Just like we had done a thousand times before
  We talked about the mission and what could go wrong
  How no matter what would happen
  We'd stay Army strong
  We checked our equipment, inspected our gear
  Bowed down our heads, the Chaplin led the prayer
  I took the lead as we rolled out the gate
  Just another day no way of knowing our fate
  Not day goes by
  That I don't fight
  The battle in my mind
  Through my eyes
  The truth in every tear I cry
  I try God knows I cry
  I know I cry

Second verse:
  The bomb was big and the noise was loud
  Med evacuated from a dusty cloud
  My heart stop beating and my blood ran cold
  Swollen, burnt so I was told
  I prayed that God would set me free
  The bomb took four and only left me
  But they are angels my guiding lights
  Assuring me that everything will be alright
  Not day goes by
  That I don't fight
  The battle in my mind
  Through my eyes
  The truth in every tear I cry
  I know I cry
  God knows I cry
  Not a day goes by

That I don't fight
The battle of the mind
The war is over
The battles still in my mind
The war is over
No, I didn't die
Not a day goes by

I served in the U.S. Army for 13 years and did four tours to Iraq, and I was injured in 2007 when I was blown up by a roadside bomb that blew up my Humvee. I was the only survivor out of five guys. I had a hard time dealing with that my first year because of survivor's guilt. I can use my sense of humor to get through a lot of stuff...to kind of block it out. But I also know that my ability to make light of things can help others too. So, I continue to laugh, and make jokes and share my story and an occupational therapist persuaded me to try stand-up comedy. That was nine years ago and I have been doing comedy ever since. I also do motivational speaking and I have been traveling all over the place for that.

I have realized over the years that we need to find an outlet and that a lot of us don't know how to find that outlet...we get lost...but finding an outlet where we 'fit' whether it is woodworking, going to the gym, working with animals, blacksmithing, there is so much out there that Veterans with PTSD can discover what they like to do that, in turn, helps them to better deal with their PTSD. It is also about learning to trust yourself and your abilities in a particular genre.

I write my poetry and songs, and do my comedy, and when I go to the camp, I talk about what I do to Veterans and First Responders at the camp, so that they are exposed to additional options that they might not have thought of or been exposed to before. I have gone to the camp several times thus far. They are still building the camp up, and its mostly Veterans and First Responders passing through who are volunteering to help build or who are just coming through for a weekend visit.

For any Veterans out there, this is a place where you can bond with other Veterans. You can open up and talk freely to your fellow Veterans. You can trade secrets to how you survived different things...different situations. It is in talking to each other that we can really make a big difference.

For those who are still dealing with survivors' guilt, whether it's a situation like mine (where I was the lone survivor), or a Veteran survived multiple tours and wonder why they are still around. They beat themselves up over that question. I tell them that they have to stop asking that question and instead think about if they weren't here and if they didn't make it home. I ask them to think about what would they would want for the ones who did make it home.

Cory McKee: We went out to the camp to help out with disaster relief from the hurricane and when we were there, we were unloading trucks and organizing the relief effort and all of the supplies. It was pretty much working sun up to sun down but that's a good thing because we were all busy. We just waited on each truck to arrive, then would unload and store all of the supplies, and get the supplies ready for transport to people that needed the supplies.

It's a large camp with a lot of acreage and there's cabins on the property for guests to stay in. The main 'house' where the kitchen is, it's pretty spacious too. It's a big gathering area for people who are visiting. That's where everybody eats dinner. The ladies who volunteer to cook for us, they cook meals all day and provide meals all day. That was really awesome.

We were there a few days, and went back over Thanksgiving, to spend time with everybody out there, and it was impressionable enough to me that I went back again. Everybody there is very nice, and they all work hard and pitch in...there are no slackers...and everybody is just having a good time.

I was in the Mississippi National Guard and I went to Iraq in 2005 and, when I came home from there, I became a police officer until it got to the point that PTSD basically caught up with me. I eventually just ended up losing my career because of my PTSD. I went to the VA looking for a job because no one would hire me with the PTSD label and especially not in men line of work. So, I went to the VA desperate for work and they said I was unemployable. So, the VA started giving me my benefits then.

Five years ago, I fell into a fire, and I was hurt pretty badly. I wasn't expected to make it through the night. But I ended up making it even though I am now an amputee and lost my eye. I do have a mild TBI for Iraq and have had vertigo ever since, and that's the reason I fell into the fire, so it's all service connected.

My wife and I went to our local VFW (Chapter 1733) and we were there just hanging out one day and there were these two guys who came through with 'Mother of all Rucks' who were going cross-country to raise money for Veterans. Well, they kept in touch with us and told us about the Camp 4 Heroes organization and introduced us to its leadership, after which we were invited to come out to the camp to visit. We ended up meeting everybody when we went down to assist with the disaster relief efforts. We stayed in their single room cabins for three nights while we worked to assist with the relief efforts.

One of the nights that we were there they grilled out. They had horses, goats and even a pig that walks around out there. The horses were kept in a pen but the goats and the pot-bellied pig were allowed free range.

If any Veteran needs a place where they can feel safe, a place where they can be amongst other Veterans, that this place is very hospitable and the people running the camp are very nice people. They really care about their Veterans, and they take a lot of pride in what they do. It isn't just a haphazard kind of camp. As a combat Veteran, I felt very safe there. I wasn't nervous at all the entire time I was at the camp. It's a really big thing for people like me, a combat Veteran with PTSD, to feel safe anywhere.

They are really getting off the ground here and making things happen in support of Veterans. But they can't do it for free. Thoughts and prayers can only go so far though. It is the support of people who care about our Veterans, and who care about the mission of Camp 4 Heroes, that have, and will continue making this camp available to Veterans and their families in need of support.

Visit https://camp4heroes.org for more information.

CHAPTER 11 - CBD

Steve Danyluk

I am a U.S. Marine Corps Veteran who at one time worked with Wounded Warriors and Veterans at both Walter Reed and Bethesda Medical Centers. Recently, I arranged for a group of Veterans to go to the U.S. House of Representatives to talk with members of the House Veterans' Affairs Committee. While I was in a position working wounded issues when on Active Duty, I witnessed what I believe was, and continues to be, a policy of over-medicating wounded men and women with opiates and other toxic medications.

After leaving Active Duty, I continued to work with wounded Veterans through a number of non-profits that I was affiliated with. It was during this time that I noticed that a significant number of Veterans were self-medicating with Cannabis in an effort to get off of the medications that they were being prescribed by the VA and that they felt were killing them. I have never been an advocate for marijuana, and because of my military background and current career as a commercial airline pilot, I personally cannot use marijuana. However, because of what I experienced, I ended up starting a company that offers an alternative and non-addictive remedy, known as Warfighter Hemp, which contains CBD made from the hemp plant.

It contains less than .3% of THC, which is the chemical that makes you high. Because the THC level is so low, it is in compliance with the 2014 Farm Bill and therefore can be sold in all 50 States. However, even tough legal, the VA not only will not prescribe it, they will not even conduct research into its efficacy. But there is little doubt that it works, particularly with Post-Traumatic Stress Disorder (PTSD).

"One way of thinking about PTSD is an over-activation of the fear system that can't be inhibited, can't be normally modulated," as stated by Dr. Kerry Ressler of Emory University. Basically stated, the brain can't downshift out of overdrive.

For anyone who may not be familiar, CBD stands for Cannabidiol, and is one of more than 100 cannabinoids found in Cannabis Sativa, the Latin name for Cannibis or Hemp and are the natural chemical constituents of Cannabis and Hemp. CBD is one of the most well-known and well-researched cannabinoids. Another you may have heard of is tetrahydrocannabinol (THC).

Information on the Warfighter Hemp site can be found at http://www.warfighterhemp.com. On this site you can also read about CBD via the Cannabidiol FAQ page. My mission with Warfighter Hemp is to provide our nation's Veterans with an organic, non-addictive, non-psychoactive means to manage pain, lower anxiety, and improve the overall quality of their lives. Warfighter Hemp believes that our 23 million Veterans can lead the way in demonstrating that there is a viable alternative to the over prescription of addictive medications and offer a pathway out of the opioid epidemic currently plaguing our Veterans.

Two goals of the Trump administration are in conflict. President Trump says he wishes to care for Veterans, but his attorney general made moves against states that chose to legalize marijuana. I get feedback like this all of the time. The testimonials often come from Veterans who never thought they'd favor legalization. CBD is not Marijuana. Whatever can help vets with PTSD or chronic pain is worth a try, especially if it's not an addictive, opiate painkiller like the VA often prescribes. What a Veteran told me recently was with all the medications that he's on and his buddies were on, he said, you know, the VA's doing a far better job of trying to kill us than the Taliban ever did.

Above all else, one should be aware that the World Health Organization (WHO) issued a report that contradicted the DEA's stance that oil derived from Cannabis has a high possibility of abuse with no medicinal value. According to the National Institute of Health, "There is significant preliminary therapeutic value of CBD. And while it is not yet sufficient for broad support of drug approval, it highlights the need for rigorous clinical research in this area. There are barriers that should be addressed to facilitate more research in this area." Legislators, including Senator Cory Booker, have introduced legislation that would get Congress to repeal Schedule I designation.

Veronica Wayne and Christine Clayburg are two of the Veterans who attended the meetings on Congress, and both of them agreed that Hemp oil made a big difference in each of their lives. Wayne took opioids for 17 years before trying Hemp oil and getting the relief she needed. Clayburg was able to stop taking what she called a "VA zombie cocktail" in exchange for CBD oil. Not long after she was actually able to feel joy for the first time in over two years. It was obvious in these two cases alone what the benefit is from these alternative treatments via CBD or Hemp oil. I can only imagine how many more could be helped if legislation would advance to the point that vital research is permitted and conducted by the necessary federal agencies.

We asked legislators to sign a letter to the Department of Veterans Affairs then Acting Secretary Robert Wilke asking him to green light a study into CBD derived from industrial Hemp. This provides much of the relief that these Veterans seek, at a fraction of the cost, without the psychoactive side effects, making it an ideal alternative to the various psychotropic and toxic medications in the VA's dispensary. The members of congress are still debating whether or not to allow testing but, according to Representative Earl Blumenauer, "I'm actually cautiously optimistic if we get something on the floor, that it will pass."

CBD has drawn interest as a treatment for neuropsychiatric disorders. Due to the lack of opportunity to run official research and testing relating to CBD and THC, researchers have had to resort to using empirical evidence of an epidemiological, human experimental, clinical and preclinical nature. Overall, evidence seems to indicate that CBD has good potential as treatment for anxiety disorders. The question on the table is when will we be able to conduct current research and testing. There is no doubt how much potential there is for helping our Veterans with PTSD and related issues.

In a letter to U.S. Representative Tim Walz, former Department of Veterans Affairs Secretary David Shulkin said that the "VA's ability to research medical Marijuana is hampered by the fact that the drug is illegal federally." According to Shulkin, the "VA is committed to researching and developing effective ways to help Veterans cope with Post-Traumatic Stress Disorder and chronic pain conditions. However, federal law restricts VA's ability to conduct research involving medical Marijuana, or to refer Veterans to such projects." This comes as 29 states and the District of Columbia, Puerto Rico and Guam have legalized the use of medical Marijuana, and despite the fact that CBD derived from industrial hemp is federally legal.

According to Walz, the House committee's ranking member, the "VA's response not only failed to answer our simple question, but they made a disheartening attempt to mislead me, my colleagues and the Veteran community in the process. They claimed, without citing any specific law, that VA is restricted from conducting research into medical Cannabis, which is categorically untrue. They also go on to make additional excuses while demonstrating a severely limited understanding of existing medical Cannabis research in the process."

"What America's Veterans need prioritized right now is for Cannabis to be treated as a health policy issue," said Nick Etten, founder and executive director of the Veterans Cannabis Project. "We're desperate for solutions for the conditions we're dealing with." In December of 2017, the VA urged patients to discuss medical Marijuana with their doctors. This shift in thought will permit doctors and patients to possibly determine what effect such a drug might have on individual treatment plans. Regardless, VA doctors still cannot refer their patients to state medical Marijuana programs due to federal restrictions. Despite the federal illegality, there are no restrictions to performing scientific research on the drug, and Universities conduct such research studies on a consistent basis. On the flip side, the VA has said that it will not do research on medical marijuana for Veterans with PTSD, even as veteran groups are advocating for use of the drug as a viable alternative to opioids and anti-depressants.

"We've got young men and women with PTSD and Traumatic Brain Injuries coming to us and saying that Cannabis works," stated Joe Plenzler, a spokesman for the American Legion. Plenzler said that, "Veterans had turned to medical Marijuana as an alternative to so-called "zombie drugs," including opioids and antidepressants, that they said adversely affected their mood and personality, up to and including thoughts of suicide." The Legion also asked Congress to remove the drug from the list of Schedule 1 narcotics — a class that includes heroin, LSD and other drugs that have "no accepted medical use" and a high potential for abuse – and reclassify it in a lower schedule.

In November of 2017 the American Legion published a phone survey of over 800 Veterans and Veteran caregivers in which 92% of respondents said they supported medical Cannabis research for the purpose of treating mental or physical conditions. As a comparison, a Quinnipiac University poll released in April of 2018 found that a record 94% of all Americans supported doctor-prescribed medical Marijuana usage. According to Nick Etten and the current U.S. Attorney General, Jefferson Sessions, "Is putting politics, antiquated policies and his own personal opinion ahead of the health needs of Veterans in this country." Representative Matt Gaetz, along with Darren Soto, co-authored a bill that would bump the drug down to Schedule 3 – the same classification as codeine and steroids. According to Gaetz, "I think my political party became too committed to this antiquated dogma of the '70s and '80s. Now we're having to pull the Ostrich's head out of the sand."

Arizona Psychiatrist Dr. Suzanne Sisley, when asked why Marijuana is better than other options, said, "I think the most intriguing thing is that a single plant can provide monotherapy for this whole constellation of symptoms." "A federally approved clinical trial of Marijuana as a PTSD treatment for Veterans is now underway in Phoenix, and results from the current phase could be ready to submit for publication in a couple of years. There is a unique neural pathway between all of those structures that deals with fear and memory. The thinking is there may be excessive firing within those structures in patients that have PTSD. So, the calming effect may reduce the neuronal firing in those structures," she says. It offers "a capacity not to forget bad memories but to not fixate on them." "Unfortunately when it comes to PTSD, we are failing all over the place. Vets are literally walking away from their pills. I have seen videos of Vets chucking their pill bottles on the floors saying, 'No, we are not going to take these anymore.'" Sisley admits Cannabis isn't a cure-all. "There is no doubt that Marijuana is a drug. It has benefits, risks and side effects. Anybody who tells you Marijuana has no side effects, well that's not true. We are trying to do a study where both efficacy and benefits are addressed."

Twenty-eight states plus the District of Columbia include PTSD in their medical Marijuana programs. The 29th state, Alaska, doesn't incorporate PTSD into its medical Marijuana program but allows anyone over age 20 to buy pot legally. As retired Marine Staff Sergeant, and co-founder of the New York-based Cannabis Collective, Mark DiPasquale, stated, "The drug freed him from the 17 opioids, anti-anxiety pills and other medications that were prescribed to him for migraines, post-traumatic stress and other injuries from service that included a hard helicopter landing in Iraq in 2005.

I just felt like a zombie, and I wanted to hurt somebody." He pushed to extend New York's nearly two-year medical Marijuana program to include Post-Traumatic Stress. As the American Legion's Executive Director Verna Jones stated during a conference in November 2017, "When Veterans come to us and say a particular treatment is working for them, we owe it to them to listen and to do scientific research required." "The sooner we allow them to live and experience the kind of emotions we do, in an abstinence-based paradigm, the sooner that they are returning home," said Senator Thomas Croci, former Navy Intelligence Officer and current Reservist who served in Afghanistan. Dr. Thomas Berger, head of the Vietnam Veterans of America's Veterans Health Council said, "You wouldn't have cancer treatments that aren't approved done to yourself or your family members and Marijuana should be subjected to the same scrutiny."

H.R. 5520, the VA Medicinal Cannabis Research Act of 2018, was introduced on April 16, 2018 and the bill has the support of top Republicans and Democrats on the House Veterans' Affairs Committee as well as other key lawmakers. It would not only clarify that the VA has the authority to research Cannabis, but also requires regular reports from department leaders on how seriously they are taking that responsibility. Tim Walz explained, "While we know Cannabis can have life-saving effects on Veterans suffering from chronic pain or PTSD, there has been a severe lack of research studying the full effect of medicinal Cannabis on these Veterans." That is why I am so proud to introduce this legislation. Simply put, there is no department or organization better suited to conduct this critically important research than VA, and there will never be a better time to act."

Thousands of military Veterans have asked federal and state legislators to legalize medicinal Cannabis, pointing out that is would reduce suicide among current and former military personnel. New York Governor Andrew Cuomo chose Veterans Day of 2017 to change his state's medical Marijuana program to include PTSD as a qualifying condition. "Despite the limited research, many scientists have recently shifted focus from THC to CBD – even if many patients have not," says Marcel Bonn-Miller, a Psychology and Psychiatry professor at the University of Pennsylvania's Perelman School of Medicine. "Think of CBD as a shotgun," she said, "It hits many receptors that people are still trying to understand it." "If you want to actually treat PTSD, most of the evidence is pointing toward CBD. But most people with PTSD are gravitating toward [Marijuana] products with high THC levels, which may help in the short-term but are likely to worsen their symptoms over time."

Regardless of the current legislative 'workings', Cannabis research still advances slowly. There are still multiple challenges, laws, and limitations on testing material with which to conduct actual studies. Dr. Suzanne Sisley, who was mentioned earlier, is the lead for Phase 2 of the study, which is part of the Multidisciplinary Association for Psychedelic Studies, better known as MAPS. The organization is a research institute that is focused on exploring uses of Cannabis and psychedelics on a medicinal basis. Sisley's project specifically on how Cannabis affects Veterans with PTSD. Her project initially received approval from the Public Health Service in 2014; and later that same year, the Colorado Department of Public Health and Environment awarded a $2 million grant to complete the research. A little more than a year after the research began, in January of 2018, Sisley's project is in its official Phase 2 Clinical Trial Phase. Sisley is hopeful that, at the completion of the project, she will have a more concrete understanding of Marijuana and its impact on PTSD and, in particular, how medicinal Marijuana can be used to assist military Veterans with PTSD.

Last year, the CDC reported that 66,000 Americans died in the opioid crisis. That is more than twenty 9/11's. If these Veterans can finally find a safe, effective alternative to the "zombie cocktail" of opioids that have been forced on them, it is worth having the VA at least study CBD. If we really want to honor our Veterans, we should stop poisoning them with a deadly array of opiate based medications and start listening to them when they tell us in their own words what works. Wouldn't that put some meaning behind the standard platitude, "Thank you for your service?" **Visit https://warfighterhemp.com for more information.**

CHAPTER 12 - CHANGING THE BRAIN THROUGH MOVEMENT - THE FELDENKRAIS METHOD OF SOMATIC EDUCATION AND POST-TRAUMATIC STRESS DISORDER

Kira Charles, JD, GCFP - Written on behalf of the Feldenkrais Guild

Moshe Feldenkrais D. Sc. (1904-1984), the creator of the Feldenkrais Method®, was a man who knew trauma. As a child, he survived pogroms (organized massacres of the Jewish population) in the Ukraine. He lived through two world wars. In 1940, he fled Paris only hours before the arrival of the Nazis and managed to escape on the last refugee ship to leave France for England. Many of his relatives were killed in the concentration camps. As a young man he lived in Palestine, where the threat of attack on Jews, who were not allowed to carry weapons, was so prevalent that he developed techniques to block knife attacks. In the newly created Israel, he worked with Holocaust survivors and, after the Six-Day War, with returning soldiers.

Dr. Feldenkrais began his study of human movement by working on himself. As a young man in Palestine, he injured his knee playing soccer. After his escape to England, he aggravated his knee doing anti-submarine research for the British Navy. A physician advised him that he had a fifty percent chance of a permanently extended knee if he underwent surgery. He refused surgery but combined his studies of the then current literature on human movement, biology, evolution, psychology, human development, and learning theory with his own background in engineering, physics and Judo to discover a way that he could continue to function despite severe injuries. He created a method of dealing with human limitation and the potential for growth through the use of movement and awareness. As he put it, "What I'm after isn't flexible bodies, but flexible brains." It is difficult to change how we think, how we feel and how we sense, but to change how we move is immediate and observable.

He called the hands-on work he developed Functional Integration lessons. Later, he realized that he could reach and teach a large number of people at once through ingenious movement explorations he called Awareness Through Movement® (ATM) lessons.

What is the Feldenkrais Method?

For many Veterans encountering it for the first time, the Feldenkrais Method seems a strange anomaly. The name is unusual and difficult to pronounce (it is pronounced Fell-den-krice – rhymes with rice) and its precepts run contrary to how Veterans have been trained for years by their drill sergeants, personal trainers and almost everyone else.

The Feldenkrais Method is a type of somatic education – a way of learning through movement and awareness. The word somatic means "of or relating to the living body." A somatic movement is "one which is performed consciously with the intention of focusing on the internal experience of the movement rather than the external appearance or result of the movement."

Humans are prone to having fixed ways of moving and of dealing with life. While most of these habitual ways of moving are useful and efficient, we also develop patterns of movement that can be the underlying causes of discomfort, stress, and pain. Many patterns of movement are below our level of consciousness. We are simply not aware of them. But they can be changed.

Conventional treatments assume that the ways we move are dependent on the underlying body structure and its limitations, whether they are inherent in the structure or caused by injury. The Feldenkrais Method comes from a functional point of view — the ways we move are determined by what we have learned and the habits we have developed. Our habits are based on are the ways we have explored movement as babies, on social conventions (in the military, soldiers always start marching with their left foot), on how we accommodate our physical structures and on our histories of injury or illness. Habits are learned preferences that can restrict our options and contribute to dysfunction and pain. The question is how to unlearn our habits in ways that help resolve movement problems, reduce pain and create more options in life, regardless of physical structure and history of injury.

The path to unlearning these habits lies in the ability of the brain to change and reorganize itself. This characteristic of the brain is called neuroplasticity. Neuro refers to neurons, the nerve cells that are the building blocks of the brain and nervous system and plasticity refers to the brain's capacity to change throughout life. Our brains create maps, or unconscious images of our bodies, which are updated as we move, explore and learn. Recent neuroscience shows that not only do the patterns of neurons firing change with learning, but the physical structure of the brain also changes. We use these maps to guide our senses and movement. As we explore new ways to move, we can make the maps more detailed. We can also make the maps less detailed when we limit our ways of moving. The brain has an extraordinary ability to change, adapt and acquire more efficient patterns of movement and action if given the right environment.

The aim of the Feldenkrais Method is to create that environment. Dr. Feldenkrais designed the Method to allow us to modify these internal images of the body — using the intimate relationship between moving and sensing that is essential in all our actions. As you make movements and direct your attention to observations like where your body is located in space; your relationship with the floor; and sensations of effort, direction and ease you develop a clearer image of your body. Dr. Feldenkrais developed processes that value lack of effort, moving slowly, attention to personal sensations, focus on the qualities of movement and curiosity and choice. Using this greater precision of perception helps you move more comfortably, with less pain and greater ease.

Most people have an unclear idea of how they move. They don't realize that they have choices in how they move. They have an inaccurate picture and limitations due to this image of self. For example, if someone does not know that her shoulder blade can move and is, in fact, the primary mover for the arm, then she can cause herself injury when reaching, perhaps tearing a rotator cuff muscle. Someone who has recovered from an injury may not realize that he is still holding on to patterns from the injury. If he has broken his leg, he will shift his weight onto the uninjured leg and may never shift the weight back. Many of us have never learned certain ways of moving. Each of us have developed habits so deeply engrained that they don't seem changeable. Our habitual ways of moving are difficult to detect because they are so much a part of us, even when they cause pain or discomfort. Inefficient movement leads to internal stress, muscular tension and shearing forces — forces that push one part of a body in one specific direction and another part of the body in the opposite direction.

As we mature, the brain continues to refine our movements by shedding what it perceives as unused movement patterns. We begin to rely on fewer and fewer patterns of action. These limited patterns cause dysfunction — moving in a way that undermines the system. Certain muscle groups and joints do most of the work while others remain inactive. These habitual and repetitive movement patterns can cause injury, pain, stiffness, compression of the spine, limited movement and poor posture. We don't give old habits up until we acquire a better way of moving to replace the old. Dr. Feldenkrais said, "In order to change our mode of action, we must change the image of ourselves that we carry within us."

Feldenkrais lessons direct attention to qualities of sensation, such as how we allow the floor to support us, skeletal support, ease of movement, the sense of the physical dimensions of the body, and how body parts move through space. Having more ways to sense your body gives you more choice in how to move.

Feldenkrais practitioners guide clients in revisiting developmental paths, such as how to roll and crawl. We explore functional themes, such as coming to stand from sitting. We look at movement from different perspectives. We explore what is it like to roll the pelvis while lying on the back, in sitting, and in standing. We bring lost or spastic areas into a person's awareness. Many people hold their pelvis rigid so it is unable to support the spine and head. We help people to breath more easily and fully.

Both group and individual lessons are often done lying down. This is to reduce the load on the nervous system and puts us in a different relationship with gravity. By doing lessons in a non-habitual orientation to gravity, we have a chance to address aspects of ourselves that are too locked into postural habits. This allows us to explore new options safely.

These explorations build sensory-motor patterns, introduce variety into behavior and promote dynamic stability. You can move from experiencing disability to experiencing ability.

Two Ways of Doing The Feldenkrais Method

Awareness Through Movement

In Awareness Through Movement or ATM group classes, practitioners verbally guide students through movement sequences that help them learn to move their bodies more intelligently. Practitioners don't demonstrate the movement; they encourage students to explore their personal ways of moving rather than trying to imitate another person. These are not exercises like aerobics or Pilates, nor do participants stretch or hold positions as in Yoga. Each student is involved in an internal and personal process of discovery where old habits can easily be replaced with new skills, and a new sense of awareness. These explorations are keys that students can use to unlock their own best self-use in class and in life.

Throughout the lesson, the practitioner directs attention to particular things to feel or notice, such as the effort used, the path of the movement, and where the movement is initiated. Sensations are more important than the movements themselves. At the end of a lesson, students tend to feel differences such as lightness or heaviness, a sense of grounding and greater range of movement. They may report feeling more relaxed.

ATM lessons typically last 30–60 minutes. Practitioners generally teach a different lesson in every class. Dr. Feldenkrais created over a thousand lessons, varying in difficulty, complexity, position and focus. We explore all aspects of human function and all levels of movement ability. Although a lesson may have a particular theme or part of the body on which it is focused, it often has a more universal application. Thus, a lesson about tilting the legs from side to side can be useful in changing movement habits that affect several other areas of the body. Each lesson provides the students with a repertoire of movements that they can do at home. The focus of the lesson may be on a certain function but students may experience changes in other aspects. After a lesson about rotating the various joints of the legs, an 89-year-old Veteran with severe Kyphosis found himself standing significantly more upright.

Practitioners consider the current capabilities and pain levels of students and make accommodations so that movements that seem difficult become possible and easy. We remind students to avoid pain and to perform movements within comfortable ranges. Movement sequences develop from simple to complex as students evolve in their ability and awareness. Time is given to allow each student to assimilate the idea of the movement and the leisure to get used to the novelty of the movement. Learning is a highly individual matter; students are encouraged to learn at their own pace in a non-competitive manner.

Functional Integration

Functional Integration or FI lessons follow the same principles as ATM lessons but learning tends to be more rapid because the practitioner is working with a student's specific issues. Practitioners use exploratory movement and subtle touch rather than words to teach the student, although practitioners may also ask questions or offer some verbal instruction/observation.

Practitioners are looking at the whole person in movement. The touch is informative and questioning. We look for where the student moves easily, where it is difficult to move; where movement is isolated, where it connects throughout the body. We ask, "Are there places where the student could move but is unaware that it is possible?" We suggest new ways of moving. The emphasis is on discovering the student's particular habits of movement and on guiding them to safely find new alternatives. The goal is to engage the ability to use the skeleton both to provide support and to allow for free movement. When the skeleton is operating optimally, less muscular effort is required. Movement therefore becomes easier, more expanded, more comfortable, and more efficient. Pain is often reduced or eliminated.

FI offers the ability to make profound differences and can change the quality of a Veteran's life. Learning must be slow and varied. When a person is given many paths to explore, then options appear that may not have been available before.

Each lesson is designed to meet individual needs and is custom-tailored to the student's unique organization at that particular moment. Each lesson is also related to a desire, intention or need the student has. The practitioner's goal is to create an environment for learning comfortably.

Strategies That Make the Feldenkrais Method Work

For many Veterans, the concepts and principles of the Feldenkrais Method may seem foreign especially because they run counter to long-held beliefs about physical fitness. For others, there are familiar aspects. Engineers, physicists, and mechanics may see scientific principles enacted through the body. Dr. Feldenkrais trained first as an engineer, then earned his doctorate in Physics from the Sorbonne in Paris. Veterans familiar with Judo and other martial practices may see martial arts roots in his work. Dr. Feldenkrais was one of Europe's first black belts in Judo and, at the request of Judo's creator Jigaro Kano, he introduced Judo to France during the 1930s.

We focus on the skeleton rather than the muscles. Many people with some familiarity of the Feldenkrais Method believe that it is solely about flexibility. It is not. We look principally at how a person organizes their skeleton, which provides both stability and flexibility. Most people don't trust their skeleton to support them, because they don't know how to let their bones do their work. When your skeleton works efficiently your muscles don't have to overwork to hold you up, no single part does more than its fair share of the work and force transmits throughout the skeleton without torsion, shear, or compression, causing less wear and tear on the body.

Movement should be performed as slowly as possible. The human nervous system, which controls our posture and movement, learns new things slowly. When we do movements quickly, we are not learning anything new — we are simply reinforcing existing learned patterns. Fast action at the beginning of learning is synonymous with strain and confusion.

Movement should be done consciously and with attention. Conscious attention is key to the learning process; we can't learn something new if we aren't aware of what we're doing. In a keynote address before the American Society for Cybernetics, Feldenkrais trainer Lawrence Goldfarb said, "The problem encountered in learning a new way of moving is that an old and often habitual pattern interferes. It is not possible to simply do something new. Learning a new movement means learning about what is already happening, so as to understand what to change. It also means figuring out which aspects of dynamics to attend to, that is, learning a new movement means learning what to notice."

This concept of learning what to notice can be very important for Veterans with Post-Traumatic Stress Disorder (PTSD) who often have difficulties being present in the moment and with enjoying their experiences. With their hyper-alertness, they can notice too much in their environment. Feldenkrais lessons can channel that alertness into a beneficial attention to the details of movement and to the kinesthetic sensations experienced during a lesson. The act of noticing, in and of itself, can create new patterns of movement and new patterns of thinking. As Dr. Feldenkrais said, "When you know what you're doing, you can do what you want."

Less is more. For many people, trying to change something about themselves means trying harder and then finding that this strategy does not work. Dr. Feldenkrais proposed that compulsive effort leads to movement that is carried out on automatic pilot and uses more effort and physical energy than necessary. Compulsive effort increases muscular tightness in parts of the body not even associated with the movement, and risks pain and injury. That non-functional effort becomes shearing force in joints and muscles. The resulting impact, friction, and heat damages our soft tissue in the short term, and our bones in the long term. In addition, the more force we use, the less sensitivity we have to how we are doing any movement — inhibiting our ability to sense ourselves more accurately in action.

Dr. Feldenkrais believed that learning does not occur when we try as hard as we can. He postulated that the smaller the stimulus, the easier it is to sense differences, and that the lighter the effort we make, the faster we learn a new skill. Students are asked to reduce effort where possible. Muscle tension can be reduced by using awareness to notice how we unintentionally contract muscles that are not necessary for a movement. Sensing these differences creates potent and lasting neuromuscular change. The Feldenkrais Method focuses on the quality of our movements (light, easy, soft, slow, smooth) over quantity (we don't do many rote repetitions and rarely use big ranges of motion). It is only when you are able to sense a difference that you have a choice. By interrupting the cycle of repetitive damage, Veterans can heal and even improve.

Feldenkrais also suggested doing the movement short of reaching the pain threshold. Acting in spite of pain causes the tissues and joints to become irritated and inflamed. Gently repeating the movement short of pain will enable you to extend the range of your ability more than you would accomplish by overcoming pain.

Variation is the spice of movement. Our earliest experiences in learning how to move were when we were infants. Dr. Feldenkrais observed that the kind of random movements that babies do, driven by stimulation from the environment and by their own curiosity, leads to new movement patterns. Learning is not linear, especially not the type of organic learning that happens in every Feldenkrais lesson. If we practice each movement as if for first time, we will notice something new and learn something new each time. Practicing somatic movements is quite different than doing sit-ups or push-ups; it's not about the quantity, it's about the quality.

Pursuing an ideal movement in a regimented way does not lead to the kind of movement improvement stimulated by Feldenkrais lessons. In both ATM and FI lessons, practitioners use a number of strategies to generate the kind of variation that leads to learning: going slowly, breaking movement patterns into parts, reversing movements, and introducing novel movements that we would not normally do in everyday life.

Often "mistakes" occur. Sometimes the students do not understand the instructions; sometimes they have no comprehension of how to do a movement because they have never done it before. Mistakes may open whole new vistas and are sometimes incorporated into the lesson. In these conditions, the nervous system can begin to identify and reproduce the new movement options that are best for each student.

Feldenkrais believed that striving to do everything correctly can inhibit the possibility of learning from the natural variation that occurs in our performance from "errors." Moreover, thinking in terms of error or negative judgment puts a person's mind and body into a tense state that doesn't help learning.

Why use the Feldenkrais Method if you have PTSD?

There can be several obstacles to moving on from trauma. Where trauma has occurred, self-protective mechanisms are triggered, which can lead to stiffness, pain, lack of movement and a sense of losing oneself. Emotions such as anger, fear and anxiety can become fixed in posture. Veterans who have suffered from trauma may not recognize their own feelings and reactions. They respond to reminders of the past by automatically engaging in physical actions that were appropriate at the time of the trauma but are no longer relevant. They may have problems with sustained attention and memory. They may have difficulty attending to their inner sensations and perceptions. They often feel overwhelmed. Traumatized individuals lose their way in the world and the Feldenkrais Method is uniquely equipped to help them create new neurological maps.

Veterans with PTSD may experience muscle tension, joint pain, headaches, back pain, temporomandibular joint syndrome (TMJ) and teeth grinding, or other types of pain. Fight-or-flight mode is a primal defense mechanism that prepares the body for physical threats, causing muscles to contract. These habitual defense mechanisms are resistant to change. Repeated encounters with triggers can keep their bodies tense, operating on high alert, without giving their muscles time to relax. They may experience exhaustion or fatigue due to a constant state of hyperarousal.

A person in pain may not realize the connection between their pain and a traumatic event. But for some the pain may actually serve as a reminder of the traumatic event, which in turn may intensify PTSD symptoms. Some people who develop PTSD and chronic pain also experience depression. Many Veterans armor themselves, holding their ribs rigid and limiting their breathing.

How People With PTSD Have Benefitted from the Feldenkrais Method

Each individual has his or her own way to of reacting to injury and trauma. Some people continue to protect an injured area long after the injury has healed, as did a Veteran who was shot in the shoulder while on foot patrol. He remained hunched over the shoulder for several years and was unable to lift his arm above shoulder height.

During FI sessions, he learned how his ribs could open and close when he bent to the side. By taking his attention away from the shoulder itself and asking him to move in places he had not considered to be related to his issue, he was able to develop full use of the arm within a few weeks.

Some Veterans have difficulty finding stability and are seeking a sense of support. When an exploding IED threw a Veteran through the air, he lost his ability to find support in his own body. He could not sit without leaning against the back of the chair and without several pillows behind him; sitting unsupported provoked waves of anxiety. When standing, he often felt like he was falling. Over a series of lessons, we explored the relationship between his pelvis or hip area, his spine and his head. The pelvis, situated in the center of the body, is the base of support for the spine and a mobile pelvis can help improve head and spine alignment. His pelvis was rigidly tilted back so he was sitting on his tailbone, giving his spine no support. His upper spine and neck were also rigid but pushed too far forward leaving the hyper-mobile lower back to take the brunt of holding him up. It was not until he could soften his chest and begin to roll his pelvis forward and back that he was able to find support and relief.

When hypersensitivities develop to stimuli such as sound, light or touch, the system needs to receive messages that will calm it. A young woman's hyperactive nerve reflexes caused her to become dizzy and nauseated and she sometimes lost her balance. Over four Feldenkrais sessions, we did minimal movements of touching the face. I also taught her to move her hands in a soft wavelike way, similar to the movement very young infants do with their hands. These movements tuned down the activity in her brain and allowed her to relax. She felt more grounded and more connected in her body. She was able to successfully navigate a potentially overwhelming family visit. She was less scared because she could feel when her system was becoming irritated. "It feels good to feel myself," she said.

Conclusion

Most Veterans ascribe to the philosophy of "no pain, no gain" and to the idea that you have to keep pushing through no matter the cost. While these concepts might get the mission done or save a life in combat, they are not useful for learning. By slowing down, doing less and focusing on the process and the experience rather than the end result, the Veteran can feel and regulate the input and the changes that are occurring. Because stimulation takes place below the usual threshold of discomfort and awareness, it avoids evoking the body's habitual defense mechanisms which are resistant to change. Patience, compassion, gentleness, and flexibility are necessary when recovering from trauma.

Movement and emotion are always intertwined. Our thoughts and emotions live in our physical body and can only be expressed through our bodies. We might manifest fear in the way our breathing changes or anger in the way our muscles contract. Changing our physical self can change the way we experience our thoughts and emotions. Individuals affected by brain injury, trauma, physical or emotional abuse, or symptoms of PTSD often find the Feldenkrais Method a resource to restore a sense of calm and balance. It can bring a Veteran into a profoundly different way of being with himself or herself.

Humans are unique in their capacity to make choices about how they respond to the world. We have the ability to discover new ways of dealing with information and can modify our responses on the basis of the lessons we learn. However, this capacity to respond in a flexible manner can be easily disrupted by PTSD. With the Feldenkrais Method, we can do many things that invite changes into the nervous system without triggering a traumatic experience.

Feldenkrais practitioners monitor cues to adjust lessons to students' needs. Practitioners continually attend to comfort and pain levels. Throughout lessons, we observe students' behavioral states including: relaxation and alertness, quantity and content of speech, facial expressions, emotions, breathing characteristics, muscle tone, skin color, and movement characteristics including smoothness, transmission of forces through the skeleton, and changes in range of motion. The importance of self-care is emphasized. It is made clear to students that they have permission to do whatever they need to take care of themselves, whether it is crying, falling asleep, not doing the lesson, or leaving the room.

Because of the slower pace, the lack of goal and the directed attention in Feldenkrais lessons, students often find a greater sense of "me." They feel more grounded, straighter, lighter, more solid, taller. They can move more easily, with less pain, with a clearer sense of themselves and with more purpose. They can find a way to stem anxiety, gain self-confidence and unlock new potential.

Benefits of the Feldenkrais Method

Improving posture, flexibility, balance, and coordination
Enhancing physical well-being
Reducing chronic pain, fatigue, stress, and muscle strain
Quieting the nervous system
Increasing function in cases of orthopedic or neurological problems
Developing awareness, attention, and thinking ability
Increasing confidence and self-esteem
Expediting recovery from injury
Utilizing a greater portion of the thousands of individual movements available in the human body

Many free Awareness Through Movement lessons can be found through the internet.

A few of Veterans Administration Hospitals provide Feldenkrais in their facilities. To date Awareness Through Movement lessons are available at the James J. Peters VA Medical Center in the Bronx, New York and at the McGuire Veterans Hospital VIP Center in McGuire, VA. Both Functional Integration and Awareness Through Movement lessons are available through Feldenkrais clinics at the Brooklyn and Manhattan Campuses of the VA NY Harbor Healthcare System.

Veterans interested in Feldenkrais lessons can find Guild Certified Practitioners in their area through the Feldenkrais Guild® of North America, the organization that certifies Feldenkrais practitioners at www.feldenkrais.com.

CHAPTER 13 - DOGA

Suzi Teitelman

I started DOGA in NYC after 9/11. I was living in New York, and a lot of things changed after that. One of the things I wanted to finally have my own dog. I didn't want to share a dog with a boyfriend or to take care of someone else's dog. I wanted my own dog...a dog to love as my child. I was and still am an actor, but when you are an actor in New York, you may get a job and have to leave at the last minute, so having a dog made that impossible. But I was ready to settle down and to make my dream happen of finally having my own dog. So, when my dog Coali, a black Cocker Spaniel, who was born a couple days after 9/11, came into my life, he came to me to teach DOGA to the world through me.

I was already a Yoga teacher...that was my settled life choice. I was still doing some acting, but I was teaching Yoga full time. I was also the Yoga Director at Crunch Fitness. When I got Coali, he wouldn't leave me or my Yoga mat. Because of this I started to add him into my Yoga poses. I did this when I was at home, when I was teaching private lessons, and even snuck him into my classes at Crunch...and we started doing Yoga together. It wasn't the same without him. We loved to be together, it felt good to be together, and yoga felt good for the both of us. It also seems like something I really needed...especially in a time like it was right after 9/11. I needed to feel close to something and Coali and Yoga became that 'something' for me. It all felt good to me and, as the Director of Yoga at Crunch, I created the dog related Yoga classes, which I called "Ruff Yoga" at that point in time. It became a worldwide hit! Eventually, when I left Crunch five years later to move to Florida, I would then rename the practice DOGA, which is what it is known of as of today.

DOGA was natural and organic in its beginnings. I didn't start Yoga to really bring it to the world it was something I was doing with my dog because it made me feel better it was something that I did because I loved Yoga and I loved my dog. Afterwards I realized that other people might also love to do the same thing that I was doing by including my dog in my Yoga practice. It stood to reason that there were already plenty of people who were practicing Yoga at home on their own with their own dogs.

It just seemed logical to incorporate movements and include their dogs in the Yoga poses and thereby creating an actual class. For someone who is new to Yoga, you can do bits and pieces of it throughout your day, and you don't need to do a full class to be able to benefit from the practice. You can do shorter sessions any time during the day and still benefit from it. Yoga and meditation are not something you will need to stop doing as you age. You can do it your entire life and still benefit.

If you have Post-Traumatic Stress Disorder (PTSD) you can call on the practice like it is medication or vitamins that you have to take daily...and this is especially true when you have your own Service Dog because they might be able to participate alongside in the practice of DOGA. Watching the men and the women received their dogs at Canines for Warriors was so beautiful to see. I could understand how they were going to rely so much on an animal to give them so much support. I was privileged to teach DOGA classes with Canines for Warriors in Jacksonville, FL (https://www.k9sforwarriors.org/). Adding Yoga and Service Dogs to help 'care' for our Veterans helps make their lives better in more ways than you can possibly count. The purpose in life for these Veterans is to help them to feel better, to be a companion, to assist them with mobility issues, and so many other things. If a Service Dog can help us in this way, then why not reach for them in every possible way we can, including doing DOGA. This can be an immediate solution and tangible medicine with no side-effects except for happiness and an unfailing sense of acceptance from your canine.

To learn how to do DOGA all you have to do is to sit on your Yoga mat and let your dog come to you. It is important for you to take some Yoga classes of your own first so that you know something about the basic moves before you start adding your dog. You can learn DOGA by watching my video or reading books on Yoga or just experimenting. There are no perfect Yoga poses just as there are no perfect DOGA poses. It's about what feels good for you and your dog. There's so much that a dog teaches us that we need to remember about being happy, peaceful, and content about living in the moment. Dogs bring us more knowledge on the Yoga mat than any teacher out there possibly could. They live in the present moment. They are already happy and joyful loving beings. That's all we wish to be. It is our function and purpose in life to be joyful. So, if we find that PTSD has been triggered in us and a bad moment is happening we must reach for Joy ... and our dogs are pure joy. Add that to the practice of DOGA, meditation and breathing and then hopefully we can all be well.

Just give yourself 5-minutes and the next day 10-minutes and then the next day 15-minutes and then the next day 20-minutes and then move on from there. You can always reset and go back to 5-minutes every day then build back up from there whenever you feel the need. Use the power of Yoga and the power of your dog to bring you to a new level. Even if for just a moment, if you find a piece of clarity in a piece of peace it's better than where you were before. Every day is a new day, and our bodies are different every day.

The practice of Yoga is going to be different, and our dogs are going to be different every day, but if we just realize that joy can be the same...happiness can be the same...peacefulness can be the same and we can find that through the practice of DOGA.

It may seem overwhelming to start a Yoga practice let alone add your dog into it. But when you have your dog with you on the mat things are only better. If we are only trying to make ourselves feel better by doing something then why not choose to do the most loving, soothing, healthy and positive action we can make ourselves physically and mentally better. Yoga is something that everyone should do. But when you have PTSD you need it even more. When people say they don't have time to do Yoga or it is too hard for them or they would never be able to do it, they are just not giving themselves the chance to try. Yoga and DOGA is something that you can and should do for the rest of your life. You have to just start doing it and not stop. It doesn't have to be a full hour on the mat every time you get time to sit and be with your pup and be with your breathing. It is about being consistent for the rest of your life with being joyful and happy even if it is only for 15 or 20-minutes while on the mat. It will extend into the rest of your life if you continue to do it daily.

You just need to allow Yoga and DOGA to cure. Don't be afraid of trying something new if it's new to you. Take time to just sit on the floor and if you don't have a yoga mat try a big towel or a big blanket and have your dog just be there with you. Just sitting with your back up-right and your heart open you will be able to allow good things to come to you and will also be able to do things like feeling the energy of your dog going in and feel the energy of you going out. You don't have to do any fancy poses...you can do just sitting or standing and folding/pending forward then touching your dog. Three great poses to do every single day are a seated pose with your legs crossed with your dog in front of you or your legs wrapped around your dog (with your dog in your lap). Another is sitting with your legs wide, your dog in front of you and your arms around your dog. The third is standing and then folding/bending forward with your dog beneath you.

The best thing you can do is to learn some simple Yoga moves on your own and then just incorporate your dog into your Yoga practice in any way that feels natural. Just allow yourself to use Yoga with your dog through DOGA like it is a medicine. Do it every day, be consistent with it, be patient, and allow it to become a part of your life forever.

For more information about DOGA please visit my website at: http://www.dogadog.org/.

CHAPTER 14 - ESOTHERAPY®: A HOLISTIC THERAPY THAT HEALS POST-TRAUMATIC STRESS DISORDER

Gerald Whitehawk

Preface: The Story of Esotherapy®

I pioneered the art and science of Esotherapy® along with its co-founder, Tahlia F. Denny. This holistic, transpersonal approach focuses on the spiritually mediated attainment of mental, emotional and physical health and wellbeing by means of consciousness integration. The results very often exceed those achieved by conventional psychology, psychiatry, and medicine.

After over two decades of transpersonal therapy experience in Australia and the U.S., and a lifetime of awareness practice in the natural realm, I developed a talent to see how your positive and negative qualities and life experiences fit together. In Esotherapy, I meet you where you are and compassionately guide you towards restoring inner peace and harmony, optimal health, and the higher goal of self-actualization.

Although I graduated with highest honors in psychology from one of the top 15 universities in the world, UC Davis, it seemed to me that there was something missing in the psychological paradigm I had learned there. In therapy people were learning to cope with their situation, but coping is just getting by, which is not the same as fully living, free of suffering. People deserve to get better, to live full exciting, healthy lives and enjoy themselves... not just sometimes or somewhat.

I thought a fresh look at therapy was needed... a look from a different perspective, a paradigm shift, a different path... but such paths did not yet exist. I was inspired by the Australian Aboriginal saying,

Stranger, there are no paths! Paths are made by walking.
Marching to the Beat of a Different Drummer

Why take a different path to understanding the world and who we are in order to create a new therapy? Because, after over two decades of working with clients, I came to understand that the limitations of the current therapies are not of the sciences themselves. Rather, they are the limitations of the dualistic level of consciousness such sciences emerge from.

As Albert Einstein explained: "No problem can be solved from the same level of consciousness that created it."

To offer a better therapy, then, it was necessary to step outside the dualistic paradigm, altogether, and shift to a higher level of consciousness, known as "non-dualistic", which became the springboard for the new therapeutic paradigm shift outlined here.

While conventional counseling and psychotherapy rely on logical verbalizing, human existence extends far beyond conceptual reasoning. My professional practice taught me that these existing approaches deny some very basic facts of how life is actually experienced, hence they lack grounding in basic experiential reality. People's negative feelings are not based on logical, thought-out decisions. Why then assume that logic can alleviate their suffering?

While working in the mental health fields in Australia and the U.S., I ultimately realized the reasons for their limitations. Western knowledge is largely focused on emphasizing and labeling differences that creates the view of a world made of different and separate entities with little or no overlap. Such a conceptually mediated worldview, known as "dualistic", causes a pervasive tension between the continuous nature of reality and the individual fragmented view of the world from which the discordant, stressful life-experiences emerge.

Esotherapy explains that our many "diseases" are but different facets of this inner tension and fragmentation that this dualistic, words-mediated perception creates. In Esotherapy, we believe that this fragmentation is the crux of all ills, and what we call diseases are mere symptoms of the same dualistic consciousness across different facets of life (mental, physical, social, etc.)

If fragmentation is the root of illnesses, it would follow, then, that healing entails restoring the sense of being an **INSEPARABLE** part of an integrated world, a worldview known as "mystical" or "esoteric". This awareness integration, which is the main focus of esotericism and mysticism, decreases this dualistic sense of disconnection and the ever-pervasive tension it produces. While mystical spiritualities aim to develop a non-dualistic consciousness, they do not harness the therapeutic skills needed for teaching how to integrate dualistic life-experiences into healing wisdom, something that psychology attempts to do. On the other hand, therapies like psychology, which are rooted in the dualistic paradigm, actually reinforce the client's dualistic perception. To overcome these inherent limitations of both conventional dualistic therapies and non-dualistic esoteric spiritualities, I realized that a "spiritual development therapy" that utilized the best of both was needed.

Who are You?

I believe that a person's True Self is a part of the fabric of conscious, non-dual or undivided continuum of energy that makes up everything, including ourselves. I believe this continuum is made of conscious, living energy. As such, it is the foundational, abiding consciousness of all things... indeed a True-Self or Higher Consciousness that is shared with all forms of existence. Being Undivided, meaning Whole or "Holy", I call this foundational Consciousness the "Great" or "Holy" Spirit. Since all things abide in it, I see it as everyone's True Self or Spirit-within. Thereby, I believe that all people, and all of life, share in a common True Self, meaning that nothing is separate from the greater, Whole/Holy Spirit that fills the earth, all animals, the sky, mountains, ocean, rivers, and all the green things that live. Esoteric Wisdom Therapy™, or Esotherapy, explains that it is in re-connecting our awareness with this common True Self that all healing lies. This transpersonal view is considered "esoteric".

Knowledge-Based Conventional Therapies versus Wisdom-Based Healing

During my 20+ years of therapeutic experience in the U.S. and Australia, I noticed that imparting healing without esoteric, transpersonal wisdom is like installing a strong door on a house where thieves come through the window. Conversely, I noticed that processing life events through esoteric wisdom pieced together the results of previous counseling with clients' personal experiences into stable life-transformation. However, it was not until 2010 that I formulated the foundational understandings that helped me formalize this method, which I had always practiced. I, now, call it "Esotherapy", meaning, a therapy grounded in esoteric wisdom.

The effectiveness of this therapy for those suffering from trauma, as well as other mental, emotional, and physical diseases has been validated in thousands of healing sessions in different countries. I have summarized these understandings and present two cases in this chapter for the reader to get a sense of what Esoteric Wisdom Therapy is and how effective it is in healing PTSD.

The Medical and Clinical Directors of three of the world's foremost treatment centers endorse the effective, rapid, and enduring results of Esotherapy:
"Most impressive about Esotherapy is its efficiency. It gets rid of the emotional charge of flashbacks and memories involved in Post-Traumatic Stress Disorder (PTSD), depression, anxiety, grief, addictions, explosive disorders, parenting problems. In a handful of sessions the clients we shared made tremendous progress, that would have taken quite a bit of time with conventional psychotherapy and...some of these changes would have been practically impossible with today's available therapies." — Dr. James Seymour, Trauma Services Director, Sierra Tucson (former Medical Director of Cottonwood). (https://www.sierratucson.com/about/staff/james-seymour/); watch his video endorsement: https://www.youtube.com/watch?v=VyQwxjldPPo)

"... to a person, every single one of those patients has reported to me, voluntarily, that it's been one of the most transformative and profound experiences they had here." — Dr. Tena Mover, Medical Director, Sierra Tucson: (https://sierratucson.com/about/staff/tena-moyer-md/; watch her video endorsement: http://www.youtube.com/watch?v=RrZGM8R-2w8)

"In 4 or 5 sessions, I have seen our residents make a shift out of old patterns of thinking that they had been stuck in, often for many years." — Peggy Holt, LPC, Clinical Director, Sabino Recovery (about her: https://sabinorecovery.com/leadership-and-staff/)

1. What Is Esotherapy?

Esotherapy, a.k.a. Esoteric Wisdom Therapy™, is a pioneering consciousness integration approach that facilitates rapid healing of BOTH mental/emotional and physical trauma and stress. Esoteric wisdom-based integration of our minds fundamentally changes the way we see and think about events, the way we perceive ourselves, relationships and the world, and increases creative expression and problem-solving abilities. This, in turn, alters the chemistry of our bodies without the use of drugs.

Generally speaking, Esotherapy works for everyone. This therapy may be done individually, as a family, or in groups with people of all ages, genders, sexual orientation, for any form of mind and body dis-ease.

To protect the public from impersonators, we have registered this international trademark as "Esotherapy".

2. Our Unique Approach to Healing Trauma

In order to lay the foundation for any new approach that overcomes the limitations of conventional therapies, we need to examine ideas that form the very basis of our present thinking, ideas considered "common sense". Such taken for granted, common sense ideas form the underpinning foundation of today's therapeutic limitations. We need to look at diseases, and healing, freshly, from a new perspective of "uncommon sense".

Consider the following comparison: Psychotherapy processes negative events through the application of dualistic and psychological knowledge which creates a story about what happened, thus reinforcing an identification as a helpless, weak, isolated, victimized, shamed individual, and ensuring the continuance of traumatic memories.

Psychotherapy also categorizes and labels the feelings the individual experiences as depression, anxiety, insomnia, etc. Even if the story is successfully changed, the success applies only to the mental or intellectual landscape, and the underlying feelings of the event remain, stored in the body and unconscious aspect of mind, ready to resurface when a "triggering" event occurs or during the night in the form of nightmares. In addition, conventional therapies attempt to treat the labels, i.e. depression, not the unique, actually experienced feelings of traumatizing events.

By contrast, Esoteric Wisdom Therapy™ processes the same events through non-dualistic, integrative wisdom. It restores identity and consciousness to its natural spirit of unity in which all Life abides as One. In this healed state of awareness there is no conflict, discord or suffering and the individual is liberated from the role of a shattered, weak tormented, hurt or angry victim. The underlying feelings of emotional pain and suffering are simultaneously resolved, along with symptoms of anxiety, depression, insomnia and nightmares, as the peace, strength and resilience of belonging to the wholeness of creation are restored to consciousness.

Esotherapy heals from the inside out all the aspects of being, including feeling, thinking and physicality. It heals without any use of medications or drugs that remedy one problem by creating new and different imbalances, thereby perpetuating the treatment cycle.

3. The Origins Of Esotherapy

"There is a language beyond human language, an elemental language, one that arises from the land itself." — Linda Hogan, Chickasaw writer.

Esotherapy arises DIRECTLY from the guidance of the Higher Consciousness. The "still, soft inner "voice" of the Great/Holy Spirit* is not found in the din and clamor of any science OR religion. It is found in the stillness of the soul, provided we can quiet our noisy minds enough to hear it.

The sayings of Jesus and Lao Tzu are NOT the roots of Esotherapy, because our philosophy developed in parallel, as a result of our own deep meditation and contemplation practices.

The sage wisdom of these masters however, do offer two independent affirmations of the healing principles that Esotherapy is founded on, and for this reason they are quoted in the following text.

* *

*Footnote: Great Spirit, Holy Spirit, One Spirit, Great Integrity or Tao, the spirit of YHWH, are all synonymous terms used by different esoteric teachers, such as Jesus, Christian Mystics, Lao Tzu, Taoist masters, Native American and Aboriginal Australian Holy People, and Jewish mystics, in order to refer to the Living Spirit of Oneness, the Essence or Higher Consciousness that permeates and unifies all of Creation. Here, we have chosen to use Holy Spirit, not because of a personal or religious bias, but because, "holy" means "whole".

* *

The difference of what we did with the present Higher Consciousness message is that rather than organizing it into a different religion or writing books about it, we organized it as an imminently practical therapy for individuals, for families, and for the betterment of humanity.

To understand the origins of Esotherapy we need to examine the meaning of the word es·o·ter·ic (e-sə-ˈte-rik). The Greek root "eso", translated as "within" or "inner", means that Esoteric Wisdom Therapy™ is about listening to the spirit within us which tells us that "holy" means "whole" or "without divisions" and "healing" means "to make whole" or "integrate".

Thus, Esotherapy is a process of reintegrating the individual awareness and thinking with their inner Higher Consciousness, a connection that has been disrupted due to traumatic experiences. As such, each intervention is Higher Consciousness-guided for each unique individual need.

4. Dualism: The Root Cause Of Humanity's Many Forms of Diseases And Suffering

Is it possible that all illnesses and suffering arise from a single, COMMON root and, therefore, healing this root cause could heal them all? Consider the words of two sages: "Dualistic thinking is a sickness." — Lao Tzu, author of the non-dualistic spiritual writing, the "Tao Te Ching"
and
"The mind is everything, what you think you become." — Buddha

Historically, humanity has tried to figure out which master was more correct than the other, by applying divisive, dualistic thinking to teachings meant to teach non-dualism. Yet, these teachings are like pearls that strung together in a necklace are worth more than the sum of each pearl alone. Taken together, the words of the masters quoted above indicate that DUALISTIC consciousness is the root cause of all sickness and suffering.

To understand why dualism is the root cause of all diseases, it is essential to deprogram the subtle misguidance society has instilled into us. We've been taught that consciousness is something we have. However, CONSCIOUSNESS IS NOT SOMETHING "WE HAVE", BUT SOMETHING "WE ARE".

The implications of this fact are key to healing. Consciousness, in a general sense — is me, just as Consciousness, also, in a general sense — is you. It follows that, humanity taken together, is a part of a general, greater, Consciousness-at-Large embodied into many individual forms.

Hence, there exist two understandings of the world, reflected as two types of consciousness:
• Dualistic consciousness is the conventional view of our world as consisting of individual divided entities, which function separately, with little or no interchange, often competing for existence.
• Non-dualistic, spiritual consciousness is the understanding that there is only one general Essence that comprises all the temporary individual forms of existence, while only the universal Essence is enduring and important. This Oneness worldview is backed by Quantum Physics.

As Buddha said, "the mind is everything", and "what you think you become" thus, dualistic and non-dualistic types of consciousness have sweeping effects, not only on individual health, but also on the health of family, society, and the world, as well.

To understand the effects of dualistic vs. non-dualistic consciousness in our lives, let's compare consciousness to a mirror. When broken and fragmented, the mirror reflects reality in divided, sharp, injurious pieces. However, if they were "re-integrated" or "made whole", meaning, "healed", then every shard would be restored to smooth and harmless surface once again. It is the same with dualistic, injurious shards of awareness vs. non-dualistic oneness consciousness: the person with a divided, i.e., dualistic consciousness, sees or perceives a stressful, tormented world that is comprised of conflicting slivers of existence called "entities", which are at odds with each other, while competing for existence. This amounts to a tormenting inner mental and emotional life defined by internal, as well as external, rifts and conflicts that injure mentally and, if unresolved, in time they may manifest as physical and social diseases.

By contrast, consider the words of Jesus in the Gospel of Thomas, 61, (http://www.earlychristianwritings.com/thomas/gospelthomas61.html) whom many Biblical scholars believe was referring to a lost form of ancient medicine ... yet, they do not know what this form of medicine was: "It is I who come from that which is integrated [undivided]. I was given some of the things of my father. Therefore, I say that such a person, once integrated, will become full of light; but such a person, once divided will become full of darkness." These words of Christ, from a distant culture, with little or no connection to China where, Lao Tzu lived more than 500 years prior to Jesus, clarify:

1. "Divided" consciousness, a.k.a. dualistic consciousness, is NOT JUST A sickness, but THE ROOT of ALL illnesses and forms of suffering, the "darkness" Jesus refers to in the Gospel of Thomas quote, above.

2. The integration of dualistic consciousness heals all illnesses and suffering, which arise from this state of divided consciousness.

Jesus further explained how this medicine works in the Gospel of Thomas, 22, (http://www.earlychristianwritings.com/thomas/gospelthomas22.html) "When you make the two one, and when you make the inside like the outside, and the outside like the inside, and the upper like the lower! And if you make the male and female one, so that the male is no longer male and the female no longer female, then you will enter [the Kingdom]!"

Consider that the Kingdom Jesus is referring to is not a place per se, but a state of consciousness, and the ancient medicine Jesus was explaining was using non-dualistic, esoteric wisdom from above (i.e., Higher Consciousness), which is without division, "undivided" (James, 3:17) to integrate the dualistic thinking that was called by Lao Tzu "a sickness." "But the wisdom that is from above is pure, filled with peace, meek and attentive, filled with love and good fruit, without division and does not show partiality." — James 3:17 (https://biblehub.com/aramaic-plain-english/james/3.htm)

What is this universal wisdom that arose at different times in different areas of the world? It is an elemental wisdom that arises from the ubiquitous Essence of Existence. This timeless wisdom, generally known as "esoteric" or "mystical", emanates from the Higher Consciousness through sages worldwide.

What Jesus, Lao Tzu and Buddha held in common, was the knowledge that the only necessity to heal all of the ills of mankind is integration of dualistic consciousness through the non-dualistic wisdom of undivided Higher Consciousness. The same healing and self-realization principle Jesus expressed is the essence of Taoism, Buddhism and Sufism, the crux of aboriginal spiritualities of the Americas, Australia, and many Pacific Islands. This wisdom from within, like its Higher Consciousness source, is undivided (James, 3:17); hence, such wisdom has no religion and no nationality.

5. What Does Esotherapy say about Trauma and Other Diseases?

"The mere formulation of a problem is often far more essential than its solution." – Albert Einstein

Humans are but a microcosm of nature; the same elemental laws that underlie the spiritual balance and harmony of nature can cue us how to process traumatic events and heal other illnesses. Yet, rather than utilizing natural wisdom, healing sciences such as psychology, psychiatry, and medicine in general use ego-derived, man-made knowledge that confuses cause and effect.

This misperception is hard to detect only because it is widely accepted as conventional "common sense" thinking. For example, let's reconsider depression, a common component of trauma. Conventional therapies consider depression to be a type of extreme sadness. Psychology and psychiatry take this "common sense" assumption for granted, and base many of their theories on it, although it is not a research-validated fact.

For instance, think of a time when you may have felt depressed for a significant period of time. Likely, before you came to feel disheartened, you first lost your appetite, had no interest in activities that made you happy, couldn't get out of bed, you were unable to sleep or had restless, non-restorative sleep and felt constantly fatigued and drained of energy. This was a loss of vitality. Naturally, you became sad ABOUT the loss of vitality and the doctor prescribed you medication to dull your sadness. As a result, you may have been living a numb life that lacked vitality. Of course, to consider depression as loss of vitality or life-energy would make it a spiritual illness, which traditional forms of medicine around the world know as "shen-losing-its-home" (Taoist-based Chinese Medicine), "will or power-loss" (Dine spirituality), or "soul-loss" (Siberian shamanism). A continued experience of this state causes feelings of powerlessness, anxiety and stress, which, alone, accounts for 75% to 90% of all doctor visits.

The understanding that depression is a spiritual disease is not limited to remote forms of traditional medicine. Rooted in the Greek word "psych", which means "soul" or "spirit", psychotherapy, psychology, and psychiatry were meant to be spiritual approaches to healing. Yet, paradoxically, they have come to deny these spiritual aspects, reducing the living, breathing person to a faceless statistic, and promoting the idea that the SPIRIT OF LIFE can be replaced by a few chemical compounds.

6. How Does Esotherapy Heal Trauma And Other Emotional Imprinting Events?

Out yonder, past our ideas of possible and impossible, past our illnesses and understandings of healing, past wars and raging political, race and gender battles, there is a field carefully guarded by the spirit of division of dualistic thinking.

This spirit does not only teach misinformation, it socializes which questions are permissible and which are not. Questions such as, "is there a common root of all illnesses?" are forbidden so that we cannot even conceive of asking them, and if we would, the "common sense" answer would be "No, there is not!". However, what if common sense, i.e., dualistic consciousness, ITSELF, is the problem?

Esotherapy marches to a different drummer. It considers all illnesses to be mere manifestations of dualistic consciousness, which sages like Lao Tzu and Christ described as the root sickness. Thus, the integration of the divided, dualistic consciousness heals all the illnesses that arise from it.

Speaking about certain states that may arise from consciousness integration, which Abraham Maslow, father of humanistic psychology, described as "peak experiences" or "transcendent moments of pure elation, wonder, awe, or ecstasy", Maslow wrote:

"It is my strong suspicion that even one such experience might be able to prevent suicide, for instance, and perhaps many varieties of slow self-destruction, e.g., alcoholism, drug addiction, addiction to violence, etc. I would guess also, on theoretical grounds, that peak-experiences might very well abort "existential meaninglessness," states of valuelessness, etc.," (http://www.bahaistudies.net/asma/peak_experiences.pdf)

Again, to understand Esotherapy, it is important to debunk our deep-seated, socially accepted "common sense" understanding that consciousness is something "we have". Consider the words of world-renowned Neuroscience researcher Dr. Candace Pert: "Your body is your subconscious mind." She reaffirms that consciousness is us. It is "who we are". Integrating consciousness integrates us. It fundamentally changes the way we see past and present events as well as the world; this alters the chemical imbalances of our brains and bodies, thereby healing mental and physical illnesses alike.

Esotherapy is a consciousness integration therapy that processes trauma and other emotional-imprinting events through an amalgam of phenomenological inquiry, esoteric healing talk and touch, meditation, and spiritual ceremony, as well as contemporary psychological knowledge that switches perception from a divided, ego-centered perception to an integrated, spirit-centered state of consciousness.

Esotherapy is an amalgam of timeless, wisdom-centered medicine, such as the one that Christ and Lao Tzu voiced, integrated with modern understandings of illnesses. However, as opposed to other past attempts of integration, in Esotherapy, it is the non-dualistic, Higher Consciousness wisdom that drives the use of modern understandings, not vice-versa.

7. How does the Mindfulness-Based Stress Reduction (MBSR) Best Practice Compare to Esotherapy?

Mindfulness meditation is a microcosm of the esoteric spiritual disciplines it belongs in. To strip it of the esoteric context, in order the fit it into a secular therapy milieu, is to strip it of its spirit, as well as its power. Without its spiritual connection even the "best practice" of MBSR offers little more than banal, meaningless experiences that are but a shadow of true life. "I had learned how to live in the present [through Mindfulness–Based Stress Reduction] but appreciating the value and experience of each moment was only reachable through Esotherapy." — an Esotherapy client

The student quoted above used mindfulness meditation to attain a state free of anxiety and depression, only to find himself feeling embedded into a hopelessly meaningless sense of living a meaningless life in an equally meaningless world. Esotherapy restored a deep and fulfilling meaning to his life, a meaning richer than he had ever experienced, a significance more abundant than he could have ever imagined.

Esotherapy returns Mindfulness Meditation to the spiritual esoteric milieu it is an emanation of. It restores us to our natural, non-dualistic awareness, inherent peace, balance and harmony. It re-establishes mental clarity, positive self-esteem, and a hopeful outlook on life, which leads to unbounded mind-body healing and growth.

8. What are the Outcomes of Esotherapy?

Esotherapy heals trauma and the ACTUAL causes of illnesses by quickly returning consciousness and life experiences to their natural interconnectedness and wholeness, rather than maintaining them in a state of fragmented and repressed isolation, like dualistic, secular sciences do. This produces transformative outcomes such as the ability to be resilient when faced with life stressors, and the restoration of the parasympathetic nervous system functions of relaxation, calm, mental and emotional quietude and clarity, and the function of restorative sleep. It frees individuals from fear and anxiety, nightmares, flashbacks, shame, guilt, emotional and physical pain, and suffering.

This transformative consciousness integration "shift" heals the mind, as well as the body, thereby resolving trauma and many other ailments that arise from dualistic awareness. The results are durable and stable.

9. Can Esotherapy help me with my PTSD and/or other problems?

Ethically speaking, no one could tell you so, until AFTER talking to you. However, are your problems similar to the ones this Medical Director, below, speaks of? Please watch https://www.youtube.com/watch?v=BCS1NrZsHSo. The results of Esotherapy are endorsed in this video by the Medical Directors of the world premiere health centers, who report that ALL of their clients stated, compared to other therapies, Esotherapy helped them get BETTER, astoundingly FASTER, and with LONG-TERM, stable results.

Since Esotherapy is also a personal growth approach it is very suitable for spiritual development, as well as resolving existential and identity crises. Learn more about Esotherapy at: https://www.esotherapy.com.

* *

Healing Stories from Veterans With PTSD

Middle East Veteran

A Veteran came seeking help for trauma he had incurred during a military assignment in the Middle East. He had gone shopping off base and had to dress in civilian clothing. While shopping in a store he heard terrified people screaming and saw a man, apparently scrambling under his partially opened coat to detonate bombs strapped on his body. People in the store realized that he was a suicide bomber whose "bomb belt" had malfunctioned. Our Veteran jumped on that man and tried to immobilize him on the ground. As he was trying to restrain the man's hands without much success, the suicide bomber continued struggling to touch together the wires that would have detonated the bombs. This Veteran realized that the suicide bomber would either successfully connect the wires, or that the struggle itself would cause the wires to touch. He stated, "I had no choice ... I did not even have a knife ... I had to kill him with my bare hands. I am a man who never killed even an animal."

My client's trauma consisted of memories of the convulsions, twitching, and fluttering of the bomber's eyelids as he strangled him to death. My client explained that he could not sleep for years, because when he would begin to fall asleep, he would see the suicide bombers eyelids fluttering and feel his convulsions and twitching. Such a memory would take a very long time to heal by means of traditional counseling, because it is not a matter of having a logical realization that there could have been no other choice, or that the bomber would have died in the explosion anyway. There were muscle, tactile and visual memories that logic is incapable of influencing, that kept this client from sleeping and caused his flashbacks.

However, from the viewpoint of Esotherapy every emotion associated with a memory, as well as the memory itself, is energy, which are gateways allowing entry into the experience itself. I confirmed to the client that, indeed, he had no other choice; and then I neutralized the energy of the associated feelings and memory by means of Esotherapy. Later my client stated that for the first time in years, he was able to sleep that night...and he had slept not only the whole night, but well into the next day. Six months after this one treatment we met, incidentally, and this client stated that he was still able to sleep through the night and the flashbacks had not returned. This man told me that without the help of Esotherapy he would probably have killed himself.

Iraq War Veteran

A Veteran of the Iraq War came in for therapy due to heavy meth use. Unlike other users, he would go out into the desert where no one could see him, alone, to use the drug. He understood that he was killing himself slowly but did not care. He had been in counseling for many years, with almost no improvement. He explained that seeing his nephew around him was a big trigger and, since he was from an extended Spanish family living together on the same ranch, he would see his nephew frequently.

He explained that during the war in Iraq, he was an MP and one night, he was in the watchtower. From the corner of his eye, he saw a silhouette that had jumped the fence and entered a building before he could react. He was on the radio communicating, when the silhouette exited the building and tried to jump the fence back out. Thinking it was an enemy that had planted a remote-controlled bomb, he aimed and fired. The silhouette slid off the fence and onto the pavement. He ran over to the body and saw a 14-year-old boy whose shirt was soaked in blood. There were potatoes on the ground, and some potatoes were still rolling out from under his bloody shirt. The boy had been hit in the head and chest and was dead. The client stated he was frozen with guilt and horror; realizing that the boy had come to steal potatoes, probably to feed his family, since the war had had created a condition of famine where people were starving to death.

My client said the boy's face looked just like his nephew's...as if they were twins. He said that after he came back to the U.S., every time he saw his nephew, he was reminded that it could have been his nephew he had killed. Because of that he could not stand being around the boy and seeing him around every day brought back the memories as flashbacks. The client stated that he wanted to die because he could not live with the flashbacks and the lack of sleep, and he lacked even basic feelings that confer a sense of reality to life.

We did a ceremony in which he communicated with the soul of the Iraqi boy telling him that he did not mean to kill him. At that point a feeling arose that helped to bring the regretful event to a conclusion, like "pieces" of a puzzle falling into place and creating a sense of completion. My client was then willing to let the energy of the memory be neutralized through Esotherapy. With the flashbacks gone, my client was able to re-connect with his nephew. As well, he was able to sleep, to experience normal feelings, and to enjoy life once again. Without the old trauma-related feelings, the need and desire to use meth had vanished.

* *

To Contact Our Esotherapists

Do you require individual sessions to heal traumatic memories, flashbacks, nightmares, anxiety, grief, or depression? Contact Gerald Whitehawk, Primary Esotherapist at #(520)300-0553.

Do you need to fundamentally transform your life and re-integrate into civilian life? Our Esotherapy Intensive Outpatient Program was created for such demanding, closely monitored work. Call Tahlia Denny, Esotherapist, at #(503)847-7083 or contact her from the website:

For more information visit https://www.esotherapy-iop.com.

CHAPTER 15 - FLOATATION THERAPY, FLOAT BROTHERS

Trey Hearn and Chris Hearn

Lance Bozek: "The themed rooms include an Ocean Room, a Nature Room, a Space Room and a Patriot Room, each dimly lit to enhance the relaxing atmosphere. There is also a lobby serving herbal tea where patrons can wait for their float time and relax before leaving the spa." Trey Hearn: "The sense of the water is the same as your skin, so you can't feel the water. The water is heated to 93.5 degrees, the body's normal skin temperature. If you think of your brain as a computer, you turn off all the apps so your muscles can relax, your joints can relax and your brain can focus on healing itself faster."

"This is just a place to connect with yourself," added Chris. "I think of it as the training wheels for meditation; this takes away all distractions for you. We first tried float therapy in Orlando. I've always been into natural, holistic ways of healing and this really works in reduction of stress."

"I remember I was so nervous going in," said Trey, "but when I walked out I felt amazing, like I had a full body massage and I was completely relaxed. It's like a reset button for your brain. If you think of your brain as a computer, you have all these apps that are going to the hard drive, and you're letting it all reboot. In a study done by the Laureate Institute for Brain Research to see how float therapy can help patients they found the same results they could see visually in the brain that are exactly comparable to the use of anti-depression medication. It's the same if not more of a relief than the drugs."

According to Chris, "As Air Force Veterans we are proud to support our brothers and sisters in arms and we offer a special program to military members at Float Brothers. We have a PTSD program here where any military or veteran medically diagnosed with PTSD can float for free in our spa – that's our way to give back. The science is very simple, but the benefits are amazing and plentiful. You break away from your everyday life to float effortlessly free of gravity in super-saturated Epsom salt water, free of sight, sound and touch. This decrease in sensory input, being gravity-free and the Epsom salts all allow your body and mind to heal and recover like never before–just what we need in our over-stimulated society."

Lance: "Our state-of-the-art float pods allow patrons to customize their experience to their own comfort level. We provide the option to have multi-colored lighting and listen to music/audiobook in the pod if desired. The ultimate relaxation experience comes from being completely removed from all your senses. You have your own room, which includes a shower and a float pod. We ask that patrons rinse themselves off of oils/lotions before getting the pod nude (you can wear a bathing suit if preferred). Once in the pod, you just lay back and float effortlessly. We offer a 60-minute or a 90-minute float session. There is no better place to meditate or get to the Theta wave state that so many meditators strive for. You are in a distraction-free environment where you won't have anything to take you away from a meditative practice. Additionally, since all you will be able to hear is your breath and heartbeat, it is much easier to be mindful and get to the meditative state much faster."

Trey continued, "Our goal is to raise as much awareness as we can about how floating is helping with PTSD. As military Veterans, Chris and I know firsthand the devastating effects PTSD that is having on the military/veteran community.

We allow any military or Veterans medically diagnosed with PTSD the opportunity to float for free in our spa in the Patriot Float Room. As Veterans, both of us are working hard to spread the word about how float therapy is helping with PTSD. The sensory-free float pod allows an individual with PTSD a comfortable environment where they have no external stimuli so complete relaxation is possible. Additionally, the meditative environment allows them an opportunity to potentially think about and hopefully overcome some of the traumatic events that are causing them so much suffering."

"The lack of stimuli allows the brain to confront images or memories they have previously suppressed. What's actually helping people on our PTSD program is, when they get into the tank and get to that point, now they can address it in a calm environment where there's nothing else there that could hurt them. They can feel like it's secure, and they're safe, and they can approach the traumatic events in more of an internal counseling session with themselves. Floating is only a tool, but many military/Veterans are getting great relief from their PTSD symptoms from floating. It's a very unique therapy that's great for a mental and physical break.

We have had very good experiences with local Veteran clients with PTSD and we have received referrals from both private therapists and from those working as contract employment on military bases."

"Float therapy is also known as sensory deprivation. You can be free of touch, sight, sound, and gravity. It just allows your body to decompress and destress as well as your mind. For folks who feel they can't shut their brain down enough to relax, all you have to do is try it one time. Your brain is going to get into this fade away state of brain waves and when you get into that state it allows your body to recover in a way that you would as if you were sleeping."

"Inside the pod, there's the 150 gallons of water and 1,000 pounds of medical grade Epsom salt that's dissolved in that water. This allows you to float effortlessly on the surface of the water just from the sheer density of the salt. The salt also helps reduce inflammation. Once you float effortlessly, your spine will decompress, and your muscles and joints will instantly start letting go and start relaxing. You'll be free of gravity cause you're floating effortlessly. You can be free of touch because we heat the temperature of the water to 93.5 which matches the outside sensory touch of your skin so within a few minutes of floating you'll lose sense of the water."

He continued, "We have the Patriot themed float room. Use of this room is free for Veterans and Active Duty service members who have been diagnosed with PTSD. Because of our military background and having deployed, we have lots of friends who have PTSD. It really gives us the drive to help our fellow brothers and sisters in the military. We have had more than 140 Veterans join our PTSD program. Some have floated only once or twice; some have floated more than 50 times. We are finding folks under the program who tell us about how they're weaning off their anti-anxiety medication and their pain medication. So, it's not only me telling you, it's actually proving itself through these folks."

"We are utilizing the PCL-5 (PTSD Checklist for DSM-5 criteria self-assessment questionnaire) to apply pre and post-float effectiveness measures for our Veterans with PTSD. This allows us to measure the effectiveness of the float sessions. Similar data is also being collected in more controlled medical studies being performed by the Laureate Institute for Brain Research in Tulsa, OK." Jamie: "Let me share a little bit about how floatation therapy has helped me deal with PTSD. I was finishing a CrossFit workout when I first heard of Float Brothers, and to be honest I thought it sounded cool, but I don't think I'd be able to do it.

The idea of being in a capsule for 60-90 minutes seemed like way too much time in my own head. After all I've been actively avoiding specific thoughts and memories from my past. So after a few minutes of talking about the claimed benefits of floating I figured that, if I was uncomfortable, I could just get out and at least I would get the relief of soaking in Epsom salt. When I finally mustered the courage to go to the spa I decided I would go there with an open mind. Sensory deprivation meant the pod would be completely dark which also meant there would be no visual distraction. The water temperature would be approximately 94 degrees, the same temperature of the skin's surface, which means no tactile distraction. Earplugs would minimize noise so and, as long as I didn't swallow any water by accident, my five basic senses would not be a distraction. I was able to alleviate a lot of my anxiety by knowing that, at any time, things such as LED light and ambient music were at my fingertips from right inside the Pod. I entered the pod with an open mind and was determined to try to tolerate going into complete isolation. The novelty of the experience made me focus my attention of how much I couldn't see, hear, or feel. I thought I could see some colors, perhaps some light source from outside the pod, but something as simple as waving my hand in front of my face proved to yield zero visibility (while making sure salt water did not fall in my eyes). So these colors I thought I was seeing were just a figment of my imagination. A few minutes went by and as I lay very still I realized I couldn't feel the water. Right then and there, the notion of being in a confined space had totally disintegrated. I started to feel as if the pod was huge...so huge that it was almost as if the pod itself didn't exist. Yet strangely enough I felt connected to everything in the universe. I become aware of thoughts that seemed to simply appear out of nowhere in my consciousness. It was as if they were authored by someone else. I had no way to block them and I couldn't ignore them, nor did I try. I simply acknowledged the thoughts as they arrived and moved from one thought to another as each made its way into my awareness. Then I began to examine the way I think and how emotions got the best of me in many of my conversations. I thought about how I could change the outcome of some of my interactions if I could just be aware of what I was feeling as it was occurring. Then, I started reliving conversations I had in the past, except this time I was occasionally able to do so without the emotional charge they had carried when the conversation originally took place. I could see past the sarcasm and attitude I got from my wife during an argument and understood the message she had intended to send me through her words. I found myself standing in the middle of my garage, which looked like an abandoned storage room, with unopened boxes from my time in the Army.

I had avoided doing this for two years but I could vividly see myself opening one box, knowing exactly what items were in the box and finding a place for each item, whether stored inside the house, in the garage or thrown out. I then moved on to the next box, and the next, and I saw the entire process in my head, one box at a time until there were no more boxes left. And just like that, my time was up. I spent the entire time in the pod in my own head and sensory deprivation had allowed me to avoid distractions and acknowledge my own thoughts. I left the spa with a very clear and realistic plan to clean up my garage. Since then I can say I have been very aware of my emotions. This doesn't mean I don't get anxious or have panic attacks. It simply means I am aware of and can make plans that counter that state-of-mind as it occurs as opposed to wandering lost with no explanation for my actions."

Chris: "It is exciting to see the progress that is being made over the last couple years with the scientific studies. Hopefully someday soon there will be enough peer reviewed data that float therapy could be adopted as a legitimate treatment for PTSD. In order for that to happen we need to create more public awareness of floating in general and ask that more studies are done to demonstrate its efficacy. This would then allow governmental agencies and insurance companies to help cover the cost of treatments, thus providing it to a much wider audience."

"In the meantime, we highly recommend that any Veterans suffering from PTSD search for a float location near you. By simply searching online for "float center + (enter your city name) you should find that most major cities have a float center within an hour drive."

Visit Float Brothers Floatation Therapy at http://floatbrothers.com/.

CHAPTER 16 - GAMERZ4VETS

Nate Gonzalez and Bennie Sullivan

Source: Chapter Author

Nate Gonzalez: I was hurt back in 2001. I had just finished a tour overseas and was getting sent to 29 Palms for Staff NCO school, and also had my officer package put in, so I was waiting for that. I had just reenlisted, had a good signing bonus, got a promotion to Sergeant, I was doing great. I came home on leave and brought my motorcycle with me. A drunk driver ran a stop sign and hit me on my bike less than a mile away from my house. That pretty much ended all of those things on my career path. Luckily the military took care of me so I am on full retirement, full benefits...if it weren't for the military I wouldn't be here today.

About two years ago, I went in for a blood clot, and it was supposed to be a quick procedure, only 30 minutes, but when they put me under sedation, they ended up losing my heart rate...O2...everything. They ended up putting me into a medically induced coma for a month trying to figure out what was going on because every time they tried to take me off oxygen and life support, they kept losing me. It took them about a month to figure out what was happening. I have late stage pulmonary hypertension. Basically, one side of your heart pumps blood throughout your body and the other part of your heart is just to get oxygen from your lungs. The vessels in my lungs are very constricted and hardened so they are not able to open up, so my heart has to work twice as hard to force the blood through the veins. The first warning of that was that I was getting very bloated. When I got out of the coma, my body was in a condition that they said I only had three to five years to live. That was my life expectancy. With medications I have been taking, I am doing a little bit better now. I am a Class 2 rather than a Class 4. Before the only thing that was going to save me was a lung transplant. Now I have seven to 10 years...maybe more.

I kind of gave up on playing video games because I only had the use of one arm...so I figured that I wasn't going to play video games ever again. Then along came a friend of mine who managed to find a one-handed controller for me to use. It had all the buttons on this one controller so that I could play the video games with just one hand. So, I started playing like that and I got pretty good at it. The PlayStation 2 came out with the dual sticks and again I figured that I was done with video games because of my limitations. I finally got to the point that I decided that I had to learn how to play with what was available. So, I started using my mouth as the left side and held the joystick on my right side. As the controllers kept getting more advanced, I kept telling myself that's it, I'm done, but I always seemed to end up figuring things out.

Bennie and I, we pretty much got hurt within a week of each other. I would see him at the hospital every time I would go to the VA, and he was volunteering his time there, and he would bring his PlayStation, and he was there at the Recreation Center trying to get people engaged with playing video games. When I first got hurt, other Veterans who were disabled or paralyzed would come in to my room and would try to break the ice and talk, but I would always kick them out of my room and would say I didn't want to hear their story, or didn't want to hear whatever they wanted to tell me. When the coin was flipped and I was going into other guys rooms trying to be positive, they would react the same way I used to.

We figured out that there had to be a way to bridge that divide and we kind of wanted to use gaming as the keystone to build that bridge. I figured that all of us had played video games at some point. We thought that if we got them gaming, then maybe we could get them talking, and then just continue building from there. There are just a lot of positive benefits to gaming. It helps with concentration, focus, socialization, task-making, goal-setting, etc.

Well, I told Bennie that we could make the whole gaming concept bigger if he wanted. I put some stuff together and got with a non-profit organization here called San Antonio Area Foundation and met with a lady there and started up a not-for-profit with me and Bennie with the focus of trying to make adaptive controllers.

Both Bennie and my backgrounds were in electronics, from our time in the military, but Bennie is more of the guy who does the fabrication of the controllers. I am more of the face-to-face guy, the business connection, the person working on getting and maintaining funding and sponsorships. I also do shooting and video editing.

Because of my health issues, this is my way of giving back. We aren't curing cancer or anything like that...we are making adaptive controllers for video games. We are also trying to bring disability awareness into the gaming community as a whole.

Bennie Sullivan: I'm a C5-C6 burst fracture injury. I'm also a Quadriplegic just like Nate Gonzalez. I was actually injured in Hawaii while I was on the All Air Force Volleyball team. We were running on the beach and the wake of the water rushed up and took my feet out from underneath me, and I flipped over on top of my head and snapped my neck. It was pretty much a freak accident. I got hurt back in August of 2001. They are doing this because I got involved with Microsoft and I built controllers with my disability and whatnot.

147

Starting just a little bit after I got hurt, my kids were two and four years old. I was an avid gamer and I wanted to be able to play video games again but I couldn't wrap my head around what I could do or how. So, I actually reached out to the only company I knew of at that time that I thought could help...Able Gamers...and they never contacted me back. They just left me hanging like hard core and had to figure things out on my own. I actually started experimenting with the PlayStation 2 and I had an old Nintendo 64. Anyway, I started experimenting with them, trying to re-teach myself how to play video games.

Now my quadriplegia doesn't allow me to use my fingers at all so what I ended up doing was I found a way to actually play with these controllers by holding the controller in my hand and using my finger up underneath the joystick, and I would tilt the controller with my other hand. That would allow me to get access to the left joystick so that I could move around. I used my lip on the other joystick, depending on the game, so that I could look around. I would just use my tongue and lip to press the buttons on it. So, I kept trying this out and perfected it a little bit and was able to play video games really well considering my disability.

I used to do computer classes over at the VA hospital where I would have people bring their computers in, and I'm a software engineer so I'm really good at computers. So, what I did was I kind of changed my scope in that, if they wanted to bring in their computers, I would help younger Veterans like myself, and tried to get them into gaming as well. I would bring my own console in and we would try to goof off and try to find different ways for the other Veterans to play.

Well, I started researching on the internet for different peripherals and things like that we could use and a lot of them were really expensive. Well, I kind of started putting together stuff on my own because I worked aircraft weapons with electronics and on top of that I had my software background so I was able to put those two together and make jerry-rigged controllers for people. So, we could get into it and enjoy playing again.

It wasn't until around 2014 when the PlayStation 3 came out and there were actually a couple of devices that came out that allowed you to change the buttons. And with those devices that came out, I was able to write code onto the devices and change the buttons so that it made it a whole lot easier for me to play video games because if you put the buttons that I needed, where I needed them, and the ones I didn't need that often elsewhere, it worked out great. So, with that knowledge and with that equipment I was able to help other Veterans to do the same sort of thing.

Around that time when I got that device there was a recreational therapist at the VA by the name of Jose Laguna. Well, Jose suggested that we make this a weekly thing and we did. On Mondays we started from 1:00-3:30 and made it a thing where I would bring my console and we'd get all the equipment that I had amassed over the years, and I kind of made it into a gaming clinic that we would do every Monday.

In around 2015, I met a quadriplegic named Travis who introduced me to Hardline, an online multi-player game. I started playing that online game and at first I was horrible. But after a while I started working my way up the scoreboards up around the middle area. I got pretty good at it. I got picked up by a clan, which is a group of individuals who get together and fight other groups/clans. Because it was a first-person shooter game we would go ahead and do that. Well, while we were doing that, these guys were the elite. They were way up on the leader boards. They came in first through third easily. They would wipe the floor with everybody. They basically taught me what I was missing in online games, and when that happened I jumped all the way up to the top of the scoreboards. When they were on I was usually fourth or fifth place but when they weren't I was first or second most of the time when I played on my own. So, they gave me those tools on how to win first person shooters and that's around the time that the PlayStation 4 came out so I kind of became addicted to first person shooter games.

I was doing those every Monday, trying to find as many people as I could because I wanted other people to be able to experience what I was going through...basically the joy of starting off down at the bottom and worked my way up through hard work and learning things...and I wanted my fellow Veterans to experience the same things.

When Nate came out of his coma, he saw me there doing my Monday 'thing' and working with everybody else. Nate and I literally got our injuries weeks apart from each other. He was like, why don't we just make this thing go big as a non-profit, and that's really how the Gamerz4Vets started for us...and that was back in March of 2017. He got most of the paperwork together, and Gamerz4Vets was born. At first things went really slow. Nate's computer classes ended up making computer games for our Veterans. They were making them specifically for individuals.

We had a couple of quadriplegics who couldn't use their arms at all, they only used their mouth, so for one in particular, we ended up getting her a controller that she could use with her mouth as a sip and blow. The university created a video game with the knowledge that she had this controller and could play it. It all came off pretty well. They weren't super-polished video games because they were just students but it was still a great effort. It was wonderful that their teacher, John Quarles (Assoc. Professor of Computer Studies, University. of Texas at San Antonio) got them involved.

**For more information visit gamerz4vets.org, call us at #210-831-8891, or e-mail us at info@gamerz4vets.org.

CHAPTER 17 - HOMES FOR OUR TROOPS

Tom Landwermeyer, President

Homes for our Troops (HFOT) is a publicly funded 501(c)(3) nonprofit organization that builds and donates specially adapted custom homes nationwide for severely injured post - 9/11 Veterans, to enable them to rebuild their lives. Most of these Veterans have sustained injuries including multiple limb amputations, partial or full paralysis, and/or severe traumatic brain injury (TBI). These homes restore some of the freedom and independence our Veterans sacrificed while defending our country, and enable them to focus on their family, recovery, and rebuilding their lives.

HFOT was started by a Massachusetts General Contractor who offered to build a home for a former Massachusetts National Guard Soldier in the town of Middleborough. The Veteran agreed to have him build a home as long as he continued to do the same for other Veterans as well. Since inception in 2004, we have built over 280 homes in 42 states and currently have over 80 active projects nationwide.

We build four-bedroom, two bath, specially adapted energy efficient homes of just over 2,800 square feet. We think this provides the right size home for a Veteran to comfortably raise a family while limiting expenses for utilities. The home design allows a Veteran to do a complete 360 in a wheelchair anywhere in the home. This is key to restoring some of the freedom and independence our Veterans sacrificed defending our country.

Our tag line is "Building Homes, Rebuilding Lives". Rebuilding Lives is the most important aspect of our mission; therefore, we stay with our Veterans after home delivery. HFOT provides a pro-bono financial planner for three years to assist in financial planning and household budgeting, in addition to homeownership education and warranty coverage to ensure that the Veteran is set up for long-term success as a homeowner. One staff section's sole focus is following up with our Veterans, and we also have a peer mentoring program consisting of Veterans in the HFOT program. To improve our post home delivery support, we continue to expand our network of non-profits, corporations, and government entities to provide assistance with employment, education, training, health, and other issues. We strive to provide the linkage between the Veteran and the assistance he or she needs. Other differences include a comprehensive selection process, building where the Veteran wants to live, and spending nearly 90 cents on the dollar to support the Veterans since our inception in 2004.

HFOT is a publicly funded non-profit, with approximately 65 percent of our operational budget generated by individual donors, private and family foundations, and community fundraisers nationwide who step up to help our American Veterans by coordinating everything from lemonade stands to golf tournaments. The remaining 35 percent comes from corporate supporters in the form of cash and donated materials.

Results from a recent survey of our Veterans reveal we are making a lasting impact in the lives of our home recipients.

After receiving their specially adapted custom HFOT homes, a large portion of Veterans have regained a substantial amount of independence. More than 80 percent of our home recipients say they are able to heal in a safe environment. Over 90 percent of Veterans say they regained freedom and independence after receiving the home.

Once they regain their freedom within the home, many home recipients, and their caregivers/spouses, have the time to pursue an education or trade. The number of Veterans who have obtained or are pursuing a degree or trade certification increased from 12 percent to 69 percent after receiving their specially adapted custom homes. The number was even higher for spouses/caregivers, growing from eight percent to 90 percent.

Since they are able to rest and recover comfortably in their homes and their spouses/caregivers no longer have to worry about their safety, many home recipients feel empowered to return to the workforce. The number of Veterans employed grew by 67 percent after receiving their HFOT home. The impact was even more significant for spouses/caregivers, with their employment rate increasing by over 300%.

Receiving a donated home gives home recipients the ability to save for the future. After receiving their HFOT homes, 58 percent of our Veterans decreased family debt, 57 percent increased savings, and 37 percent increased family income.

Living in a safe and stable environment gives home recipients the ideal environment to start or expand their families. Over 150 babies have been born to HFOT families since 2010. The number of Veterans who are married increased from 59 percent to 79 percent. The average American household size remained unchanged at 2.6 from 2005-2017, according to the U.S. Census. During that time frame, the average HFOT family grew from 2.7 to 3.8.

Many Veterans feel so grateful for receiving an HFOT home, they want to continue serving others. After receiving the keys to their homes, the number of Veterans able to pay it forward by volunteering grew from 12 percent to 67 percent.

Corporate Partners include Armstrong Flooring, Budget Blinds, Whirlpool, CertainTeed, C.H.I. Overhead Doors, Ferguson, Kohler, Liberty Creek Wines, MI Windows and Doors, OakCraft Elegant Cabinetry, Progress Lighting, Rev-A-Shelf, Sherwin-Williams, Texas Roadhouse, Veterans United Foundation, Harvey Building

Products, H-E-B, HARDI, Silestone, Thompson Creek Window Company, #1-800-PACK-RAT, WB Liquors & Wine, Channellock, American Fire Sprinkler Association, Rinnai, J.G. Wentworth, Boeing, Santander, AirMedCare Network, Shaw, Ferguson, and the Wounded Warrior Project.

"We see our mission as a moral obligation of our country to care for these Veterans and families who have willingly sacrificed so much so the rest of us can enjoy the daily freedoms we hold so dear."

Please visit https://www.hfotusa.org for more information.

CHAPTER 18 - INTIMACY AND TRUST AFTER MAJOR TRAUMA

Scoba F. Rhodes, MSW

I was born in January of 1966. I graduated Bowdoin College in 1987 and joined the Navy Nuclear Power Program in 1988 and received a Bronze Star and numerous other service and merit-based related awards during my time in the Navy. I graduated University of Southern California (USC) with Master of Social Work 2016. I am currently a member of the Paralyzed Veterans of America (PVA) California Chapter, a monthly columnist for the Paraplegic News (PN) magazine, and I authored a book titled "Rules of Engagement: A Self-Help Guide for Those Overcoming Major Personal Trauma," am currently serving on City of Tustin Board of Appeals, and am also currently a Career Agent for Ohio National Financial Services. I have been married the past 10 years to Sonia and am currently living in Tustin, CA.

I joined the United States Navy in March of 1988 and was accepted into the Navy Nuclear Power Program. Although I had already graduated from a small New England College, I found the academic regimen in the Navy the most difficult I had ever encountered. I endured and graduated with a respectable grade point average and was enjoying life as a teacher's assistant at a Naval Nuclear Power training facility in New England. Then a Middle Eastern dictator named Saddam Hussein invaded Kuwait, and as with all members of the military, my life and my future were changed forever. Within a few months, I received orders directing me to San Diego and specifically to the Nuclear Cruiser **USS LONG BEACH (CGN-9)**. I served in Desert Storm, earning the Bronze Star. After leaving the Gulf region the ship returned to the Pacific Ocean, joining up with a Drug Enforcement Agency (DEA) team and engaging in anti-drug enforcement operations. After six years of active duty service, I transferred to the Naval Reserves for two more years, and received an honorable discharge from Naval Service in 1996. Although I had reasons to visit a therapist shortly after completing my service, and had been in some dangerous situations, I was not diagnosed with any type of Post-Traumatic Stress Disorder (PTSD), and as I look back, I was suffering more from guilt and depression, not PTSD. Thirteen years later however, my life would change again.

In 2005, I was in an aerobics exercise class and felt an unfamiliar rip in my chest. I went to my doctor and after running some tests, was referred immediately to a heart surgeon who informed me I had suffered an aneurysm burst in my aortic arch, the artery that acts as a conduit for the blood leaving the heart and distributes it to the rest of the body. The open-heart operation repair was successful and after 30 days I was discharged and after three months I returned to work.

Unfortunately, I didn't change any of my bad habits that probably contributed to my health, namely smoking. I guess I was still feeling like the invulnerable Veteran, because three years later, I was driving on the freeway, drinking a cup of coffee and smoking a cigarette, and began feeling a pain in my chest, and woke up four days later in a hospital room. I was told I suffered another aneurysm in the thoracic region of my aorta and had to undergo emergency repair. This was my second open heart surgery, and like before, I was discharged from the hospital in 30 days.

This time the surgeon described the unhealthy condition of my arteries and informed me there was another aneurysm in the abdominal region of my aorta, but due because the medical staff felt to repair the third aneurysm would require too much time under anesthesia, and I should give my body sufficient time to recover from the previous operation. I waited a year and scheduled the operation for November 2nd, 2009. I had every expectation this operation would play out as the last two. Little did I know how wrong I was. I was given a pre-operation brief, and expected the operation to take around six hours, and I would be back at work in thirty days. This time however, I awoke two weeks later, hands tied to the railings, using a breathing apparatus, and unable to move my legs.

I was barely conscious, and the doctors attempted two unsuccessful attempts to remove the Bilateral Positive Airway Pressure (BiPAP) machine. On the third attempt, I could barely breathe on my own. My father and my then girlfriend, Sonia, took turns watching over me as a fought to simply breathe. It took all my strength to simply expand my lungs and take in air. After a few hours, I sent my Sonia out of the room and stopped fighting. I was too tired to continue, and I was about to give up and let myself die. My father came back in the room and essentially ordered me to keep fighting. I looked at him attempting to say I couldn't go any farther, and he simply kept ordering me to keep fighting and keep breathing. When Sonia returned for her turn to watch over me, she let me know in no uncertain terms that I was not going to be able to kick her out of the room again. I resigned myself to the situation and just began to focus on the next breath. Eventually, my lungs began to clear, and my breathing became close to normal. It was only then I was able to ask how long I was going through this, and I was told by the doctor it was just short of eight hours.

It was a bit later that I would learn that my battle to stay alive was far from over. When the doctor explained to me that the aneurysm had burst, and I lost blood flow to my Spinal Cord resulting in my paralysis, the doctor explained that my internal organs also suffered damage. My kidneys were rendered completely inoperable, my bladder and bowel, small and large intestines, possibly my liver and gall bladder had suffered major damage too. Additionally, I had developed bed sores on both my legs and my lower back. I felt helpless as I would lie there and watch the nurses change the dressings on my chest, the dialysis technicians sit there and run their machines, all the while internally wondering if I was going to survive another day. Additionally, some of those doctors, nurses, and technicians were indifferent to cruel, and I believe that contributes to the fears and bad memories many people have regarding medical care. One of my brighter moments was when Sonia would stop by and give me a vegetable smoothie to drink about four to five times a week. A few weeks later, a nurse noticed there was urine in the Foley catheter drainage bag. My kidney function was returning.

After a few months, I was transferred to the nearest Veterans Administration Hospital (VA) and the medical staff labeled in the transfer documents my condition "good". But my first night at the VA was far from that. First, I was given two units of blood. The reason that is important is because a normal human being carries between 10–12 units of blood, and the loss of twenty percent of blood leaves the patient dangerously vulnerable. Remember my wounds that were formed at the first hospital? The report said they were healed, yet the wound care specialist at the VA removed the scab tissue and found the ulcer had deteriorated almost all the way to the bone and was infected. If these wounds had not been treated and I had been simultaneously given antibiotics intravenously (IV), it was possible I could have died. My condition was far from good. Yet, co-incidentally my insurance stopped paying for my hospital stay, so a miracle occurred, and my condition was stable enough to be transferred to the VA hospital. As it turns out, that transfer saved my life. If I had stayed in that hospital another week, I have no doubt I would have perished, and no one would have known why.

Did I have PTSD? Most definitely. However, I had other issues to worry about. I had to heal, and undergo two more surgeries, this time for the wounds that occurred while I was in the hospital. Then I had to listen and absorb the news that due to the nature of my injuries I would most likely never walk again. That's when I learned my next lesson, doctors rejoice in giving good news, and talking about their success stories. The failures, and bad news however, not so much. Yet, my condition was not going to change, and I my choices were few. For the first few months I simply went through the paces, and I had one hour of counseling a week, and three hours of physical training a day. Distraction is a powerful thing.

I had to regain my strength and then some, If I was going to operate a wheelchair, transfer from my chair to various other pieces of furniture, and eventually operate an automobile. The workouts were hard, but I was getting stronger. Sonia was by my side the entire time, and even slept in the room with me between four to five nights a week, and almost every weekend. We even got married while I was in the hospital. Eventually my time for discharge arrived, and I was nervous. I was unsure how my life would unfold. That I learned my third life lesson, just as a person can be sick, but not sick enough to go to the hospital; a person may not be fully healed, but can be well enough to leave the hospital. It was then I began to experience what it means to have PTSD.

This is the physical side disability I am living with, and although I did experience some emotional issues when I left the military in 1996, I recovered quickly and without any major incident. This experience was a different matter. Having your life placed in danger changes your entire life perspective. Most people don't think about how dangerous it can be driving on the freeway, eating in a restaurant exposed to any crazy person who can come in through the door and let loose a spray of bullets, or how similar a sledgehammer being operated by a construction worker sound oddly similar to a machine gun. I believe PTSD does not even occur when your life is placed in danger, because for the military person, we are trained to cope with those situations. Our lives are in danger more often than most of us realize. If we were to know how many meteors almost strike the planet during any given decade, we would all be constantly nervous. How about how many car accidents we almost get into, things happening beyond our field of vision that we don't even see? Our lives are in danger almost all the time. It is that moment when we become unsure whether we will survive an ordeal, when we are faced with the real possibility of death, due to causes outside of our control, that we will eventually experience PTSD. Because we have experienced a situation, some of us many situations, where we really questioned whether our lives would continue, we become hyper-vigilant to every other aspect of our lives that we can control. Along with our hyper-vigilance, we become extremely reluctant to place our well-being into the hands of another individual, whether it is a doctor, nurse, counselor, or spouse. We become the ultimate control freak, and we make no apologies about it.

Car accidents, traffic jams, crowds, car engines backfires, suspicious looking people; folks with PTSD are usually triggered by all these events and more. So many things can occur during an everyday trip to the office that can affect our moods to the extent that the first person we run into gets a handful of negative emotions they have no idea how to respond to.

Unfortunately, the usual response is rejection. We find it hard to find a job, heck, it's almost impossible to get in the car and drive to the office, much less deal with all the stimuli we receive while on the way. The problem is, the world does not stop and wait for us to simply get better. It is up to us to find a way to heal and rejoin the world.

My paternal grandmother was handicapped, due to Rheumatoid Arthritis, and walked on crutches and could not grasp anything with her hands. She did not suffer from this affliction her entire life, but she did through mine. I don't remember ever seeing her without her crutches. She was given a life ending diagnosis back in 1960 and given six months to a year to live. She died in 1984. Living on borrowed time, and overcoming it, was part of my father's life experience. So, there was no way he was going to let me just give up. When I was discharged from the hospital, I went to one of the local Los Angeles Universities and enrolled in a Master's degree program, and earned a Master of Social Work, with a concentration in mental health, and during my time in school, learned about PTSD and its treatment, and essentially treated myself.

Understand that earning that degree was not easy. I had to do the first year from the hospital. After I was initially discharged, I developed another pressure sore, an issue which plagues me to this very day. The difference is my level of knowledge regarding my condition has increased, which is my first rule of overcome trauma, "You are your first line of defense". Thanks to help from teachers and students, I was able to observe the lectures via computer, my wife purchased my books, and the students volunteered to have the study groups in my hospital room. With their assistance I completed the first year. I began attending class during the second semester but kept dozing off. I was taking prescription medication Vicodin (two pills every four hours) for pain. One professor informed me I would not successfully complete the program if I kept falling asleep in class, and I would have to find some other solution to my pain if I wanted to graduate. With some adaptive yoga and physical therapy, I weaned myself off the pain medications, and currently take a few Tylenol as needed once every few days. I am still completely opioid free. I would have never known it was a problem until my professor pointed it out to me. You never know the changes in your life you must undertake to complete a journey, until you actually attempt that journey. This is another reason why many people with PTSD do not get diagnosed properly until years after the life-threatening event.

The truth is almost every life-threatening injury or situation will have a component of PTSD attached to it. The intensity of the PTSD is dependent on a number of factors, but each individual has a different personal experience. It was during this early stage of my injury that I learned my most valuable lesson. Regardless of the type of injury, or its level of damage, the tools we use for healing are the ones we develop before we become injured. All our adversity skills: dedication, determination, perseverance, optimism, and strength, do not mysteriously manifest themselves during our healing process, they are developed by our experiences, teachers, leaders, and parents throughout our lives. It is during our rehabilitation when we reach down and draw upon them to help get us through, but first we must get over our fear and anger in order to access them. We could avoid a lot of future emotional struggles if the individual were assessed immediately after the life threatening event with PTSD, and even if there were not any symptoms present at that moment, there were some follow up appointments made at six month intervals for a two-year period to assess if there were any delayed manifestations of PTSD.

Additionally, I have discovered, it is the same process with intimacy, sexuality, and trust. As individuals, we do not lose our sexual drive because we have endured damage to our bodies. We may lose our self-esteem, self-worth, and our self-confidence thus preventing us from having romantic and sexual moments with our partners, or even worse, initiating any type of romantic engagement with our spouses, but the sexual drive is still within us. Unfortunately, I have seen it manifest in some individuals with PTSD in an unhealthy manner, from inappropriate interactions between hospital staff and caregivers, to solicitation, and an unhealthy amount of time spent pursuing sexual online activities, unfortunately whether married or not. Please do not misunderstand. I support a healthy self-image with healthy flirtation if proper respect for personal boundaries is maintained. And for those who are married or in a committed relationship, maintaining a proper acknowledgement of your loved one's emotions is included here. I have no moral objection to a healthy inclusion of creative sexual practices in one's lifestyle if both partners find it exciting. What I am talking about are the unhealthy activities I have previously observed that end up damaging an otherwise healthy romantic relationship.

If our self-worth was secure before our accident, then it stayed secure after. We see this frequently in those who although now disabled, are still engaged in wonderful relationships, working in great careers, even conquering mountains and competing in sports events. Many others, however, suffer with healing, employment, substance abuse, and their relationships, romantic and otherwise. Where popular opinion is incorrect however, is that it is the injury that has damaged the relationship, and not that the relationship was not strong enough to cope with the injury. As I mentioned before, all we were before the injury is what we bring into the life after it. The same circumstance applies with our relationships, and the strength of our bond with our loved ones. As the late Dana Reeve, wife of the late Christopher Reeve, said to her husband after he suggested she divorce him, "Nonsense, you are still you!" My father said the same type of statement to me when I was struggling with my injury, "Did you get this far in life because of your legs, or because of your brains and personality?"

Once I have explored many of the failed relationships that have occurred after an injury, it was easy to discover many issues stressing the strength of the relationship, and a strong case could be made that the injury was simply the proverbial straw that broke the camel's back. Additionally, those spouses/mates that attempt to stay and end up leaving later, have reported that they felt pushed away by the very individual they were trying to stay with. Being in that same situation myself, I have come to understand that those that are injured need to come to a level of peace with their injury, and that moment does not always come quickly. However, every moment that the patient delays in self-healing is a moment the spouse/mate feels being pushed away. Eventually, they can be pushed so far away that it becomes too far to bring them back. I have developed a set of rules that the patient can use to help maintain the relationship and possibly make it even stronger. As proof, I submit that my wife and I are still together, and all is well.

First, all couples whether married or not, need to perform an honest assessment of their relationship prior to making any major decisions regarding the future of the relationship. No major decisions should be made under the cloud of anger and fear. I recommend waiting three months or so. However, if the spouse/mate immediately says they will stay, the injured person needs to immediately accept that the spouse is dedicated and allow the spouse to be as active as part of the rehabilitation process as he/she is willing. The more engaged the partner is in the rehabilitation, the stronger the relationship becomes. Remember, it is easy to stand together when times are great, but it is the bonds formed during our struggles that have a more durable weave.

Secondly, realize and accept the power of support. Every successful endeavor was never accomplished alone. Every mountain climber who has reached the summit will tell you how wonderful their guide was. The person who holds the world record for reaching the top of Mount Everest is not a celebrated famous mountain climber, it is Kami Rita Sherpa — a local mountain guide. He has reached the summit 24 times, guiding other people to the top. During your rehab, that's the kind of friend you need by your side. You know, the one you avoid when you are trying to quit smoking. The one who will hold you accountable to reaching your goals. Often, that person is the one closest to you, but having been there myself, we can be too entrenched in our own self-pity to realize it. We can't make it too difficult or too frustrating for our mates to help us through tragedy. Not to be confused, most mates are aware of the difficulties ahead for us. What happens is our own anger, self-pity, and depression compounds the obstacles for those attempting to help us, many times to the point of breakup, then we rationalize their leaving as their unwillingness to stick around, when the truth is that we pushed then away. The sooner we make peace with our injury, the sooner we can recover and rebuild our lives.

The reason these two advisories are so important is because one of the main bonds of any relationship is intimacy, and that is attached to trust. Trust is not built from one action, many times trust is the result of many actions, eventually convincing the other person in our lives that we can be trusted. Not just with their physical bodies, but with their financial and social futures as well. We need to realize all these issues are rolled into one. However, although it takes many efforts to create enough trust in our mates, it can be destroyed much easier. If our mates don't believe we can eventually function with our newly acquired disability, that distrust can plant a seed that will eventually grow into other parts of the relationship and erode it to the point where the mates eventually leaves. I am convinced that the main reason I am still married even being paralyzed from the waist down, is that I am still independent enough that my wife can still have her own life, leave me alone without worrying if I will be okay. She even spent a week vacationing in Mexico, and I stayed home since I couldn't get away. As grateful as I am to Sonia, I am also determined to not turn my wife into just a personal nurse or caregiver. Yes, she helps me, but she also knows that to help me is her choice, and that I can get by alone if she is not around. Your hospital social worker may or may not be competent to provide you with all the information you need, but there are a few books that can help you.

ADDITIONAL:

The list below is just the beginning. As you read these books, other books will be suggested that are more in line with the issues affecting your life. The more you know, the better off your life will be. As with all things in life, the final decision is yours. I wish you all the best you can achieve in your journey.

The Diagnostic and Statistical Manual (DSM) of Mental Disorders (commonly called the DSM-5) - LINK: https://www.psychiatry.org/psychiatrists/practice/dsm — Know your own symptoms and understand the treatment options for PTSD. Awareness and information are the best ways to combat the accompanying fear that comes with any life-threatening injury or situation.

Paralysis Resource Guide — issued by the Christopher Reeve Foundation - LINK: https://www.christopherreeve.org/living-with-paralysis/free-resources-and-downloads/paralysis-resource-guide — contains not only has information on various injuries, it also contains valuable information on support networks helping us to live a full and productive life after being discharged from the hospital.

Sexuality and Physical Disability: A Disability-Affirmation Approach to Assessment and Intervention Within Health Care, by Eisenberg, Andreski and Mona - LINK: https://link.springer.com/article/10.1007/s11930-014-0037-3 — Sexuality does not have to end with disability. Anyone born with a disability can tell you that.

Rules of Engagement: A Self-Help Guide for Those Overcoming Major Personal Trauma - LINK: https://www.amazon.com/Rules-Engagement-Self-Help-Overcoming-Personal/dp/1483677427 — By Scoba F. Rhodes, MSW (as mentioned in the chapter above)

CHAPTER 19 - LONELY SOLDIERS: THE ISOLATING TOLL OF WAR TRAUMA AND PTSD

Jacob Y. Stein, Ph.D., I-Core Research Center for Mass Trauma and Bob Shapell School of Social Work, Tel Aviv University, Israel

English poet John Donne (1572-1631) has famously asserted that, "no man is an island." This iconic proclamation connotes that we are all connected and inter-depended in one way or another. Indeed, from the dawn of civilization humans have been social creatures, living together and forming families, communities, states, societies, and cultures. We depend on one another for countless different things, from the most rudimentary and mundane tasks of our lives such as public transportation and getting our groceries to the most intimate of companionships sought in aromatic relationships. From an evolutionary perspective, our inclination to seek closeness with others has been entrenched into our nature by evolutionary processes spanning from prehistoric times, when men had to hunt together, to modern times, when social media reigns. The fact is, that for most of us, being alone makes it that much harder to face the adversities of this world. Therefore, "sticking together" and fostering benevolent social relationships emerge as imperative for our survival as a species (Holt-Lunstad, 2018).

Stemming from this fundamental aspect of human nature are several togetherness-promoting mechanisms, the most conspicuous of which is our proneness to feel lonely when social ties dwindle (J. T. Cacioppo & Cacioppo, 2018; J. T. Cacioppo & Patrick, 2008). From an evolutionary perspective, loneliness is viewed as an internal signal that there is need for to remedy social compromise. This works much like the manner in which thirst and hunger operate as internal signals that the body needs liquids or more substantial nourishment. It is this view of loneliness and social relationships that has led to the bourgeoning field of social neuroscience. Indeed, social neuroscientists have conducted voluminous amounts of research indicating that loneliness, if not attended to, may not only lead to extremely detrimental outcomes, including hindered well-being, poor mental and physical health and even premature death (J. T. Cacioppo & Cacioppo, 2018; S. Cacioppo, Grippo, London, Goossens, & Cacioppo, 2015); but may be embedded into various physiological systems (J. T. Cacioppo, Cacioppo, Capitanio, & Cole, 2015; S. Cacioppo, Capitanio, & Cacioppo, 2014).

Unfortunately, loneliness presents a real problem for many Veterans. To exemplify, in a study among aging Vietnam Veterans, 44% reported feeling lonely at least some of the time, and of these, 10.4% reported feeling lonely often (Kuwert, Knaevelsrud, & Pietrzak, 2014). Another study, among Israeli Veterans, indicated that for Veterans who experienced a mental breakdown on the battlefield, loneliness rates remained high for decades after the war (Solomon, Bensimon, Greene, Horesh, & Ein-Dor, 2015).

This pervasiveness places Veterans at increased risk for loneliness' aforementioned deleterious impact. Indeed, scientific work focusing specifically on Veterans' loneliness, albeit surprisingly scarce (G. Wilson, Hill, & Kiernan, 2018), indicates that this loneliness may be strongly related to and exacerbated by Veterans' psychiatric conditions (e.g., their depression as well as acute and chronic post-traumatic stress reactions; Kuwert et al., 2014; Martin & Hartley, 2017; Solomon et al., 2015), and highly conducive of suicidal inclinations (i.e., suicide ideation and attempts; Bryan & Rudd, 2012; Teo et al., 2018). It is for these reasons that it is vital to address Veterans' loneliness with utmost seriousness and concern.

That said, the guiding notion of this chapter is that loneliness is anything but a homogeneous experience. I will elaborate on this in a moment, but at this point it is important to realize that this implies that if we wish to adequately address and alleviate a person's loneliness, it is paramount that we first and foremost understand its nature within the specific context wherein it transpires (Stein & Tuval-Mashiach, 2015b). Therefore, in the present chapter, I primarily explicate the nature of the experience of loneliness as it stems from being a combat Veteran and elaborate upon the manner in which Post-Traumatic Stress disorder (PTSD) adds additional strata to this loneliness, exacerbating it and making it considerably more difficult for Veterans to breach their subjective solitary confinements and overcome their loneliness. I will conclude with intervention strategies that may be and are employed by clinicians, Veterans and their support networks. As a preliminary step, however, it is necessary to attend to the constituting elements of loneliness and its multifariousness.

Loneliness: Definition and Heterogeneity

It is common to think that loneliness is tantamount to isolation and thus that increasing social interactions is the remedy for loneliness. However, one merely needs to observe the instances wherein loneliness transpires and instances where it fails to do so, to realize that this is not exactly the case. After all, as many may reflect, being alone is not always such a bad thing. Indeed, we often thrive in seclusion; we create and give birth to our most esteemed work when away from the hassles and distractions of the world and the nuisance of dealing with other people. It is in isolation that we may often experience our most profound breakthroughs in life, and in detachment we often find safety and reassurance. This kind of oh-so-blessed isolation is not loneliness. Rather, this is what may better be termed solitude (Storr, 1988), the positive side of being alone (Gotesky, 1965). To make things slightly more complicated, loneliness, as the term is used in the social sciences (Stein & Tuval-Mashiach, 2015), may be experienced with all its anguish and torment when completely surrounded by other people, whether in a crowd or buzzing social event. Indeed, as I elaborate more thoroughly below, sometimes, it is precisely when one is embedded within a social interaction that loneliness manifests in its most overwhelming, agonizing and relentless form. This understanding may in itself be redeeming, as Veterans try to understand why they feel so utterly alone although their families are so welcoming and embracing. So what is loneliness if not an artifact of physical isolation?

Defining "loneliness" may be less intuitive a task than appears at first glance. However, most simply, it may be argued that loneliness is the subjective experience of undesired painful isolation (Stein & Tuval-Mashiach, 2015b). Let me explicate this definition. Loneliness is subjective in that although it may be precipitated by an objective social reality, it stems more from perceptions and appraisals of that reality than the reality itself. Underscoring the painful or aversive aspect of the experience is important for discerning loneliness from aloneness, which may be neutral in the feeling or emotion that it engenders, and solitude, which is positively experienced and at times deliberately sought (Gotesky, 1965; Storr, 1988). Additionally, and often taken for granted, any experience of loneliness necessarily involves an experiencing subject (i.e., a lonely person or consciousness) and an Other, in relation to whom and for whom one is lonely. Being lonely for something or someone gives rise to the realization that loneliness forever involves an discrepancy between the person's desired and attained social relations (Perlman & Peplau, 1981). The extent of the discrepancy typically corresponds with the severity or intensity of the loneliness at hand and the extent to which it is undesired. As the famous aphorism goes: the higher the expectation, the greater the disappointment. Loneliness reflects a bitter shattering of social expectations and desires. Moreover, this discrepancy always relates to a relational need or provision that is experienced as lacking. The lonely, it may therefore be argued, are those that most direly need someone for something, but alas, find no one at their side at their time of need.

Conversely, people may be lonely in very different ways. I therefore argue that in order to understand a given experience of loneliness one must identify a) the social identity of the experiencing individual (e.g., widow, orphan, bullied adolescent, bereaved parent, ostracized immigrant, stigmatized mental-health patient, Veteran, etc.); b) the relational needs and provisions that are compromised (e.g., romantic love or intimate companionship, friendship, parental care, etc.); c) those who are expected to fulfill these relational needs (e.g., friends, family, colleagues, etc.); and by extension d) realize the mode of isolation that must be attended (Stein & Tuval-Mashiach, 2015b). For instance, Weiss (1973) discerned loneliness of social isolation, denoting the sense of isolation within social networks, from loneliness of emotional isolation, denoting a sense of loneliness within intimate relationships. Others have added collective isolation, the sense of being detached from a greater collective (J. T. Cacioppo & Cacioppo, 2012), and existential isolation, which connotes a detachment from all being or existence as a whole (Ettema, Derksen, & Leeuwen, 2010; Mijuskovic, 2012; Moustakas, 1961). From an existential perspective, to paraphrase John Donne's aforementioned assertion, "every man is an island." Against this backdrop, we may now explore the loneliness of Veterans, and more so that of traumatized Veterans.

The Soldier Comes Marching Home... Alone

As I was conducting research with the aim of understanding the Veteran's loneliness, one Vietnam Veteran send me an e-mail with the following disclosure. I think his words capture the multifariousness of the experience, albeit in a nutshell:

In an abbreviated sense, being lonely is fighting for acceptance in your original world, being ripped away and then enduring the same process in a new world but under horrific circumstances, then returning to your original world only to discover that you are not understood, do not belong there the same way you did before, and the new world you have just left no longer exists, leaving you alone. Even when there are still the trappings of the world you once knew, they are no more, and there is no one to comfortably talk with about these things, so you keep these feelings inside and withdraw into them unless distracted by work or some crisis or some event powerful enough to draw your mind away from simply feeling like you no longer belong, anywhere really.

In what follows, I will do my best to unpack this description, so as to make the experience and its unfolding as explicit as I can manage for the sake of Veterans and their support-networks.

A soldier becomes a Veteran the moment he or she sets foot off the battlefield and departs for the journey home. Though for many this journey is full of excitement and anticipation towards reuniting with family and friends, often these may be overshadowed with a sense of loneliness. This loneliness may engulf the Veteran almost instantaneously upon departure, or it may gradually settle in. Recall that loneliness invariably entails a cognitive discrepancy wherein one evaluates his or her existing social connections against the backdrop of prior or imagined social relations that are more favorably desired. Thus, to understand and appreciate the Veterans' loneliness, it is crucial that one gain an understanding of the military culture and the kind of bond that soldiers have. Because from the initiation of this bond, it will frame any social experience thereafter.

Researchers, much to their surprise, have found that the loneliness experienced by active duty military personnel is different from that which is experienced by civilians. Specifically, they found that it does not seem to be influenced by familial bonds and socioeconomic backgrounds, as it typically does among civilians, but rather it reacts to fluctuations in social connection within the military unit (J. T. Cacioppo et al., 2016). What these researchers failed to realize, is that for those who served, the military unit is the "family." It cannot be overstressed that the bond formed between combat soldiers runs deeper than blood and ultimately renders them "brothers-in-arms." It is a kind of bond that can rarely, if ever, be emulated in any other context. The consolidation of this bond begins early on in the enlistee's military experience.

Basic Training (i.e., boot camp) aims both to create soldiers and form cohesive combat units. It does so by breaking old civilian habits and replacing them with a strict military ethics. The "soldier identity" is often instilled by an abrupt detachment from one's former social ties (i.e., family and friends) and the employment of a rigorous training regimen that will make much of that was once so familiar, seem completely irrelevant. Soldiers are "broken in," so to speak; and as they break as individuals they are re-molded into an organic unit. However, it is ultimately the joined participation in war that forges the unbreakable bond between soldiers.

The stressors of war – the fear of annihilation, the sight of mutilated bodies, the moral conflicts, the loss of friends, the physical and mental strain, the fatigue and the uncertainty, to name but a few (Nash, 2007) — are of such magnitude, that enduring them together creates an extraordinary shared experience that incommensurably exceeds the mundane involvements of everyday life. It is an experience that makes the statement "I was there" a defining feature, an identity that separates the us and the them (Hynes, 2001). The battlefield is an alternative universe wherein killing and dying are commonplace and survival is a normal mode of existence.

The bond between soldiers is acquired also via a discursive channel, as common terms change their meanings. As soldiers undergo war together, they learn anew, and more forcefully than ever, the meaning of comradeship, solidarity, courage, loyalty, trust, reciprocity, interdependence, sacrifice and loss. These "concepts" no longer designate for them what they meant prior to the war, what they mean still to civilians. Indeed, when civilians speak of such things, when they enunciate these words, or when they idly mention names of people and places that have sustained the dire toll of war, Veterans might feel that these have been uttered in vain.

More fundamentally, the military binds soldiers by employing a unique military lingo, the discourse that becomes the bread and butter of warriors' discursive interchange: codenames, nicknames, acronyms, locations, military slang and common jokes, these are all embedded in soldiers' everyday discursive exchange. These become part of the defining features of the Vet's world. Nevertheless, this discursive practice also contributes to the Veteran's isolation upon departure from that world. As former U.S Army Intelligence officer and Veteran of the Gulf War, Ray Starmann notes, How do you talk to civilians about "fire for effect" or "grid 7310" or "shake and bake" or "frag orders" or "10 days and a wake up" or a thousand and one other terms that are mystifying to the real world? You can't. (Starmann, 2015). Conversely, Benedict (2009) notes that the military language, almost as an undeclared purpose, strives "to maintain a secretive culture that shuts out civilians" (p. 8). And so it does.

Indeed, and unfortunately, all of the aforementioned factors that serve to bind soldiers to one another, also work to sever the repatriated Veteran from the civilian world, particularly from family and non-military friends. The all-encompassing Army life that soldiers grow so accustomed to is a paradoxical one. While deployed, one may become homesick, longing to reunite with the family left back at home; and yet, when back at home, one can often think and speak of nothing but the military. An important aspect of the soldier's isolation is, therefore, their severance from family life. American sociologist of the military and World War I Veteran, Willard Waller, notes that "Sometimes even the most sophisticated soldier is shocked when he suddenly recognizes the gulf that has arisen between himself and his loved ones" (Waller, 1944, p. 30). As one World War I soldier wrote in a letter to his young wife: "All the time I was with you, I had the most curious feeling that I was waiting to go back to go "home" to Camp X. Now I realize why. I'm really home now, hard as it is to say this. But that's what happens, it seems, when you join the Army. You don't feel that you belong anywhere else you can't when you're in a uniform. The Army seemed strange when I first got into it, but now everything else but the army seems strange." (p. 31)

Being a warrior is an identity that one can hardly shake off (Hoge, 2010; R. T. Smith & True, 2014), and rarely wishes to do so (see footnote 1 below). However, it becomes challenging and alienating after repatriation. This sense of estrangement resurfaces in accounts of British and American Veterans of the conflicts in Iraq and Afghanistan (Ahern et al., 2015; Brewin, Garnett, & Andrews, 2011; Orazem et al., 2017) as it has been for Veterans of the World Wars (Schuetz, 1945; Waller, 1944), the Vietnam War (Figley & Leventman, 1980; Shatan, 1973; Shay, 2002), and Israeli Veterans of multiple conflicts (Stein & Tuval-Mashiach, 2015a). Veterans' sense of belonging often shifts dramatically from the family to the military, thus rendering them alien in their own homes. In their investigation of the challenges of Afghanistan and Iraq Veterans' transition from military to civilian life, for instance, Ahern et al. (2015) identified three dominant themes in American Veterans' accounts: a) the military environment as a "family" that took care of them and provided structure; b) the notion that normal is now alien to them; and c) the search for a new normal as a strategy to reconnect. As one Veteran in the study noted, "I can tell stories all night long and [my family] probably won't really grasp what's going on" (p. 5). Similarly, in a study with British Veterans of Iraq and Afghanistan (Brewin et al., 2011) one Veteran lamented "our lives are completely alien to civilian lives. I think it always will be a them-and-us situation' while another noted that "it's hard to fit back into Civvy Street. I've been out 18 years now. I'll never do it. It's just, y'know, I talk like a squaddie, I act like a squaddie" (p. 1737). Thus, the first fundamental need that may be critically compromised for returning Veterans and thus give rise to their loneliness is the human need to belong (Baumeister & Leary, 1995). As Hynes (2001) notes of war: if it makes men, it also isolates them from other men — cuts off the men who fought from older and younger men who did not share that shaping experience, and intensifies the feeling every modern generation has anyway, that it is separate, a kind of secret society in a world of others. (p. 6)

1. It is important to note that identity issues may differ between individuals, and more so between armies. In conscript armies (e.g., in Israel), wherein a large percentage of the population serves for a predetermined period of time, the "warrior" identity may be less dominant. Nevertheless, as I argue below, PTSD may fortify that identity regardless of whether service is mandatory or not.

Contributing to this sense of alienation is Veterans' conviction that civilians would never really be able to understand and Veterans will never really be able to explain, not fully, not sufficiently. The experience of war is ineffable. After all, how does one explain the experience of taking cover in the face of incessant enemy fire, losing a friend, or deliberating whether to pull the trigger when confronted by a child carrying explosives, and doing so, or the uncertainty of the battlefield, or collecting mutilated bodies (friends' as well as foes'), or myriad other experiences? Therefore, there is a loneliness of communicative isolation almost inherent to war. Samuel Hynes (2001), in his seminal book, The Soldier's Tale, notes that "War cannot be comprehended at second-hand. . .it is not accessible to analogy or logic" (p.1). If men are from Mars and women are from Venus, then soldiers inhabit their own world, and it is different from that of civilians. As a Canadian soldier fighting on the Italian front in the Second World War, writes to someone at home:

The damnable truth is we are in really different worlds, on totally different planes, and I don't know you anymore, I only know the you that was. I wish I could explain the desperate sense of isolation, of not belonging to my own past, of being adrift in some kind of alien space. (Hynes, 2001, p. 9, italics in the original)

Such alienation carries on to the home front. Alfred Schuetz (1945) underscores that the challenge is even greater, as each Veteran's experience is unique. Thus, while Veterans wish to feel a sense of commonality in their experiences, they may also sometimes wish that their experiences not be reduced to a title and thus lose their uniqueness. As Schuetz notes: ... whatever occurs to him [the homecoming Veteran] under these particular circumstances [of war] is his individual, personal, unique experience which he never will allow to be typified. When the soldier returns and starts to speak — if he starts to speak at all — he is bewildered to see that his listeners, even the sympathetic ones, do not understand the uniqueness of these individual experiences which have rendered him another man. They try to find familiar traits in what he reports by subsuming it under their preformed types of the soldier's life at the front. To them there are only small details in which his recital deviates from what every home-comer has told and what they have read in magazines and seen in the movies. So it may happen that many acts which seem to the people at home the highest expression of courage are to the soldier in battle merely the struggle for survival or the fulfillment of a duty, whereas many instances of real endurance, sacrifice, and heroism remain unnoticed or unappreciated by people at home. (p. 374) And then there is the matter of gaining an attuned and empathic audience. Veterans may get the impression, often justified, that people just do not want to hear their stories. Dan Bar-On, who studied Holocaust trauma, has made the distinction between the "indescribable" and the "undiscussable" (Bar-On, 1999); the former connoting the notion that there are things that can never be adequately described due to the ineptitude of language, while the latter regards the notion there are topics that there is just no place wherein they can be discussed. This is the bedrock of a conspiracy of silence, and while Veterans are both conspirators and victims of that acquiesced pact of mutism, society shares a great part in the conspiracy. American historian and Veteran of World War II, Paul Fussell, addresses this issue very poignantly in his attempt to shatter the romantic view of the war: One of the cruxes of the war, of course, is the collision between events and the language available – or thought appropriate – to describe them. To put it more accurately, the collision was one between events and the public language used for over a century to celebrate the idea of progress. Logically there is no reason why the English language could not perfectly well render the actuality of trench warfare: it is rich in terms like blood, terror, agony, madness, shit, cruelty, murder, sell-out, pain, and hoax, as well as phrases like legs blown off, intestines gushing out over his hands, screaming all night, bleeding to death from the rectum, and the like. Logically, one supposes, there's no reason why a language devised by man should be inadequate to describe any of man's works. The difficulty was in admitting that the war had been made by men and was being continued ad infinitum by them. The problem was less one of "language" than of gentility and optimism; it was less a problem of "linguistics" than of rhetoric. . .The real reason is that soldiers have discovered that no one is very interested in the bad news they have to report. What listener wants to be torn and shaken when he doesn't have to be? We have made unspeakable mean indescribable: it really means nasty. (Fussell, 2013/1975, p. 184, italics in the original)

We all have a need to sense that our experiences are shared by other people around us, and our primary tool to achieve this is discourse (Echterhoff, Higgins, & Levine, 2009), and particularly narratives. The incommensurability of military life and civilian life critically undermines this need and may lead to a deep sense of isolation. Journalist Sebastian Junger (2016), who accompanied American troops in Afghanistan, argues that our modern individualist society just makes things worse in this respect. Veterans who are used to never being alone, always having at close reach someone to speak to who has shared their strife, return to an alienated society wherein each person is out for him or herself. This alienation makes Veterans long to go back to their units, where they are understood and where they belong. Thus, the loneliness at hand is experienced within the Veteran's family, but ultimately also vis-à-vis one's community and society at large. When war becomes traumatic and PTSD develops, this adds additional strata to this experiential isolation and thus exacerbates the Veteran's loneliness and deepens it. As George Atwood poignantly stresses: The loneliness of the trauma victim is of the most extreme kind that one can imagine: It has as its essential feature that it is felt as absolute, never to be relieved. The loneliness is cosmic, rather than terrestrial. It extends throughout the universe and seems, to the person suffering it, to be eternal. It is not conceivable that it can ever be addressed, diminished, soothed, escaped. It is damnation. (Atwood, 2012, pp. 128-129)

The Isolating Burden of PTSD

Findings indicate that having PTSD may implicate survivors' loneliness (van der Velden, Pijnappel, & van der Meulen, 2018). Developing PTSD may be isolating in multiple manners. First, there is the matter of identity. PTSD is the case wherein past experiences remain pathologically and unrelentingly present in one's conciseness. It is, as patients often stress, not so much the case wherein one cannot let go of the past, but rather it is the past that does not let go of the person. PTSD, therefore, strengthens three interrelated identities: a) the "Veteran" or "warrior" identity, b) the "trauma survivor" identity, and c) the identity of a person whose mental health has been compromised.

Above, I discussed the manner in which the "Veteran" identity may sever the person from society. Reliving the war repeatedly, drives that identity deeper and adds to it the torment and strife associated with mental injury. When one sustains an injury on the battlefield, its presence serves as a reminder of the battle wherein it was sustained. The same process occurs with combat stress injuries but more forcefully because the unrelenting memory and reliving of the experience is inherent to the injury. Moreover, being mentally ill is an identity in its own right (e.g., Cruwys & Gunaseelan, 2016). Having PTSD then nourishes two additional identities, that of a trauma victim or survivor and that of a mentally ill person. Both identities may be accompanied by self-stigmatization, shame, and guilt (J. P. Wilson, Drozdek, & Turkovic, 2006), and thus increase one's inclination to withdraw from social interaction. Such withdrawal amplifies the discrepancy between what is experienced within and what is outwardly visible. This ultimately increases one's isolation and loneliness and drives him or her further away from necessary professional help and social support Michalopoulou, Welsh, Perkins, & Ormsby, 2017).

Furthermore, PTSD adds to this loneliness by the virtue of its constituting symptoms: intrusive re-experiencing, avoidance, alterations in mood and cognition, and hyper-arousal and hyper-vigilance (American Psychiatric Association [APA], 2013). At first, Veterans face the challenge of figuring out what it is that they are experiencing. Indeed, it may take some time before they put the pieces together and realize that their symptoms have a name, and that they are not the only ones who are experiencing these symptoms. Until then, they may lack the words and knowledge to describe their PTSD and feel utterly ashamed that they cannot get their act together. As Canadian Lt. Colonel Stephane Grenier attests in the aftermath of his peacekeeping mission to Rwanda, "I thought that I was the only one feeling this way, and I was terribly ashamed that I was not coping" (Grenier, Darte, Heber, & Richardson, 2007, p. 263).

Doubtlessly, each of PTSD's symptom clusters may contribute to the exacerbation of this isolation. A hallmark of the intrusiveness of trauma related thoughts are the flashbacks: the reliving of parts of the experience in an extremely vivid manner (e.g., Hackmann, Ehlers, Speckens, & Clark, 2004). These overwhelming experiences instantaneously take Veterans back to the battlefield, the noises, the smells, the dread and trepidation all come gushing in as if one is actually there. As Veterans return to the battle, they dissociate from the engagements of the here-and-now, and become engulfed in a world of their own. Not only does this set them away from social interactions, but it is itself beyond description. Whether triggered by the coincidental shatter of a glass in a restaurant or otherwise waking up in the middle of the night, screaming and howling, covered with sweat from the nightmares that haunt their sleep, these are very lonely experiences.

The avoidance symptoms of PTSD are likewise extremely conducive to loneliness. Trying to refrain from any reminder of the trauma gradually minimizes Veterans' social interactions. Among such avoidances one can enumerate avoiding conversations about the trauma, avoiding crowded places, and avoiding social interactions. Often, Veterans' withdrawal from social life may be attributed to their attempts to avoid reminders or triggers that may reactivate their PTSD. As they engage in avoidance and concealment of their strife, their loneliness' reign strengthens.

Since loneliness is predominantly interweaved with cognitive and affective phenomena (J. T. Cacioppo & Hawkley, 2009), the alterations in cognitions and mood are central to this experience. Indeed, according to the Diagnostic and Statistical Manual of Mental Disorders (DSM-5; APA, 2013), "Feelings of detachment or estrangement from others" are examples of this symptom cluster (p. 272). Trauma undermines and disrupts global schemas, such as our view of the world as a safe place, of people being mostly benevolent and ourselves being generally competent, lovable and good (Janoff-Bulman, 1992). Trauma survivors, Veterans included, may lose trust in people and generate a negative view of themselves as part of the meaning-making process that ensues participation in war and the emergence of PTSD. This may exacerbate in cases of moral injury (Litz et al., 2009). Moral injury may be defined as follows: Disruption in an individual's confidence and expectations about one's own or others' motivation or capacity to behave in a just and ethical manner. This injury is brought about by bearing witness to perceived immoral acts, failure to stop such actions, or perpetration of immoral acts, in particular actions that are inhumane, cruel, depraved, or violent, bringing about pain, suffering, or death of others. (Drescher et al., 2011, p. 9)

The conviction that one is not good is an isolating one, and one that in due course results in more loneliness (J. T. Cacioppo & Hawkley, 2009). Indeed, moral injuries are a source of immense shame but also anger and a sense of betrayal. Veterans often feel that their commanders have stranded them to preform missions that, as Shay

(1994) notes, "betray what is right." Such violations of moral values haunt the Veteran long after the deed is done and manifest as psychopathological symptoms similar to those of PTSD (Litz et al., 2009). Thus, anger wells inside. Moreover, as these domains of experience are often those that no one wants to hear about, they are shrouded in a conspiracy of silence that is the sources of immense loneliness. For some Veterans, the burden is so great that even the civilian gesture of thanking Veterans for their service feels alienating rather than embracing (Sherman, 2015). As one Veteran of Iraq notes: "I . . . resented the strangers who thanked me. I suspected that they were just trying to ease their guilt for not serving. Instead of thanking me, I wanted them. . .to make some sacrifice greater than the amount of lung effort necessary to utter a few words." (p. 41)

Finally, having PTSD impedes social functioning in several manners. Being incessantly on edge, or otherwise being easily irritated, makes the temper of Veterans who suffer from PTSD extremely volatile. Bursts of rage are not uncommon within Veteran families, as PTSD Veterans may more readily get into conflicts that they cannot adaptively resolve (Miller et al., 2013). Gradually, Veterans who struggle with PTSD may choose to withdraw to alcohol consumption or other substance abuse to avoid the pain of dealing with their past and present alone. Others may contemplate suicide (Bryan & Rudd, 2012) and too many actually pull the trigger.

Women Veterans' Isolation

Much of what I described above is relevant and true for women Veterans as it is for men (Benedict, 2009). However, there are additional elements that make female Veterans sometimes even more susceptible to experiential isolation than male Veterans. For one, women are far more likely to return to a society that does not believe or even assume that they have been to combat. As one Veteran attests, "We don't get the same respect, we have to fight for it. I don't even tell people about seeing death and being shot at anymore, 'cause they don't believe me. They assume all I did was office work" (Benedict, 2009, p. 199). War is still very much constructed along masculine stereotypes and meta-narratives (Hinojosa, 2010; Hutchings, 2008) and, therefore, it is difficult for women Veterans to claim the "warrior" identity they have rightfully earned. As if forced out of that identity, women Veterans may feel even lonelier in civilian society than their male comrades.

A second domain wherein women may feel greater isolation than men regards sexual trauma, both sexual assaults and sexual harassment on behalf of their unit members (Mattocks et al., 2012). Falling victim to military sexual trauma is much more prevalent among women than men, though it is not unique to women (Surís & Lind, 2008). Indeed, military sexual trauma may be extremely isolating for men as well (Monteith, Gerber, Brownstone, Soberay, & Bahraini, 2019). "People worry about their loved ones' encounters with the enemy, but for females, sometimes the enemy eats, sleeps, and works right next to them" (Benedict, 2009, p. 5). Findings show that being a victim of military sexual trauma increases the risk for severe PTSD both because the sexual trauma may induce PTSD and because it may diminish the social support of the combat unit and thus facilitate war-induced PTSD (Scott et al., 2014). Moreover, sexual trauma within the military unit is often not addressed because it is silenced. This is what has been termed institutional betrayal (C. P. Smith & Freyd, 2014), which is also associated with greater traumatization. It is therefore no surprise that sexual trauma within the military is the source of loneliness for women Veterans (Benedict, 2009), as they cannot speak about it with peers for fear of disbelief or accusation of impeding unit cohesion (Burns, Grindlay, Holt, Manski, & Grossman, 2014; Turchik, Bucossi, & Kimerling, 2014) nor can it be discussed within their families. The dynamics of silence relating to sexual assault and rape (e.g., the shame, the fear, the societal disbelief, etc.) are key here, but they are beyond the scope of the current chapter. At this point it is sufficient to say that military sexual trauma complicates everything, and hence adds additional factors of perceived isolation.

What can be Done?

Regardless of the ostensibly grim picture painted above, hope is not and must not be lost. Advances are being made on multiple fronts. On the military front, it is important to take the time necessary for demobilization. Teach Veterans about the challenges of civilian life and educate them as to what they should expect and how it is different from the military. In contrast, on the clinical front, there are calls for therapists to immerse themselves within the Veterans' experiences, so as to share them together, regardless of the emotional difficulty involved (e.g., Carr, 2011, 2013). By doing so, clinicians may breach the mechanisms that accommodate the conspiracy of silence (Danieli, 1984) surrounding the Veterans' traumas and their aftermaths. Furthermore, it is increasingly acknowledged that in order to treat Veterans, clinicians must get familiar with the military culture (Beder, 2017; Hall, 2011; Litz, Lebowitz, Gray, & Nash, 2016; Meyer, 2015). A recent study has found that Veterans prefer being treated by therapists with a military background, typically a Veteran (Johnson, Ganz, Berger, Ganguly, & Koritzky, 2018). It is assumed by Veterans seeking mental-health services that such individuals may have a better chance of understanding their patients' military experiences and thus are more likely to assist in alleviating the Veterans' loneliness rather than exacerbate it. Getting familiar with military culture may facilitate similar processes.

Alternative therapies are also being developed. For instance, acknowledging that Veterans' bifurcation of society to the us and the them is the foundation of their isolation has given rise to various peer-support therapies wherein Veterans work together towards healing, once again establishing the comraderies they had in the military (Caddick, Phoenix, & Smith, 2015; Hundt, Robinson, Arney, Stanley, & Cully, 2015; Pfeiffer et al., 2012). It is recommended that Veterans locate such a peer-support program to be part of, so they have a safe haven wherein they can feel better understood. Similarly, a novel therapeutic approach entitled "I was There," utilizes film-making workshops wherein Veterans team up to create a short film that will tell their story (Tuval-Mashiach, Patton, & Drebing, 2018). Participants do not only work together with those who understand them, but also get to give voice to their experience and have it appreciated by others, thus reducing their experiential isolation twofold. As one female Veteran who participated in the program attests: It's almost like, two recovering people. In a program, like, of addiction. Only one addict can know another addict. Only one alcoholic can understand another alcoholic. That's how the program actually works. Cause if a regular person came and talked to them about their problem, they probably wouldn't even listen to him, cause they don't feel you relate. This is the same thing with PTSD. For me, this is my opinion. That if I'm talking to someone who understands how I'm feeling, it's. It's lighter. The load. It feels... it's, I'm recovering at that moment. That I'm talking to someone who understands.

Ultimately, however, since Veterans feel isolated and alienated from civilian society, it is society that must accommodate traumatized Veterans' return and work to minimize their loneliness. In this respect I concur with Nancy Sherman that, "Recovery is a matter of shared moral engagement," and, therefore, "the afterwar belongs to us all" (Sherman, 2015, p. 3). This may be accomplished both by engaging Veterans to tell their stories and share their experiences and by de-stigmatizing war-induced trauma. As Paula Caplan (2011, p. xvi) notes: Simply sending frightened, angry soldiers off to therapists conveys disturbing messages: that we don't want to listen, that we're afraid we're not qualified to listen, and that they should talk to someone who gets paid to listen. The implication is that their devastation is abnormal, that it is a mental illness, and this only adds to their burdens. Yet since there's intense debate even among experts about the definition of mental illness, it's all the more important for the rest of us to let returnees know that we don't consider them weak or crazy for having problems.

To overcome the stigma of mental illness, there have been attempts to change the terminology being used. Rather than speaking of mental disorder or illness, it is becoming increasingly popular to speak of mental injury. As Shay (2007, pp. xvii-xviii, italics in the original) notes: When a military service member's arm is shot off, do we say he or she suffers from Missing Arm Disorder? That would be ludicrous, and we do not. I have been agitating for some time to acknowledge that the diagnostic entity we now call Post-traumatic Stress Disorder is an injury, not a malady, disease, sickness, illness, or disorder. The language we use may do much to remedy the wounds of war and the loneliness they foster. Thus, I join the implorations above, and argue that each and every one of us may do something to ameliorate Veterans' loneliness and redeem them from their isolation.

Friends and family may be the most critical circle of support, and thus may benefit from various strategies for empathic engagement with their beloved Veteran (Lyons, 2007). They too should educate themselves as to the military culture, trauma and its aftermath with an emphasis on PTSD and comorbid symptomatology (e.g., depression, substance abuse, anxiety, suicidality, traumatic brain injury, etc.; Recommended in this respect for both Veterans and their families is the book "Once a Warrior Always a Warrior" by Charles Hoge, 2010), and most of all engage Veterans with sincere invitations to share whatever they choose of their war experiences. That said, it is also imperative that family and friends respect Veterans' desire not to speak. They will do so when they see fit and feel ready.

Notwithstanding, much of Veterans' escaping of the entrapments of loneliness remains up to them. Sherman (2015) speaks of the development of self-empathy. Veterans must find ways to minimize their own misunderstandings of what happened and what that means, reduce their self-stigmatizing and come to terms with what has happened. In this respect, Paulson and Krippner (2007) recommend that Veterans embrace their loneliness as an existential predicament and thus reconnect with themselves.

Alternatively, Veterans may educate themselves about trauma and PTSD so they may better communicate their experiences, or otherwise learn and exercise manners in which experiences may be better communicated to others e.g., Stein & Tuval-Mashiach, 2017). Finally, seeking professional counseling may be essential in reducing Veterans' loneliness and gradually facilitating reintegration into civilian society, regardless of PTSD (Castro, Kintzle, & Hassan, 2015).

Conclusion

War ultimately and irrevocably changes a person (Gill, 2011). This change must be acknowledged in order to overcome the alienation of the returning Veteran (Hoge, 2010; Schuetz, 1945; R. T. Smith & True, 2014), who retains his or her well-entrenched military identity years and decades after the shooting is well done. As I delineated above, this identity – constituted by experiences of the past and the present, as well as various discursive mechanisms — is at the heart of the Veteran's loneliness. Let us come to know that identity, know the person who returns from war, know that which he or she has undergone, and learn to accept him or her for who they are now. Only then may we breach the solitary confinements fortified by the horrible experiences they have endured and their psychiatric residuals.

About the Author

I have a Ph.D. in Rehabilitation Psychology from Bar-Ilan University, Israel. My research focuses on various aspects of trauma's aftermath, particularly the interpersonal domain with a special interest in loneliness. I am currently conducting multiple research projects as a research fellow under the auspices of the Israel Center of Research Excellence (I-CORE) for the Investigation of Mass Trauma, located at Tel Aviv University, Israel and headed by world-renowned trauma researcher, Prof. Zahava Solomon. In my studies, I have explored long-term effects of trauma, primarily among combat Veterans and repatriated prisoners of war. Employing qualitative research methodologies, such as phenomenological and narrative inquiries, I seek to hear the stories of trauma survivors and lonely individuals in the first person with the hope to understand and shed light on the idiosyncratic intricacies of traumatized as well as lonely individuals' lived experiences. In my quantitative research endeavors, I also seek to understand the complex psychosocial, and at times psychobiological, mechanisms through which trauma takes its toll decades after the war. I have published numerous papers and book chapters on these topics in leading journals and books in the field.

References:

Ahern, J., Worthen, M., Masters, J., Lippman, S. A., Ozer, E. J., & Moos, R. (2015). The challenges of Afghanistan and Iraq veterans' transition from military to civilian life and approaches to reconnection. PloS one, 10, e0128599.

American Psychiatric Association. (2013). Diagnostic and statistical manual of mental disorders (5th ed.). Arlington, VA: Author.

Atwood, G. E. (2012). The abyss of madness. New York, NY: Routledge.

Bar-On, D. (1999). The indescribable and the undiscussable: Reconstructing human discourse after trauma. Budapest, Hungary: Central European University Press.

Baumeister, R. F., & Leary, M. R. (1995). The need to belong: Desire for interpersonal attachments as a fundamental human motivation. Psychological Bulletin, 117(3), 497-529. doi: 10.1037/0033-2909.117.3.497

Beder, J. (Ed.). (2017). Caring for the military: A guide for helping professionals. New York, NY: Routledge.

Benedict, H. (2009). The lonely soldier: The private war of women serving in Iraq. Boston, MA: Beacon Press.

Brewin, C. R., Garnett, R., & Andrews, B. (2011). Trauma, identity and mental health in UK military veterans. Psychological Medicine, 41(108), 1733-1740.

Bryan, C. J., & Rudd, M. D. (2012). Life stressors, emotional distress, and trauma-related thoughts occurring in the 24 h preceding active duty US Soldiers' suicide attempts. Journal of psychiatric research, 46(7), 843-848.

Burns, B., Grindlay, K., Holt, K., Manski, R., & Grossman, D. (2014). Military sexual trauma among US servicewomen during deployment: A qualitative study. American journal of public health, 104(2), 345-349.

Cacioppo, J. T., & Cacioppo, S. (2012). The phenotype of loneliness. European Journal of Developmental Psychology, 9(4), 446-452. doi: 10.1080/17405629.2012.690510

Cacioppo, J. T., & Cacioppo, S. (2018). Loneliness in the modern age: An evolutionary theory of loneliness (ETL). Advances in Experimental Social Psychology, 58, 127-197. doi: https://doi.org/10.1016/bs.aesp.2018.03.003

Cacioppo, J. T., Cacioppo, S., Adler, A. B., Lester, P. B., McGurk, D., Thomas, J. L., & Chen, H. Y. (2016). The cultural context of loneliness: Risk factors in active duty soldiers. Journal of Social and Clinical Psychology, 35(10), 865-882.

Cacioppo, J. T., Cacioppo, S., Capitanio, J. P., & Cole, S. (2015). The neuroendocrinology of social isolation. Annu Rev Psychol, 66, 733-767. doi: 10.1146/annurev-psych-010814-015240

Cacioppo, J. T., & Hawkley, L. C. (2009). Perceived social isolation and cognition. Trends Cognitive Science, 13(10), 447-454. doi: 10.1016/j.tics.2009.06.005

Cacioppo, J. T., & Patrick, W. (2008). Loneliness: Human nature and the need for social connection. New York, NY: W W Norton & Co.

Cacioppo, S., Capitanio, J. P., & Cacioppo, J. T. (2014). Toward a neurology of loneliness. Psychological Bulletin, 140(6), 1464-1504. doi: 10.1037/a0037618

Cacioppo, S., Grippo, A. J., London, S., Goossens, L., & Cacioppo, J. T. (2015). Loneliness: Clinical import and interventions. Perspectives on Psychological Science, 10(2), 238-249.

Caddick, N., Phoenix, C., & Smith, B. (2015). Collective stories and well-being: Using a dialogical narrative approach to understand peer relationships among combat veterans experiencing post-traumatic stress disorder. Journal of Health Psychology, 20(3), 286-299.

Caplan, P. J. (2011). When Johnny and Jane come marching home: How all of us can help veterans. Cambridge, MA: MIT press.

Carr, R. B. (2011). Combat and human existence: Toward an intersubjective approach to combat-related PTSD. Psychoanalytic Psychology, 28(4), 471-496.

Carr, R. B. (2013). Two war-torn soldiers: combat-related trauma through an intersubjective lens. American journal of psychotherapy, 67(2), 109-133.

Castro, C. A., Kintzle, S., & Hassan, A. M. (2015). The combat veteran paradox: Paradoxes and dilemmas encountered with reintegrating combat veterans and the agencies that support them. Traumatology, 21(4), 299-310.

Cruwys, T., & Gunaseelan, S. (2016). "Depression is who I am": Mental illness identity, stigma and wellbeing. Journal of affective disorders, 189, 36-42.

Danieli, Y. (1984). Psychotherapist's participation in the conspiracy of silence about the Holocaust. Psychoanalytic Psychology, 1(1), 23-42.

Drescher, K. D., Foy, D. W., Kelly, C., Leshner, A., Schutz, K., & Litz, B. (2011). An exploration of the viability and usefulness of the construct of moral injury in war veterans. Traumatology, 17(1), 8-13.

Echterhoff, G., Higgins, E. T., & Levine, J. M. (2009). Shared reality: Experiencing commonality with others' inner states about the world. Perspectives on Psychological Science, 4(5), 496-521. doi: 10.1111/j.1745-6924.2009.01161.x

Ettema, E. J., Derksen, L. D., & Leeuwen, E. v. (2010). Existential loneliness and end-of-life care: A systematic review. Theoretical Medicine and Bioethics, 31(2), 141–169. doi: 10.1007/s11017-010-9141-1

Figley, C. R., & Leventman, S. (1980). Strangers at home: Vietnam veterans since the war. Philadelphia, PA: Brunner/Mazel.

Fussell, P. (2013/1975). The Great War and modern memory. New York, NY: Oxford University Press.

Gill, D. C. (2011). How we are changed by war: A study of letters and diaries from colonial conflicts to Operation Iraqi Freedom: Routledge.

Gotesky, R. (1965). Aloneness, loneliness, isolation, solitude. In J. M. Edie (Ed.), An Invitation to Phenomenology (pp. 211-239). Chicago, IL: Quadrangle Books.

Grenier, S., Darte, k., Heber, A., & Richardson, D. (2007). The Operational Stress Injury Social Support Program: A peer support program in collaboration between the Canadian Forces and Veterans Affairs Canada. In C. R. Figley & W. P. Nash (Eds.), Combat stress injury: Theory, research, and management (pp. 261-294). New York, NY: Routledge.

Hackmann, A., Ehlers, A., Speckens, A., & Clark, D. M. (2004). Characteristics and content of intrusive memories in PTSD and their changes with treatment. Journal of Traumatic Stress, 17(3), 231-240.

Hall, L. K. (2011). The importance of understanding military culture. Social work in health care, 50(1), 4-18.

Hinojosa, R. (2010). Doing hegemony: Military, men, and constructing a hegemonic masculinity. The Journal of Men's Studies, 18(2), 179-194.

Hoge, C. W. (2010). Once a warrior always a warrior: Navigating the transition from combat to home, including combat stress, PTSD, and mTBI. . Guilford, CT: Globe Pequot Press.

Holt-Lunstad, J. (2018). Why social relationships are important for physical health: A systems approach to understanding and modifying risk and protection. Annu Rev Psychol, 69(1), 21.21–21.22. doi: 10.1146/annurev-psych-122216-011902

Hundt, N. E., Robinson, A., Arney, J., Stanley, M. A., & Cully, J. A. (2015). Veterans' perspectives on benefits and drawbacks of peer support for posttraumatic stress disorder. Military medicine, 180(8), 851-856.

Hutchings, K. (2008). Making sense of masculinity and war. Men and Masculinities, 10(4), 389-404.

Hynes, S. (2001). The soldiers' tale: Bearing witness to a modern war: Penguin.

Janoff-Bulman, R. (1992). Shattered assumptions: Towards a new psychology of trauma. New York:, NY: Free Press.

Johnson, T. S., Ganz, A., Berger, S., Ganguly, A., & Koritzky, G. (2018). Service members prefer a psychotherapist who is a veteran. Frontiers in Psychology, 9(1068). doi: 10.3389/fpsyg.2018.01068

Junger, S. (2016). Tribe: On homecoming and belonging. New York, NY: Hachette Book Group.

Kuwert, P., Knaevelsrud, C., & Pietrzak, R. H. (2014). Loneliness among older veterans in the United States: results from the National Health and Resilience in Veterans Study. The American Journal of Geriatric Psychiatry, 22(6), 564-569.

Litz, B. T., Lebowitz, L., Gray, M. J., & Nash, W. P. (2016). Adaptive disclosure: A new treatment for Military trauma, loss, and Moral injury. New York, NY: Guilford Press.

Litz, B. T., Stein, N., Delaney, E., Lebowitz, L., Nash, W. P., Silva, C., & Maguen, S. (2009). Moral injury and moral repair in war veterans: A preliminary model and intervention strategy. Clinical Psychology Review, 29, 695-706.

Lyons, J. A. (2007). The returning warrior: Advice for families and friends. In C. R. Figley & W. P. Nash (Eds.), Combat stress injury: Theory, research and management (pp. 311-324). London, England: Routledge.

Martin, J. C., & Hartley, S. L. (2017). Lonely, Stressed, and Depressed: The Impact of Isolation on US Veterans. Military Behavioral Health, 5(4), 384-392.

Mattocks, K. M., Haskell, S. G., Krebs, E. E., Justice, A. C., Yano, E. M., & Brandt, C. (2012). Women at war: Understanding how women veterans cope with combat and military sexual trauma. Social Science & Medicine, 74(4), 537-545.

Meyer, E. G. (2015). The importance of understanding military culture. Academic Psychiatry, 39(4), 416-418.

Michalopoulou, L. E., Welsh, J. A., Perkins, D. F., & Ormsby, L. (2017). Stigma and mental health service utilization in military personnel: A review of the literature. Military Behavioral Health, 5(1), 12-25.

Mijuskovic, B. L. (2012). Loneliness in philosophy, psychology, and literature. Bloomington ,IN: iUniverse.

Miller, M. W., Wolf, E. J., Reardon, A. F., Harrington, K. M., Ryabchenko, K., Castillo, D., . . . Heyman, R. E. (2013). PTSD and conflict behavior between veterans and their intimate partners. Journal of Anxiety Disorders, 27(2), 240-251.

Monteith, L. L., Gerber, H. R., Brownstone, L. M., Soberay, K. A., & Bahraini, N. H. (2019). The phenomenology of military sexual trauma among male veterans. Psychology of Men & Masculinities, 20(1), 115-127.

Moustakas, C. E. (1961). Loneliness (Vol. 15). Englewood Cliffs, NJ: Prentice-Hall.

Nash, W. P. (2007). The stressors of war. In C. R. Figley & W. P. Nash (Eds.), Combat stress injury: Theory, research, and management (pp. 11-31). London, England: Routledge

Orazem, R. J., Frazier, P. A., Schnurr, P. P., Oleson, H. E., Carlson, K. F., Litz, B. T., & Sayer, N. A. (2017). Identity adjustment among Afghanistan and Iraq war veterans with reintegration difficulty. Psychological Trauma: Theory, Research, Practice, and Policy, 9(S1), 4-11.

Paulson, D. S., & Krippner, S. (2007). Haunted by combat. Westport, CT: Praeger Security International.

Perlman, D., & Peplau, L. A. (1981). Toward a social psychology of loneliness. Personal Relationships, 3, 31-56.

Pfeiffer, P. N., Blow, A. J., Miller, E., Forman, J., Dalack, G. W., & Valenstein, M. (2012). Peers and peer-based interventions in supporting reintegration and mental health among National Guard soldiers: A qualitative study. Military medicine, 177(12), 1471-1476.

Schuetz, A. (1945). The homecomer. American Journal of Sociology, 369-376.

Scott, J. C., Pietrzak, R. H., Southwick, S. M., Jordan, J., Silliker, N., Brandt, C. A., & Haskell, S. G. (2014). Military sexual trauma interacts with combat exposure to increase risk for posttraumatic stress symptomatology in female Iraq and Afghanistan veterans. The Journal of clinical psychiatry, 75(6), 637-643.

Shatan, C. F. (1973). The grief of soldiers: Vietnam combat veterans' self-help movement. American Journal of Orthopsychiatry, 43(4), 640-653. doi: 10.1111/j.1939-0025.1973.tb00834.x

Shay, J. (1994). Achilles in Vietnam: Combat trauma and the undoing of character. New York, NY, US: Atheneum Publishers/Macmillan Publishing Co.

Shay, J. (2002). Odysseus in America: Combat trauma and the trials of homecoming. New York, NY: Scribner.

Shay, J. (2007). Forward. In C. R. Figley & W. P. Nash (Eds.), Combat stress injury: Theory, research, and management (pp. xvii-xx). London, Engleand: Routledge.

Sherman, N. (2015). Afterwar: Healing the moral wounds of our soldiers. New York, NY: Oxford University Press.

Smith, C. P., & Freyd, J. J. (2014). Institutional betrayal. American Psychologist, 69(6), 575.

Smith, R. T., & True, G. (2014). Warring identities: Identity conflict and the mental distress of American veterans of the wars in Iraq and Afghanistan. Society and mental Health, 4(2), 147-161.

Solomon, Z., Bensimon, M., Greene, T., Horesh, D., & Ein-Dor, T. (2015). Loneliness trajectories: The role of posttraumatic symptoms and social support. Journal of Loss and Trauma, 20(1), 1-21. doi: 10.1080/15325024.2013.815055

Starmann, R. (2015). The solitary world of a vet. US Defense Watch. Retrieved November 8, 2015, from http://usdefensewatch.com/2015/11/the-solitary-world-of-a-vet/

Stein, J. Y., & Tuval-Mashiach, R. (2015a). Loneliness and isolation in life-stories of Israeli veterans of combat and captivity. Psychological Trauma: Theory, Research, Practice, and Policy, 7(2), 122-130. doi: 10.1037/a0036936

Stein, J. Y., & Tuval-Mashiach, R. (2015b). The social construction of loneliness: An integrative conceptualization. Journal of Constructivist Psychology, 28(3), 210-227. doi: 10.1080/10720537.2014.911129

Stein, J. Y., & Tuval-Mashiach, R. (2017). Narrating for affective empathy: Verbal discursive devices that elicit experiential connection in combat related trauma narratives. Israel Studies in Language and Society, 10(1), 175-199.

Storr, A. (1988). Solitude: A return to the self. New York, NY: Ballantine Books.

Surís, A., & Lind, L. (2008). Military sexual trauma: A review of prevalence and associated health consequences in veterans. Trauma, Violence, & Abuse, 9(4), 250-269.

Teo, A. R., Marsh, H. E., Forsberg, C. W., Nicolaidis, C., Chen, J. I., Newsom, J., ... Dobscha, S. K. (2018). Loneliness is closely associated with depression outcomes and suicidal ideation among military veterans in primary care. Journal of affective disorders, 230, 42-49.

Turchik, J. A., Bucossi, M. M., & Kimerling, R. (2014). Perceived barriers to care and gender preferences among veteran women who experienced military sexual trauma: A qualitative analysis. Military Behavioral Health, 2(2), 180-188.

Tuval-Mashiach, R., Patton, B., & Drebing, C. (2018). "When you make a movie, and you see your story there, you can hold it": Qualitative exploration of Collaborative filmmaking as a therapeutic tool for Veterans. Frontiers in Psychology, 9, 1954.

van der Velden, P. G., Pijnappel, B., & van der Meulen, E. (2018). Potentially traumatic events have negative and positive effects on loneliness, depending on PTSD-symptom levels: evidence from a population-based prospective comparative study. Social Psychiatry and Psychiatric Epidemiology, 53(2), 195-206.

Waller, W. (1944). The veteran comes back. New York, NY: Dryden.

Weiss, R. S. (1973). Loneliness: The experience of emotional and social isolation. Cambridge, MA, US: The MIT Press.

Wilson, G., Hill, M., & Kiernan, M. D. (2018). Loneliness and social isolation of military veterans: systematic narrative review. Occupational Medicine, 68(9), 600-609. doi: 10.1093/occmed/kqy160

Wilson, J. P., Drozdek, B., & Turkovic, S. (2006). Posttraumatic shame and guilt. Trauma, Violence, & Abuse, 7(2), 122-141.

CHAPTER 20 - MASSAGE THERAPY IN RETREATS FOR VETERANS WITH PTS AND THEIR PARTNERS

Kathy Dunbar, New Mexico MT 1452

I have been a massage therapist since 1990, and in 2009 I was asked by Chuck Howe, President and founder of the National Veterans Wellness and Healing Center of Angel Fire, New Mexico, if I would be interested in providing massage therapy at a Veterans' Retreat. These retreats are specifically for Veterans who have been diagnosed with Post-Traumatic Stress Disorder (PTSD), and their spouse/partner/support person. Because the Veteran's PTSD always affects their relationships with those around them, it is important to include the partner, who will also be struggling with the situation.

The retreats are a week long residential in-depth immersion in healing and coping strategies. They have education classes in the mornings, in which they learn about the science behind PTSD, what happens in the brain and body during trauma, and how that causes changes over time. The participants learn to recognize it in themselves, what triggers them, and how they react. Then they are taught a variety of tools to cope with it, and have opportunities to explore and practice those tools in a safe and supportive setting. Communication skills are also taught and practiced, with help from other group members and staff if needed. In the afternoons they have a counseling session every day, and then they have a couple of other therapies, such as massage, acupuncture, Tai Chi, chiropractic, or energy work (such as Reiki or other types). They can wind down at the end of the day with a gentle, individualized Yoga class. By the end of the week they have had a chance to experience all of these healing modalities that they might not have ever tried before, and so can discover what they might want to pursue when they return home after the retreat.

At our retreats, we omit the "D" in PTSD, and refer to it as PTS, since what are considered symptoms in civilian life were often an appropriate survival response during the traumatic situation, and become inappropriate only when those situations are no longer present. Then their reactions can become harmful and not useful. Labeling them as having a "disorder" can cause feelings of helplessness, but our goal is to guide them to find healing and well-being. The retreats are free to the participants and includes lodging, meals, and all activities. They can also receive follow-up care with counseling and our other therapies after the retreat ends. Everything during the retreat and after remains confidential, which frees them to open up and be honest with each other and the staff.

I wanted to work at the retreats because I know too many Veterans of different wars and interventions who have had difficulty adjusting to civilian and family life after or during their service. Closest to me was my beloved uncle, who served in Burma in

WWII. He always carried the burdens of his experiences, physically, emotionally, and spiritually. I also had a friend who never returned home from Vietnam, and several who came back scarred or extremely ill from exposure to Agent Orange. And I was horrified by the way many of our returning service members were treated after coming home. I loved the idea of the retreats as a way to finally give them the warm welcome they deserve, and of acknowledging their sacrifices.

My role in the retreats is mainly to provide massage therapy to the participants, but I also find it helpful to be present for the initial welcome ceremony (which brings some of our guests to tears) and many of the other activities and meals throughout the week. This way we can get to know each other in a relaxed setting outside of the therapy room, so they can feel comfortable and cared for by all the staff. At our initial dinner they have a chance to introduce themselves, and we on staff do so as well. We explain a bit about what we do, and let them know we are open to any questions or concerns they may have about the therapies we provide.

When our guests come for their sessions, it is essential for us therapists to be prompt and ready, and to project calmness and openness. The space should feel safe and un-distracting, without obstacles that can trip someone or make them feel hemmed in. Some of them may have TBI (traumatic brain injury), mobility issues, or deficits in vision or hearing, so there needs to be a clear pathway to the treatment table or chair, and any necessary aids to settling in, such as a step stool or a sturdy chair they can grab onto to help them get on and off. I also let them know I am available to assist them with getting off or on the treatment table or chair, or with any undressing or redressing, if wanted or needed. Their level of undress for our session is their choice, I explain that I will work with what is comfortable for them. I always have an assortment of pillows, bolsters, and blankets on hand so that we can get them as comfortable as possible throughout their session.

I do not use any scents, since I do not know what allergies or sensitivities people may have, or even what scents may be a trigger for someone. A scent that may be fine for one person but may be a problem for the next, so I avoid using them at all. Background music is also something to consider since tastes vary. What one finds pleasant and relaxing may be jarring to another. This certainly applies to nature sounds. Forest birdsong may not be relaxing to a Veteran who is reminded of their service time in a jungle, or ocean waves can cause anxiety for someone who almost drowned in the ocean, although both of these soundtracks are well-received by most. Each person is an individual with their own set of experiences; there is no single relaxing thing for everyone. For this reason I keep a variety of music and nature sounds, and let each person choose what they want. No background sounds at all is also always an option.

On occasion I have had participants who wanted to check out the room thoroughly and see what was behind every door, and this should not elicit comment from me.

They can do what they need to feel safe so they can relax. Before we begin our session I ask what they want from their time with me. Some will want specific work on an old injury or problem area, some want relaxation, some want vigorous work to energize them. Many participants have never had a massage before and they don't know what they want, so I explain possibilities and emphasize that **THEY ARE IN CONTROL** of their session and that nothing should make them feel uneasy or unheard. If they feel they want to stop the massage at any time or change the focus, that is what we will do, with no need to explain or feel bad. If someone does not want a massage at all, I ask them to let me explain about massage, and to answer any questions they have, so that they will have some information to help them decide if they'd like to try it at another time. I never take it personally if someone decides they don't want a massage, or don't like a technique I'm using. Ego has no place in this interaction, and I must not have any particular expectations of our session other than that I will do my best.

My job is to draw upon my knowledge, intuition, and heart to do what I can to help my client along their journey of healing. It is very important to keep in mind what they are dealing with, and why they have chosen to attend the retreat. If someone wants specific work on an injury or problem area, I have been well trained in Medical/Orthopedic massage, and have actually taught it for 10 years. This modality encompasses many different massage techniques in a focused way, such as Trigger Point Therapy, Cross-Fiber Friction, Positional Release, Muscle Energy Technique, Myofascial Release, etc., with the aim of normalizing damaged or dysfunctional soft tissues. It is crucial to be knowledgeable about pathologies and injuries that I may be presented with and to know what techniques may be helpful or harmful in each case.

Since I also earned a degree in Exercise Science and was certified as a Health/Fitness Instructor by the American College of Sports Medicine, I can advise my clients on helpful exercises and stretches to address some of their simpler problems. In seeing so many Veterans, I have worked with many injuries and old wounds from their service.

One of my favorite techniques to use is Myofascial Release (MFR) and Myofascial Unwinding. These modalities are very effective for softening scar tissue, separating adhesions, and freeing up layers of tissues that have become stuck together and hardened. Since MFR doesn't push hard into the body but uses lighter pressure to actually pull the tissue layers up and apart, restoring movement and fluid flow, it is relaxing and non-threatening to an already traumatized body. Body tissues often hold on to painful memories and emotions by tightening up, forming "energy cysts" or what many people refer to as "knots". Some of the trauma that is held by the body in this way will be locked away and cause pain, and can be difficult for self-awareness to access unless unlocked. Releasing the energy cyst with slow, gentle, mindful touch can help the client let go of the difficult memories and emotions as they become aware of them. It also frees up energy that was used to hold on to those repressed feelings, and that energy then becomes available for healing and building resiliency. The release can be a huge relief, but it can also bring up intense emotions, especially during a powerful retreat week.

When someone becomes really agitated, confused or emotional during a session, or has a flashback, I work to bring their attention back to the present and their surroundings as quickly as possible. Speaking in a calm voice, having them look at objects around the room or concentrate on breathing or bodily sensations (such as wiggling toes or fingers), are some ways to bring them back to the here and now. Depending on the person and the moment, it may or may not be a good idea to touch them, but if intuition says to touch, a light but firm static touch may be best, being careful not to startle. Any issues that come up for them during our session, I encourage them to discuss with their counselor.

People suffering with PTS are often stuck in, or too easily switched into, the Sympathetic mode of the Central Nervous System, commonly referred to as "fight/flight/freeze" mode. In this state, which is essential for survival in a dangerous situation, stress neurotransmitters and hormones are released to prepare the body to respond. When the danger is over, the body should shift back into Parasympathetic mode, also known as "rest/digest/heal" mode. This is the state we need to be in to absorb nutrients, get restorative sleep, and rebuild body tissues. If a person stays in Sympathetic mode chronically or enters it too often, there can be damage to the body and brain from the prolonged exposure to the stress hormones. This can lead to health problems such as high blood pressure, heart disease, obesity, mood disorders, kidney damage, diabetes, impaired immunity, etc.

It is important to let the body and mind experience the Parasympathetic state so that a person can learn how it feels and can find ways to get there more often. Massage therapy can be very effective at bringing a person into this state, and helping them relax and feel at ease, so that it becomes a more normal state of being. We are hard wired to enter the fight or flight state more easily, since it is critical for survival in a dangerous world, but we need to be able to switch into relaxation mode when possible, for long term health and well-being.

Many of my clients at the Veterans' retreats suffer from insomnia, anxiety, hyper-vigilance, and depression. We have found that MFR, aside from the physical effects of normalizing tissues, can also induce a deep trance-like state in which the nervous system can reset the "tension thermostat" and experience profound relaxation and healing. This state is extremely restful, switching the body into Parasympathetic mode and allowing that neural pathway to become stronger. Many clients fall asleep while I'm working, to their surprise, and report to me the following day that they had their best sleep in years that night. This gives them hope and motivation to know that there is a way to find peace and rest. Myofascial Release also includes Craniosacral work, which gently works with the bones of the skull to restore the free flow of cerebrospinal fluid, which nourishes and protects the brain and spinal cord. This essential flow of fluid can become uneven or blocked in places, from trauma, tension, or illness. When the flow is hindered it can lead to many complaints including anxiety, headaches, mysterious pain or numbness in various body areas, dizziness, insomnia, and many other symptoms that seem unrelated and inexplicable.

Restoring the normal rhythm and freedom of the cerebrospinal circulation allows the body to rebalance and heal itself and nourishes the nervous system. I always try to educate and explain what may be happening with a client's body when they have pain or physical problems. When they can get a clear explanation for why they feel the way they do, it reassures them that they're not just imagining it and that there are usually self-help actions they can take. Learning strategies to help themselves gives them a feeling of having some control in their life and encourages them. The bodywork also helps them to physically experience some of the strategies they learn in their morning education sessions.

For example, practicing open communication during their massage, paying attention to bodily sensations, recognizing triggers and excess tension as it arises and practicing overcoming them. These lessons are reiterated and bolstered by all staff in many encounters throughout the week so that they become ingrained in participants by the end of the week and can be readily accessed when needed. It is exciting to watch them learn and practice and apply their new tools in different situations as the week goes by. When they leave us to return home, most feel much more confident that they can apply the tools in daily life challenges. Massage generally has many benefits for just about everyone.

Touch is extremely important for the nervous system to remain aware of what's going on in the body. It also helps increase blood and lymph circulation, enhances immune function, can help with injury healing, digestion, elimination, breathing, increase flexibility, improve sleep, decrease blood pressure, pain, and anxiety, and allow the body and mind to relax. It should give the recipient a feeling of well-being and even bliss, something we could all use more often.

Massage can be of particular benefit for our clients with PTS. It helps them experience a relaxed state, which may be rare for them and hard to attain. It can help the body to let go of old trauma and begin to heal and restore balance. A good balance of neurotransmitters and hormones will give them a feeling of well-being and will maintain long term health. The bodily awareness that gentle and focused touch can bring can make them aware of physical problems that may have been ignored or that are developing, so that they can be addressed before they become worse. Massage can bring a person "back into their body". Many people who have experienced trauma will dissociate from their body and cannot really heal from it until they fully inhabit their body. Receiving a massage, especially in the setting of our retreats, lets a person know they are cared for and acknowledged. For them to know that everyone around them, staff and fellow participants, are working towards their healing, wellness, growth, and happiness, is a powerful incentive. Especially for those who have felt isolated and removed from society, the circle of caring people surrounding them can give them strength and comfort, helping them to move forward.

When a retreat client feels benefit from their massage, I give them information so that they can find a practitioner in their home area. We also have a program for follow up care with our staff at the Veterans Wellness and Healing Center in Angel Fire, NM, where we are based. This care is either at no cost or deeply discounted for them. Many of them do utilize the continued care, and many participants keep in touch with each other and form their own support groups and continuing friendships. In the 10 years of doing these retreats we have witnessed amazing growth and progress in participants' well-being, and the entire staff is dedicated to making each retreat safe, loving, supportive, and effective.

If you are a former or potential client, or if you want more information, you can contact the National Veterans Wellness and Healing Center via phone at #(575)377-5236 or visit the website at: http://veteranswellnessandhealing.org.

CHAPTER 21 – MDMA

Brad Burge, Director of Strategic Communications
Multidisciplinary Association for Psychedelic Studies (MAPS)

Founded in 1986, the Multidisciplinary Association for Psychedelic Studies (MAPS) is a 501(c)(3) non-profit research and educational organization that develops medical, legal, and cultural contexts for people to benefit from the careful uses of psychedelics and marijuana. Since its founding, MAPS has raised over $70 million for psychedelic therapy and medical marijuana research and education. For more information, visit maps.org.

MAPS was founded to bring life-enhancing psychedelics through the regulatory system and legitimize their use as prescription medicine and, because of our due diligence, MDMA is now in phase III of medical trials in the U.S. and is on track to be rescheduled in 2021 for the treatment of Post Traumatic Stress Disorder (PTSD).

Our Work:

We further our mission by: developing psychedelics and marijuana into prescription medicines; training therapists and working to establish a network of treatment centers; supporting scientific research into spirituality, creativity, and neuroscience; and educating the public honestly about the risks and benefits of psychedelics and marijuana.

Our Vision:

We envision a world where psychedelics and marijuana are safely and legally available for beneficial uses, and where research is governed by rigorous scientific evaluation of their risks and benefits.

Our Values:

Transparency — Information is shared openly and clearly. Communications are respectful, honest, and forthright.

Passion and Perseverance — We persist in the face of challenges. We have a sense of urgency about our work and know that it's a long-term effort.

Intelligent Risk — Our decisions are informed by research. We try new things and learn from our mistakes.

Trust and Accountability — We value integrity and honesty and embrace high standards.

Our highest priority project is funding clinical trials of 3,4-methylenedioxymethamphetamine (MDMA) as a tool to assist psychotherapy for the treatment of Post-Traumatic Stress Disorder (PTSD). Preliminary studies have shown that MDMA in conjunction with psychotherapy can help people overcome PTSD, and possibly other disorders as well. MDMA is known for increasing feelings of trust and compassion towards others, which could make an ideal adjunct to psychotherapy for PTSD.

We are studying whether MDMA-assisted psychotherapy can help heal the psychological and emotional damage caused by sexual assault, war, violent crime, and other traumas. We also sponsored completed studies of MDMA-assisted psychotherapy for autistic adults with social anxiety, and MDMA-assisted psychotherapy for anxiety related to life-threatening illnesses.

MAPS is undertaking a roughly $26.9 Million plan to make MDMA into a Food and Drug Administration (FDA) approved prescription medicine by 2021 and is currently the only organization in the world funding clinical trials of MDMA-assisted psychotherapy. For-profit pharmaceutical companies are not interested in developing MDMA into a medicine because the patent for MDMA has expired. The idea of using MDMA to assist psychotherapy of any kind for any specific clinical indication has long been in the public domain.

In MDMA-assisted psychotherapy, MDMA is only administered a few times, unlike most medications for mental illnesses which are often taken daily for years, and sometimes forever. MDMA is not the same as "Ecstasy" or "molly." Substances sold on the street under these names may contain MDMA, but frequently also contain unknown and/or dangerous adulterants. In laboratory studies, pure MDMA has been proven sufficiently safe for human consumption when taken a limited number of times in moderate doses.

Expanded Access is a U.S. FDA program that allows the use of an investigational drug under a Treatment Protocol. The program is designed to address urgent and life-threatening conditions in patients who do not currently have promising treatment options. Only sites within the U.S and U.S. territories are eligible to participate in the U.S. FDA Expanded Access Program. MAPS does not have an Expanded Access program at this time but will be applying to FDA in early 2019. We hope to apply for similar programs internationally, at a later date. You can learn more about Expanded Access on the FDA's website.

If Expanded Access is approved in the U.S., new sites meeting the requirements listed below may seek approval to participate in the **MAPS Public Benefit Corporation (MPBC)** multi-center Expanded Access protocol under an **FDA** Treatment protocol, which would allow them to administer open-label **MDMA**-assisted psychotherapy for **PTSD** in line with the single approved protocol. Qualified applicants will have a team of therapy providers, a physician, and a facility suitable to conduct **MDMA**-assisted psychotherapy per Schedule 1 regulations with approval by regulatory agencies and under supervision of **MPBC**.

Research into **MDMA**-assisted psychotherapy as a treatment for **PTSD** is continuing in three countries. The first of the 15 Phase 3 trial sites in the US, Canada, and Israel started enrolling participants in November 2018.

Information about enrollment as well as an email sign-up for people interested in learning about enrolling in our clinical trials is available here: https://maps.org/participate/participate-in-research

If the clinical trials continue to show success, **MDMA** could soon be approved as a treatment for **PTSD** by federal regulators. Assuming that the Phase 3 trial results are satisfactory to the FDA, the agency would approve the treatment as soon as 2021. Once that happens, **MDMA**, which is currently a Schedule 1 drug under the Controlled Substances Act, would have to be reclassified to Schedule 2 or lower. Then, **MAPS** plans to help make the treatment available to as many people with **PTSD** who need it as possible. We are working hard to ensure as wide accessibility to **MDMA**-assisted psychotherapy as possible once it's approved, including getting it covered by private insurance and public health care plans.

We have the FDA determining that a psychedelic-assisted therapy could be a significant advance over what's currently available for mental health treatment. That's very different from the last 40 years of regulatory, political and cultural attitudes around these drugs. It's been decades since psychiatry has had a new set of tools available to it. And here we have psychedelics entering as a whole new class of pharmaceuticals that when used in combination with psychotherapy, could actually be better than conventional treatments.

It's unclear exactly why **MDMA** seems to help in the treatment of **PTSD**, but there are various theories. **MDMA** prompts the release of serotonin and dopamine in the brain, which together can help patients remember trauma and keep them motivated through long therapy sessions. **MDMA** also prompts the release of hormones associated with trust, bonding and intimacy. **MDMA**, when it's used in recreational contexts, is sometimes referred to as the 'love drug' and this is why. It creates these feelings of intimacy, of love and trust in the people around you when you're under its influence. In the context of therapy, it may help people feel more trusting of the therapist they're working with. Finally, MDMA acts in the amygdala, a primal part of the brain associated with fear and the fight-or-flight response. People with PTSD have a hyperactive amygdala on average. MDMA actually turns down the volume of the amygdala. It directly reduces activity in the amygdala, we can see that in brain-imaging studies. People can talk about the most terrifying experiences of their lives in a relatively calm and articulate way.

Current medications for PTSD are insufficient. The only two medications approved for PTSD treatment are antidepressants (SSRIs). Most patients need to take these drugs every day for many months, years, or sometimes forever in order to see their symptoms reduced. Like any treatment, SSRIs approved for PTSD can have unwanted side effects, and since they are daily medications, many people struggle with them continuously.

MDMA-assisted psychotherapy uses MDMA to improve the effectiveness of psychotherapy. The treatment involves only two or three administrations of MDMA in conjunction with psychotherapy in a controlled therapeutic setting, as part of a 12-week course of psychotherapy. In this program, MDMA is not the treatment by itself, but must be administered together with psychotherapy. Once approved, patients will not be able to take the MDMA home—they won't be filling their prescriptions at their local pharmacy. Instead, MDMA will only be available through a doctor and only in supervised therapeutic settings from certified clinicians.

MAPS has been championing and fundraising for MDMA research for 32 years and we are seeing stronger and stronger evidence that MDMA-assisted psychotherapy may be an effective treatment for PTSD, and may be a promising alternative to currently available treatment for PTSD. We intend to continue to develop and work towards approval for the treatment as diligently as we can.

NOTE: FDA Agrees to Expanded Access Program for MDMA-Assisted Psychotherapy for PTSD: https://maps.org/news/media/8008-press-release-fda-agrees-to-expanded-access-program-for-mdma-assisted-psychotherapy-for-ptsd

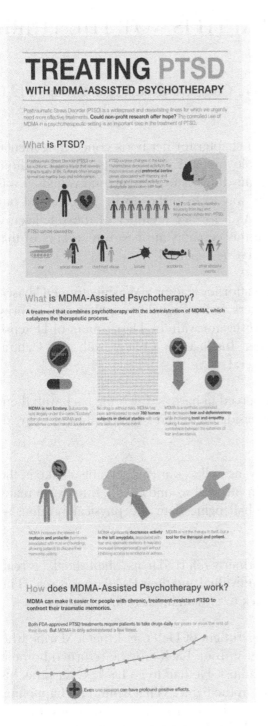

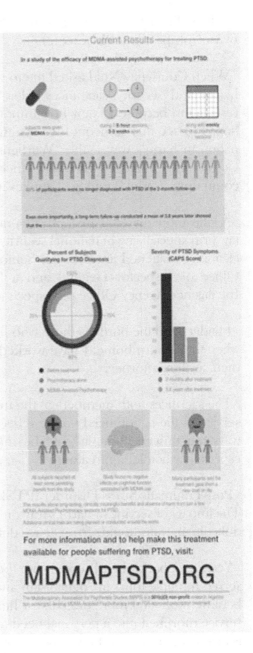

CHAPTER 22 - MENTAL HEALTH IS NOT THE THIRD RAIL IT USED TO BE

Andrew P. Bakaj, Esq., Managing Partner, Compass Rose Legal Group, PLLC (www.CompassRosePLLC.com)

When Courtenay Nold asked me to write a chapter for her book concerning mental health and security clearances/federal employment, I accepted to do so without reservation because I knew how important this topic is to so many individuals. I was happy to see that someone was leading the way to help those who have served our nation in harm's way — the "Warfighter". As a former member of the Intelligence Community, I can say with confidence that this certainly applies to members of that community as well. Frankly, it applies to everyone — period.

A little about myself: I am a private practice attorney leading a Washington, DC-based law firm specializing in national security matters, federal employment law, and security clearance matters. I am a former Senior Investigator with the Department of Defense Office of Inspector General and a former Intelligence Officer with the Central Intelligence Agency Office of Inspector General.

I understand the burdens those who have served in harm's way bring back with them when they return home. I have worked alongside them and I now represent many of them as their attorney.

The sacrifices both members of the military, as well as our civil servants, make in the service of the nation need not be reflected in physical wounds. And, frankly, in many ways the unseen "trauma" can be more challenging than the physical burdens — especially when left untreated.

Post-Traumatic Stress Disorder (PTSD), formerly referred to as "shell-shock," is real. The impact of serving in harm's way on the individual and their loved ones is real. The difficulty in transitioning from active duty back to civilian life is real.

Years ago, back when I served with the Department of Defense, I met a Marine who served multiple tours in Afghanistan and later in Iraq. Each time he returned home it became more and more difficult for him to adjust. He had to go back. Over time, his service morphed into a personal need to be "in the fight". What wound up happening is that he did not know how to be a "civilian" any longer. He did not know how to "live life" in a place other than a war-zone. He needed to be in a place where when he woke up there was a "mission" to undertake that day if not that morning. His story ends well because he eventually became a leader helping those in need globally as a humanitarian. He made the transition and he is, without question, a success story. But notice what he was fighting — the transition back home. He could not be somewhere other than a war-zone, and every time he redeployed the need to be in the war-zone was simply reinforced. His story ends well, but for many it does not.

We all know and read news stories of the mental anguish with which soldiers return home. By-products of this are anxiety and depression. Sometimes it leads alcohol and/or drug abuse. Other times it leads to physical violence. Sometimes, as we know, it can lead to suicide. I have known someone in each of those categories — and perhaps you have as well.

In my capacity as a private practice attorney, I have — and continue to — work with clients in getting them psychological help. This is often in the context of me helping them fight for their security clearance or their job. In fact, as I write his chapter, just earlier today I was on the phone with a mental health professional coordinating a referral for a client. I do this because I am helping them fight for their careers. I also do this because it is the right thing to do for them as a fellow human being.

I recently represented an individual who is a military officer and who served in highly sensitive operations overseas. Upon returning from multiple special assignments in a variety of locations, he began self-medicating as part of coping with stress. His self-medicating began with increased alcohol consumption and gradually morphed into the officer purchasing prescription drugs absent a prescription via the dark web. At one point, he had a realization that what he was doing was not just illegal, but physically harmful to himself — and his growing family.

The officer did something brave. He self-referred himself to a military hospital, informed his chain-of-command, and got help. His senior officers and colleagues were 100% supportive, and he has since rebounded tremendously. He has been successful because he became an active participant in his own recovery. He worked with the doctors and counselors in finding treatment that works, and he complies with all treatment programs. He is, by all accounts, doing well.

Now, the type of drugs he used and the means by which he acquired them became a clearance concern. Going to counselors and psychologists, however, never became a concern. In fact, because he self-referred the facts and documentation supported his good judgment and responsible actions to do the right thing. Seeing the doctors was not a liability. To the contrary: it became the underlying evidence supporting his ability to retain a security clearance. As a consequence, his career will continue to blossom because he did the right thing for himself.

Another category of clients I represent are whistleblowers — that is, individuals who lawfully disclose violations of law, rule, or regulation through authorized channels. The term "whistleblower" has been conflated to include individuals like Edward Snowden or Chelsea Manning. Those individuals are not whistleblowers — they are "leakers," and they did not engage in protected activity and in compliance with the law. "Whistleblowers," on the other hand, are individuals who disclose wrongdoing through appropriate channels — like to an Office of Inspector General or through lawful means to Congress.

I know this area well because when I worked as a federal official, I developed the legal and investigative framework for protecting whistleblowers with access to classified information. As a byproduct of working within that field, I have seen individuals who have experienced multiple tours of combat, return to an assignment within the Continental United States, see something wrong, disclose the wrongdoing lawfully, and be threatened with having an illustrious career ruined because when they came home they did the right thing and lawfully disclosed wrongdoing.

For example: years ago, there was a matter where a series of individuals reported, up through the chain-of-command, that their investigative leadership was fabricating evidence in order to obtain a guilty plea/verdict in a federal criminal matter. When leadership decided to continue in the illegal activity, disclosures were made to an Office of Inspector General of jurisdiction. That resulted in a heavy response, to include the involvement of the FBI. The result: leadership circled the wagons and the whistleblowers were targeted for reprisal through retaliatory investigations. While in private practice, I have witnessed clients' leadership manipulate their colleagues and others as a form of workplace bullying, effectively "swarming" the individual in an attempt to make their life so miserable that they ultimately quit or retire early. Such experiences can certainly create significant stress creating or execrating already present medical conditions. Furthermore, such experiences can certainly impact an individual's relationship with their loved ones.

Finally, I have colleagues and friends who have neither served in combat nor are whistleblowers. Their jobs are quite stressful and, in addition to their day-to-day challenges, have been dealt the added worry of a family member with cancer or raising a child with Autism.

This is all to say that stress need not come from seeing combat. Stress comes from a number of places. And, as it is with life, those challenges change and their day-to-day impact can ebb and flow.

In the end, we are all human and when faced with challenges, different people cope differently. Moreover, taking part in combat or special operations missions need not trigger stress-related coping that involves drugs or alcohol. In fact, here in Washington I have seen a number of individuals working "desk jobs" but in extraordinarily stressful environments. The resultant "coping" mechanisms are the same.

When a client is involved in drug or alcohol abuse, we have no choice but to send them somewhere to get help. But for those who haven't started abusing alcohol or drugs, but who are clearly under an enormous amount of stress day-in and day-out, I have to have the candid conversation about seeking professional help.

Why do these individuals not seek help on their own? Why don't they see a counselor or mental health profession? "Stigma," they'll say. Stigma from what? They'll respond with, "The assumption that something is wrong with me." Who's making that assumption? "Friends. Colleagues. Loved ones. The government — and I'll lose my clearance," — is the conclusion they'll draw. Nothing can be further from the truth.

I am not going to discuss what your friends or family may think about getting mental health treatment. And, to be frank, that is a personal matter that not "everyone" needs to know. So, the notion that people will think less of "you" is simply not true because you need NOT tell them. In other words: your business is your business.

Second, when it comes to obtaining a government job or a security clearance, the notion that seeing a mental health professional will harm your ability to get the job or clearance is absolutely false. I know the rumors because when I served in the government, I heard the same thing. The common belief was that anyone who seeks counseling in any way, shape, or form will not get through the process and, therefore, will not be granted a security clearance. Conversely, it was believed — and many continue to believe — that if you have a clearance and seek counseling or see a psychiatrist, that such action will be the basis to revoke a security clearance.

In addressing this concern, I will discuss this from the standpoint of how it impacts one's ability to obtain — or maintain — a security clearance. For purposes of our discussion here, it does not matter if the security clearance is at the SECRET or TOP SECRET level, or that you're being adjudicated for eligibility for access to Sensitive Compartmented Information (SCI) or Special Access Programs (SAPs). The adjudicative criterion is identical.

As most national security professionals know, the first step in obtaining a security clearance is filling out the Standard Form 86, typically on a computer program referred to as "e-QIP". If you navigate to https://www.opm.gov/forms/ and enter SF-86 into the search bar you will be able to bring up the current SF-86 Form from the Office of Personnel Management's website. As many of you know, there is a section entitled "Psychological and Emotional Health." In this section the government makes the following very clear: Mental health counseling in and of itself is not a reason to revoke or deny eligibility for access to classified information, suitability or fitness to obtain or retain Federal employment, fitness to obtain or retain contract employment, or eligibility for physical or logical access to federally controlled facilities or information systems. Seeking or receiving mental health care for personal wellness and recovery may contribute favorably to decisions about your eligibility.

SF-86

These are not mere words. This is true. First, when a security clearance is adjudicated the deciding official is looking at whether any "concerns" arise. These concerns fall under various "adjudicative guidelines", which can be reviewed on my firm's website https://compassrosepllc.com/adjudicative-guidelines-for-determining-eligibility-for-access-to-classified-information/)

For psychological concerns, the relevant guideline is Guideline "I". When it comes to security clearances, it is about "mitigating" the concern. That is to say, it is about alleviating the government's concern that there is an issue. Often "psychological" concerns crop up for members of the Intelligence Community because there often is a "mental health" screening as part of the application and subsequent continuous evaluation process. I will provide examples of this and how we addressed the concerns.

By way of example, reproduced are the mitigating conditions for Guideline G – Alcohol Consumption:

(a) So much time has passed, or the behavior was so infrequent, or it happened under such unusual circumstances that it is unlikely to recur or does not cast doubt on the individual's current reliability, trustworthiness, or good judgment;

(b) The individual acknowledges his or her pattern of maladaptive alcohol use, provides evidence of actions taken to overcome this problem, and has demonstrated a clear and established pattern of modified consumption or abstinence in accordance with treatment recommendations;

(c) The individual is participating in counseling or a treatment program, has no previous history of treatment and relapse, and is making satisfactory progress in a treatment program;

(d) The individual has successfully completed a treatment program along with any required aftercare, and has demonstrated a clear and established pattern of modified consumption or abstinence in accordance with treatment recommendations.

Security Executive Agent Directive 4 ("SEAD 4"), National Security Adjudicative Guidelines (Effective June 8, 2017).

By way of further example, reproduced are the mitigating conditions for Guideline H – Drug Involvement and Substance Misuse:

(a) The behavior happened so long ago, was so infrequent, or happened under such circumstances that it is unlikely to recur or does not cast doubt on the individual's current reliability, trustworthiness, or good judgment;

(b) The individual acknowledges his or her drug involvement and substance misuse, provides evidence of actions taken to overcome this problem, and has established a pattern of abstinence, including, but not limited to:

(1) Disassociation from drug-using associates and contacts;

(2) Changing or avoiding the environment where drugs were used; and

(3) Providing a signed statement of intent to abstain from all drug involvement and substance misuse, acknowledging that any future involvement or misuse is grounds for revocation of national security eligibility;

(c) Abuse of prescription drugs was after a severe or prolonged illness during which these drugs were prescribed, and abuse has since ended;

(d) Satisfactory completion of a prescribed drug treatment program, including but not limited to, rehabilitation and aftercare requirements, without recurrence of abuse, and a favorable prognosis by a duly qualified medical professional.

Finally, by way of further example, reproduced are the mitigating conditions for Guideline I – Psychological Conditions:

(a) the identified condition is readily controllable with treatment, and the individual has demonstrated ongoing and consistent compliance with the treatment plan;

(b) the individual has voluntarily entered a counseling or treatment program for a condition that is amenable to treatment, and the individual is currently receiving counseling or treatment with a favorable prognosis by a duly qualified mental health professional;

(c) recent opinion by a duly qualified mental health professional employed by, or acceptable to and approved by the U.S. Government that an individual's previous condition is under control or in remission, and has a low probability of recurrence or exacerbation;

(d) the past emotional instability was temporary, the situation has been resolved, and the individual no longer shows indications of emotional instability;

(e) there is no indication of a current problem.

Security Executive Agent Directive 4 ("SEAD 4"), National Security Adjudicative Guidelines (Effective June 8, 2017).

As you can see, much of the mitigation surrounds actually seeing a mental health professional, obtaining treatment, and following through on the treatment plan. Consider the officer who self-referred because of his drug use. That concern was mitigated because seeking counseling for his addiction meant that the acknowledged his drug involvement and substance misuse, and his seeking counseling was evidence of completing a treatment program. Conversely, the concerns about his psychological condition were never raised. Put another way: seeking mental health guidance is not a problem; it was the underlying factual <u>solution</u> that mitigated the government's concerns.

To underscore my point, I will use a more extreme example. A few years ago, I had someone retain me who had attempted suicide on two occasions. This individual self-reported the incidents on the SF-86 because they were involuntarily hospitalized. The situation was serious and, given the facts initially disclosed, we had to go through a robust appeal for their security clearance, which we ultimately prevailed in.

So, what was the evidence we provided? Well, plenty of statements from fact witnesses who knew this person well and could attest to their mental stability. However, the critical evidence came from two medical professionals: a clinical psychiatrist and a licensed clinical social worker. The clinical psychiatrist provided a letter detailing the length they provided psychological services for this individual, the treatment plan, and evidence showing that my client was following the treatment plan to a "T". The licensed clinical social worker did the same, and even provided some details about the counseling sessions. All of this evidence — proof that my client was seeing these medical professionals — was what we needed to show that she was trustworthy and possessed good judgment, meriting access to classified information (i.e., getting a security clearance).

I use the above example because it is an extreme example — and things worked out for the client. When it comes to mental health, the U.S. Government saying that seeking help will not be held against you is true; these are not mere words they're batting about. Our nation has been "at war" for many years and people need to see medical professionals for reasons beyond "PTSD". Anxiety, depression, marital counseling — life happens, and the agencies understand that.

As I stated from the outset, many individuals say that seeking mental health assistance presents a stigma that has to be overcome, but as you can see from my example, the very opposite is true. So, if you ever hear someone saying that seeking mental health counseling will have you lose a job or a security clearance, you now know, without question, that the person is full is flat out wrong.

Taking care of yourself not only includes taking physical care of yourself but includes taking mental and emotional care of yourself.

All statements of fact, opinion, or analysis expressed are those of the author and do not reflect the official positions or views of the U.S. Government. Nothing in the contents should be construed as asserting or implying U.S. Government authentication of information or endorsement of the author's views.

Visit www.CompassRosePLLC.com for more information.

CHAPTER 23 - MOVEMENT AND BREATH: THE PILATES SOLUTION TO PTSD

Catherine H. Pinnell, B.S., PMA CPT

When you think of tools that are good to help with managing Post-Traumatic Stress Disorder (PTSD), the Pilates method may not be one that immediately comes to mind. Is it for dancers? Is it just a fancy way to work your abs? Pilates was developed by a man, initially to train boxers, and addresses the whole body. One might even say it is the first advertised method of "functional training". I have successfully used the Pilates method, traditionally just known as Pilates, to not only gain strength, but connect my body to my brain, and address all of my PTSD symptoms. It is my goal to encourage the reader to try Pilates for themselves, to reap the benefits of this dynamic and life changing method of exercise. Whether it is practiced as a supplement to a regular routine or as a primary form of exercise, all participants will benefit, inside and out.

I served in the U.S. Marine Corps from 1999-2003. My trauma experience and military experience go hand in hand; I was sexually assaulted by my Staff Non-Commissioned Officer (NCO) in Charge at my first school. I told no one, and the pain and shame grew into an awful beast. PTSD has been a part of my life since early adulthood and it will be a burden I carry for the rest of my life.

It took me a long time to be able to talk about my trauma. I was ordered to stay, do what I was told, and my career was threatened if I didn't do exactly as he demanded. At first, I self-medicated with alcohol; a common way many of us begin to deal with the demons. Since the Marine Corps is well known for alcohol consumption, it was a natural place to start. The more I drank, however, the angrier I got. Instead of feeling numb, I felt a rage that was unmanageable. Unfortunately, this was accepted amongst my friends since so many of us had anger issues. I was part of the crowd, and not willing to address the underlying issues causing me pain. I drank like this for a long time. There were many ways unhealthy ways I choose to deal with my pain, and they only contributed to my shame.

After separating from the Marine Corps, I started over like all of us do after our tour of duty. There were ups and downs, successes and failures. I was able to put myself through school and earn a Bachelor's degree in Exercise Science. I taught fitness classes, held management positions, but continued to struggle internally. Through the struggles I was on a path to getting the help I needed. I became more involved in my local Veteran community and even married a man that continues to serve in the Army Reserve. Bit by bit I was able to share my story but it felt overwhelming emotionally, and even physically. Shame still ruled my life.

I was able to confront the fears, shame, and all the other issues PTSD brought when I had a miscarriage in 2014. The grief of this loss combined with the PTSD and the grieving I needed to do to recover felt overwhelming. Instead of being angry and emotional only sometimes, I spiraled into depression and anxiety. Panic attacks were a common part of my life. I was desperate. I talked to my local County Veteran Service Officer and he encouraged me to, at the very least, contact the counselors at the Vet Center in my area. This is where my counseling, and more importantly, my healing began.

Over the years, the things that helped me to manage my PTSD in the healthiest ways have been counseling (including Cognitive Processing Therapy), and exercise, and especially Pilates. Exercise in general, as I am sure you know, can help with depression and anxiety symptoms. There are many research studies to prove this, along with my own story to apply the benefit to mental health. It is not a magic pill, and I do not claim it will solve all mental health issues. But it certainly does help manage symptoms and can be a tool in your toolkit to help ease the pain you are feeling. Researchers have been studying the link between mental well-being and exercise for decades. There are a mountain of studies that have been performed on every demographic imaginable, and they all agree that exercise helps. Some of these reasons include, according to Kelsey Graham (2017):

Increased Neurotransmitter activity

Improved self-esteem (which is commonly low in those who suffer from depression)

Release of stored energy, which can alleviate anxiety

Serves as a distraction or coping mechanism

Creates opportunities for social interaction (para. 3)

Pilates has helped me achieve all of the above. From improving brain function to being an outlet for movement, Pilates has helped me achieve so much more than I had ever imagined.

The History of Pilates in Brief

Before I dissect the bulleted list, I will give a brief history and overview of Pilates so that you understand a little more about it. Joseph Pilates was born in the late 1800s in Germany and was often ill as a child. He hated being so sick and developed an exercise routine to help him combat his childhood illnesses. As a circus performer, he moved to England in the early 1900s to find work. Unfortunately, World War I emerged after a year he was in the country so he and all other Germans were interred in England for the length of the war. While at the internment camp, Pilates and other fitness enthusiasts kept their cohorts moving with his routines. They stayed healthy! His reputation preceded him and when he returned to Germany he assisted with rehabilitation of soldiers. While he was working on rehabilitation, he was also training boxers, his true passion.

In 1926 Pilates moved to the United States and decided to settle in New York City. He was quickly sought out by dancers because his exercises and equipment helped them recover from injuries much faster than other methods. This is where the dancer reputation began, but he stayed true to his roots and always loved boxing. In the beginning he called his method "Corrective Exercise" and subsequently "Contrology". Even though Joe was a pioneer in fitness ahead of his time, he was a prolific inventor. Pilates had been developing equipment to assist in training himself and others. It started when he was rehabilitating soldiers in Germany, and he continued to improve his designs. The most famous and versatile piece of Pilates equipment is called the Reformer. Also commonly used is the trapeze table, or "Cadillac," spine correctors/barrels and Pilates chairs. Almost all of Pilates equipment uses springs to create resistance. The chair is the most compact piece of equipment and was initially developed so that people could have a piece of equipment that would fit in their crowded New York apartments! All Pilates equipment has a specific benefit and can be used for a multitude of exercises.

Exercise and the Direct Connection to Mental Health

Now that you have a brief overview of where Pilates comes from, I will return to the list of how exercise directly impacts mental health. First, increased neurotransmitter activity, also called neuroplasticity. This is by far the most fascinating and scientific aspect of Pilates. It also connects directly to PTSD symptoms and treatment, since PTSD creates significant change in the brain and endocrine systems (Scaer, 2014, p. 64). These changes are adverse in nature and what cause panic attacks, negative thoughts, and other symptoms. Pilates, along with other methods of exercise, can help us create new neural pathways. New pathways mean better brain function and the ability to create new habits. Most of my PTSD symptoms are on the anxious side of the spectrum, so developing new neural pathways, or neuroplasticity, is key for managing my PTSD symptoms. For example, I frequently suffer from racing thoughts, shame, panic attacks, and feeling like the world is against me. These types of symptoms are directly affected by working on my neuroplasticity because it forces my brain to stop the cycle of anxious and negative thoughts. It was previously thought that neural pathways were set by age 25, but current research is proving this to be false. While it is not as easy to do as when we were young, it is still possible. In my opinion, the amount of work that it takes to create neural pathways has been worth every second. The more I work on this, the more I can ease my anxiety symptoms. I have the old pathways and somatic responses sometimes, but these responses occur less and less the more I work on neuroplasticity.

Second, improved self-esteem. Pilates makes me feel strong. I have no trouble moving through life, picking up my daughter, or carrying the groceries in the house. Physical pain I had experienced previously has pretty much disappeared since I started practicing Pilates regularly. The two biggest complaints I had physically before Pilates were knee pain (mostly from running in the Marines) and sciatica (from pregnancy). I used to walk with a limp, and my back was starting to have issues. There are many reasons why Pilates can help people with injuries, but the three biggest ones for me were and continue to be: physical fitness, overall flexibility, and muscle strengthening with spring tension.

One of the key tenets of Pilates is physical fitness, especially incorporating the spine with the movements. As Joseph H. Pilates (2005) said, "Physical fitness is the first requisite of happiness. Our interpretation of physical fitness is the attainment and maintenance of a uniformly developed body with a sound mind, fully capable of naturally, easily, and satisfactorily performing many and varied daily tasks with spontaneous zest and pleasure." (p. 15) I have found this to be true for me, and working on not only strengthening but mobilizing my spine has helped me heal physical ailments and sets me up to be pain free long-term. In every Pilates class, participants are guided through spinal movement in all ways: flexion, extension, side or lateral bending, and rotation. These movements simultaneously develop strength, flexibility, and mobility of the spine. When the spine is strong, flexible, and mobile, we are able to move through life with ease. While researching for this article, there was one study that came up time and time again for Pilates: Low back pain and how Pilates impacts it. Most people I know suffer from back pain of some sort, and it is common in the low back. Pilates, done well, can ease lower back pain and help it from reoccurring.

Flexibility seems to be the forgotten essential of fitness, even though it is equally important as cardio or muscle strength. In Pilates, it is definitely not forgotten! One of the unique traits of Pilates is that many exercises address flexibility and strength at the same time. For example, one of my favorite exercises on the Reformer is called 'Feet in Straps - leg circles'. Leg circles can also be done without equipment. In both exercises, muscles of the legs will stretch and strengthen at the same time. While performing the exercise, the participant uses their abdominal and back muscles to keep the body from moving. A simple leg circle is a new world from a Pilates point of view. I learned that my sciatic pain was coming from tight muscles in my hips, and when I worked to release those muscles, the pain went away.

Using springs instead of hand weights or machines has its own set of benefits. When I would lift weights, it would almost always cause knee pain. I wanted to lift more, progressed slowly, but pain was a consistent roadblock. When I started working with the Pilates equipment, however, I could increase the resistance and not feel pain. This has strengthened my muscles and joints so that my knees are better supported and my pain is practically non-existent. As referenced in the study by Natour, Cazotti, Ribiero, Baptista, and Jones (2015), it is proven that people who practice Pilates feel less pain, take less anti-inflammatory medication, and even have an increased quality of life (p. 65).

Third, release of stored energy. Pilates is physically challenging and requires precision. Once I started practicing regularly, the pregnancy weight finally came off because I was building a lot of lean muscle. No matter your size, gender, or goal, Pilates will increase your muscle tone and connection to other essential bodily systems like fascia. Fascia is connected to muscle, and is the sheath that surrounds muscles, like a vacuum sealed bag that holds muscles and muscle groups together. There are many reasons to connect to facia, including increasing flexibility, neuroplasticity, and functional movement. Pilates has not only helped me get stronger and leaner but has helped me correct poor posture and movement patterns that were the root of many of my physical ailments. It is, from what I know, the original method of functional exercise.

Another important part of the release of stored energy is the connection that mental pain has to physical pain in the body. In recent decades psychologists have well documented studies that prove emotional pain can manifest as physical pain. While everyone is different, we understand that PTSD is a great deal of emotional pain that is carried long term. At the very least, PTSD symptoms can cause tightness in the muscles because of anxiousness, and even more physical pain, especially in the areas in which the person was traumatized (Meltzer-Brody, et al., 2007, p. 905). I mentioned earlier that the muscles in my hips are chronically tight. It's no surprise that my hips are tight and have developed pain over the years; that is where I was violated. Pilates has helped me slowly but surely release the tension in my hips and the rest of my body.

Fourth, a distraction/coping mechanism. When I am practicing Pilates, I do not have the capacity to allow my mind to race. This is the most powerful part of Pilates to me. In the past, I have tried other methods of exercise to cope, and they just don't work as well. Activities like running and biking just gave me more time to think so they weren't terribly productive. Moreover, they usually exacerbated my physical pain, especially in the knees, so the reasons why I had to find something new intensified. In my Pilates classes I have to maintain a laser focus to perform the exercises with precision. My anxiety, especially racing thoughts, are no match to Pilates and the focus it requires! Even after an advanced and/or challenging session I feel energized instead of tired. It is my personal goal to make my clients feel this way after every class or session, because it feels so good.

Finally, opportunities for social interaction. For me this meant support from individuals who are open to hear about my experience and creatively assist with support and/or solutions. As someone with PTSD, especially anxiety, it became increasingly difficult for me to socialize, and I found that I frequently isolated myself. The Pilates classes I attend are small and easier for me to handle. I have been able to build new relationships with my Pilates community locally and on a national level by attending conferences. Time and time again, I have found a collaborative community and people that are open to share ideas and to listen.

When looking for a class to attend, I would inquire on the class size. The smaller the class, the easier it may be for you to attend, especially if you have social anxiety like I do. It is also common to practice Pilates one on one with an instructor, like personal training at a gym. Many Pilates studios are relatively small, and are not busy or loud, and are designed to be a calm and quiet sanctuary. It is common to ask a lot of questions before you choose a studio so don't be shy to ask about things that concern you, or to ask for a tour. You deserve to practice in a place that feels safe and brings you calm, and most of all, relief from your symptoms.

Sometimes there is a disconnect with what the Pilates method is and what people think it is. Pilates is a dynamic way to exercise, and since it focuses on breath, can be a useful tool in managing mental health issues, especially depression, anxiety, and PTSD. Pilates was initially interesting to me because I thought it was challenging, especially for the abdominals. The practice became much more than that to me after really digging into it. Breathing deeply and evenly helps me manage my anxiety, and the challenge of the exercises keeps me interested and motivated. I was able to connect my body with my breath and feel a relief from my anxiety; for me Pilates is a meditative practice in that way. Because of the breath/body connection I immediately felt refreshed, because for that hour of the Pilates class, I couldn't be anxious. I had to concentrate too hard to allow my thoughts to race. Additionally, and more long-term, my mental and physical strength grew, and I started to trust myself more and more. The trust was a new and freeing experience.

I finally realized that the cause for my trauma was the loss of trust in myself. It was immediate and felt permanent. After the trauma of the miscarriage, I lost any remaining trust I had; I felt that my body and mind were completely broken. I found myself thinking, "For goodness sakes, my body couldn't even grow a child, something my body was made to do!" The feelings of hopelessness at that time were overwhelming. This time of my life may have been the lowest but in hindsight, I am grateful for it. The experience showed me that I needed to change in order to get better. It drove me to seek help and to eventually understand that I was not broken, and the shame I had been carrying for more than a decade had been a burden I was willing to shed. It is a burden none of us should bear, but we have to work through it. We cannot change the past.

Other methods of exercise helped as a distraction, teaching exercise helped sometimes, but other times made my anxiety worse. Pilates has been the most comprehensive solution to manage my PTSD and re-build the trust I had lost in myself. If you haven't tried Pilates yet, I highly recommend you find an instructor. There are a lot to choose from, so I recommend finding an instructor that is certified through the Pilates Method Alliance (PMA), the only governing body for Pilates instructors. If the instructor has earned a certification through the PMA, it means they have completed at least 450 hours of practice and are knowledgeable of all the Pilates equipment. The PMA is more than a trusted source of Pilates teachers. According to Jojo Bowman (2015), the PMA also has a specific initiative called "Heroes in Motion" (p. 168), dedicated to helping Veterans with Pilates. It is still growing, and there are many Pilates practitioners that are using the method to help us Veterans recover from and/or manage Traumatic Brain Injuries, amputations, and PTSD. It is my personal mission to assist with the growth of the "Heroes in Motion" initiative with PTSD specifically, and will continue to reach out to as many Veterans as I can to help them find relief from their suffering by connecting their breath with the body. No matter your choice on how to manage your PTSD, I think it is wise for all of us to find things that help us create new neural pathways (learn new things), improve our self-esteem, calm our minds/bodies, help us cope, and interact with others. This has been an excellent recipe for me in managing my mental health and is a long-term solution.

References

Graham, K. (2017, August 29). Exercise to reduce symptoms of anxiety and depression. [Web log post]. ACE fitness lifestyle blog. Retrieved from https://www.acefitness.org/education-and-resources/lifestyle/blog/6537/exercise-to-reduce-symptoms-of-anxiety-and-depression

Scaer, R. (2014). The body bears the burden: Trauma, dissociation, and disease. New York, NY: Routledge.

Natour, J., Cazotti, L., Ribieriro, L., Baptista, A., Jones, A. (2015). Pilates improves pain, function and quality of life in patients with chronic low back pain: a randomized controlled trial. Clinical Rehabilitation, 29(1), 59-68.

Meltzer-Brody, S., Leserman, J., Zolnoun, D., Steege, J., Green, E., Teich, A. (2007). Trauma and posttraumatic stress disorder in women with chronic pelvic pain. Obstetrics & Gynecology, 109(4), 902-908.

Pilates, J. H. (2005). Return to Life Through Contrology. Miami, FL: Pilates Method Alliance, Inc.

Bowman, J. (2015) "Wounded Warriors": Royal Danish ballet dancers train repatriated wounded soldiers in Pilates. Pilates, Arts, & Health, 7(2), 161-171.

CHAPTER 24 - MTB VETS

William J. Langham

On January 20, 2018, 1SG (Ret) Brent Myers took his life. He left behind a wife of 25 years and two sons. It seemed on the outside he had it all, a successful wife, sons making their own way in college and the civilian sector, a getaway cabin, and friends who truly cared for him. But why did he do it? Brent no longer has to deal with any problems, however, he just passed them on to everyone else.

How do I know Brent Myers? Brent and I served as Army Ranger Instructors in Dahlonega, GA (Mountain Phase of Ranger School). He was one of the first guys I met when I arrive at Camp and we became very good friends. We also competed as a team in the 2004 Best Ranger Competition placing 7th. To say the least our families were close as well. After retirement, Brent and I would talk for several hours a week and send hundreds of texts every week. I never got the impression, nor did he hint that he was thinking of taking his life. To this day I feel I let him down by not hearing him asking for help and not being there enough. But at the end of the day, he made a choice and the choice he made angers me.

Brent, like many Veterans including myself deal with Post-Traumatic Stress Disorder (PTSD) and the horrors of combat. The difference is in how we individually choose to deal with it. I participated in Desert Shield/Desert Storm, Operation Iraqi Freedom, and Operation Enduring Freedom. For me, after serving over 22 years as an Army Airborne Ranger, and retiring as a First Sergeant (E8) in 2011, my choice was to continue working in the same type of environment with the same type of guys. I did high threat contracting in the middle east for five years. But that too started to wear on me and my family. My wife and I felt it was time to come home and be a family. My job was easy, take care of the house, dogs, take her to the airport on Mondays and pick her up on Fridays. It was the life for about six months. During that time, I started to lose my identity and I felt as though I didn't have a real purpose. I stopped going to the gym and started drinking while my wife was gone on business. I was going to a bad place and continually thinking about my time in combat and the men and friends I lost. Needless to say, I was miserable, and my mindset was not right. How did I overcome all this?

While I was contracting, I bought a high-end mountain bike but was never home long enough to enjoy it. Now that I was home, I had the time and but lack the knowledge to work on my own bike. I reached out to shop owner where I purchased it (Shawn Brunner of Fresh Bikes) and asked him what the best way for me was to learn how to work on my bike. He proceeded to tell me by working at the shop with him and he would teach me everything I needed to know. I started working there part-time and was learning while also becoming a better rider. I was having fun pushing myself on the trail and meeting new people who just enjoyed riding their bikes. I quickly found the mountain bike community very much like my military community and I loved it. I was starting to feel good about myself and this what I needed. I was feeling better at home, didn't drink as much and felt very lucky every day and why not...I had a wonderful wife (Tamara), a great son (Colin), and new friends who liked riding.

We were all having the time of our lives in 2017. My wife and I sold our house, our son had graduated from college and was moving to New Zealand. Tamara and I were traveling the world making up for lost time from my former life. We traveled to Australia, New Zealand, Ireland, Italy, Greece, and even went back home to Texas for a few months to be with family. Now Tamara and I were ready to find a home and enjoy what 2018 was going to bring us. However, the beginning of 2018 wasn't very kind, I was notified Brent Myers had committed suicide on January 20th.

Once back in Georgia, I knew I need to do something to help Veterans regain a sense of purpose and give them a path to health and happiness. I knew how I was going to do it too...mountain biking. I knew how riding my bike turned things around for me and I knew it could for other Veterans as well. I reached out to Shawn Brunner and pitched my idea to him and he was thinking the same thing. For five months I was working on a name, getting all the legal documents together, applying for non-profit status, getting insurance, applying for grants, and purchasing bikes. And then on June 6, 2018, MTB Vets, LTD, a 501(c)(3) non-profit organization became reality. Why June 6th? That is a date that's synonymous in military history..."D-Day". On that day in history, all branches of our armed forces along with our allies came together with one common goal and that goal was to crush the Nazi War machine. For MTB Vets, it's the day that Veteran Mountain bikers along with our avid civilian mountain bikers set out to help our Veterans who are dealing with PTSD. Our message is simple, suicide is not the answer and we're here for you.

MTB Vets mission statement is simple, MTB Vets exists exclusively for our Veterans. It's an honor and privilege to provide our Veterans an outlet to seek health, happiness, and purpose through a mountain biking community of comrades. We Ride - We Thrive! MTB Vets provides a mountain biking outlet and community for Veterans. But more importantly, we are Veterans who understand the potential challenges of transitioning into and thriving within the civilian community — the lack of purpose, the flashbacks to dark days and memories of good days, the longing for brotherhood camaraderie, and the loss of identity. When you join the military, you join a big family; when you leave the military, it may feel like you've left your family ... which is uncomfortable and unnerving.

We understand because we've been there.

We want to help because we've lost brothers and sisters to the darkness of those challenges.

We know we can make a difference.

As proud Veterans and enthusiastic mountain bikers, we firmly believe in 'trail therapy'.

The trail challenges the body, stimulates the mind, and soothes the soul...and your riding companions become family.

You belong.

Veterans are at their best when they are challenged both mentally and physically. And what better place to be challenged than in nature where the air is crisp and the only thing that matters at that time is you, the trail, and your ridding mates? MTB Vets provides our Veterans a mountain bike, protective gear, and transportation at no cost to them if needed. We have also partnered with several bike shops in the area as donation drop off centers. People can donate used mountain bikes to MTB Vets, and we will ensure they are safe and trail worthy. These donated bikes then are given to Veterans who cannot afford to buy their own bike. One would think it would be easy to get them out however, that's not always the case. Veterans suffering with PTSD tend to be anti-social, lack friends, don't like going out to public places, and would rather be by themselves. This leads to bad thoughts, excessive use of alcohol, prescription drugs, illegal drugs and possible suicide. Surprisingly, many of our Veterans' decline getting help because they are afraid of being labeled by society. On a positive note, over the past several years PTSD awareness and treatment has made great improvements. In the past it took months to get an appointment with the VA and when seen the doctors would just prescribe addictive medications and not treating the issues. Also, the civilian community saw our Veterans as damaged goods who they thought could snap at any moment. Many of our Veterans started to believe this and felt they had no one and had no purpose in life.

During our short existence, MTB Vets had been awarded two grants, hosted the first annual MTB Vets Charity Golf Scramble, hosted the 1SG Brent Myers Memorial Ride, attended Veteran workshops, and donated time and resources to spreading awareness about PTSD and how Veterans can enhance the community and the workplace. Every get-together, every ride, Veterans and civilians praise what we are doing to bring awareness and needed help to our Veterans. Seeing the smiles on Veterans faces after a ride, hearing them laugh about the ride afterwards, and seeing them return is why MTB Vets was created.

How does MTB Vets help our Veterans other than getting them out on the bike? MTB Vets uses the bike as a positive tool for Veterans. Our goal is to create a community for our Veterans where they feel accepted for who they are even if they don't ride. We are building a foundation for our Veterans and provide a ring of reciprocity for Veterans and their spouses. We do this in several different facets. One, there are other non-profits trying to make Atlanta the premier destination for Veterans. They have partnered with companies like Coke, Home Depot, Sun Trust, and UPS. These companies are aggressively seeking out Veterans to fill their ranks because they know the benefit our Veterans bring. We network with these other non-profits in order, if needed, to assist Veterans with job opportunities. Second, MTB Vets works with the VA Mental Health Department. With more Veterans moving to the Atlanta area this will continue to cause a strain on VA services. This is where MTB Vets comes in. For those Veterans not necessarily seeking one on one treatment are often referred to us or other non-profits. What we find is many Veterans are truly in search of a community of Veterans who understand what they are going through. We are always here to listen and assist in any way without judging. Lastly, MTB Vets has a lot of knowledge working with and dealing with the VA services. We can assist Veterans with navigating the system and even how to go about applying for and receiving other Veteran benefits they might be unaware of. It's funny how it works, we have Vietnam Veterans helping younger Veterans and vice versa. At the end of the day, MTB Vets is here for all Veterans regardless of if they ride or not. The community we are building is what's important and if you happen to ride that just an added bonus. Success is measured in many different ways. MTB Vets measures success, one smile, one, one laugh, and one Veteran at a time.

For more information please visit https://www.mtbvets.com.

CHAPTER 25 - OMEGA-3'S AND BRAIN HEALTH

Michael D. Lewis, MD, MPH, MBA, FACPM, FACN
Colonel (Retired), U.S. Army

I am an expert on nutritional interventions for brain health, the prevention and rehabilitation of brain injury and particularly the use of Omega-3 fatty acids for the prevention, management, and rehabilitation of concussions and traumatic brain injury (TBI).

I served in the Army for over 31 years. I graduated from the U.S. Military Academy at West Point, the U.S. Army Military Intelligence Officer Basic Course, U.S. Army Airborne School, and U.S. Army Ranger School before serving as an Intelligence Officer in Infantry Divisions on the Demilitarized Zone in Korea and Fort Ord, California, for five years prior to attending medical school at Tulane University in New Orleans. Following a surgical internship at Walter Reed Army Medical Center, I served as Chief of the Primary Care, Executive Medicine, and Flight Medicine Clinics at The Pentagon where I routinely cared for the highest levels of civilian and military leadership in the DoD, U.S. Congress, the CIA, and U.S. Supreme Court and was rated as a Senior Flight Surgeon. Following my residency training in Preventive Medicine and Public Health at Johns Hopkins University and the Walter Reed Army Institute of Research, I began a long period of overseas international research and as a professor at the Uniformed Services University Medical School. Altogether, I retired at the military rank of Colonel and then founded the non-profit Brain Health Education and Research Institute. My private practice, BrainCARE, is located in the Washington DC suburb, Potomac, Maryland, where I take a comprehensive and functional approach to concussion recovery, brain injury, ADHD, sports and cognitive performance, and brain health issues. My pioneering work in the military and since has helped thousands of people around the world and is regularly featured in the media, radio, podcasts, webinars, scientific conferences, and television including CNN's Sanjay Gupta M.D. show.

For centuries doctors' only treatment plan for brain injuries was rest and time. After being overseas for a number of years, I was assigned to the Uniformed Services University in Bethesda where I interacted with wounded warriors at the gym, hospital, and base exchange. I looked at the problem of military Traumatic Brain Injury (TBI) as an outsider, not trained in neurology or neurosurgery, and believed that the state of TBI management was completely inadequate.

I began to hear more and more about the Sago coal mine disaster (January 2006) and how high doses of fish oil may have helped the lone survivor, Randy McCloy, recover from carbon monoxide poisoning. I connected with McCloy's neurosurgeon, Dr.

Julian Bales. Rather than saying, "Only time will heal your damaged brain," Dr. Bales had prescribed heavy doses of Omega-3 fats in the form of fish oil that hastened McCloy's miraculous recovery. With that on my mind, I went to the head of research for the Defense and Veterans Brain Injury Center located at Walter Reed Army Medical Center and asked, "Is anybody looking at the use of Omega-3 fatty acids to help soldiers recover from traumatic brain injury?" The director was very thoughtful, looked at me and said, "No, why don't you?"

The brain's made up of fat, so we saturate it in the material that made the brain in the first place. If you have a brick wall that needs repair, you want to use more bricks to fix it. Omega-3 fats are basically the bricks of the brain.

As discussed on my website: http://www.brainhealtheducation.org/resources/omega-3s-and-brain-health/ Omega-3 fatty acids are essential fatty acids that are necessary from conception through pregnancy, and continue to support normal growth and development of infants. Throughout life, Omega-3 fats aid in the prevention and treatment of heart disease, diabetes, arthritis, inflammatory diseases, and cancer. Omega-3 fatty acids also play an important role in protecting the health of the brain, eyes, and nervous system. Over 8,000 published clinical trials have unequivocally established that Omega-3 fatty acids are important in human nutrition.

The primary source of Omega-6 fatty acids in the human diet is linoleic acid (LA) from the oils of seeds and grains. Sunflower, safflower, soy, and corn oils are particularly rich in linoleic acid. Evening primrose oil, borage oil, and black currant oil are unique due to their relatively high content of the health-promoting Omega-6 fatty acid, gamma-linolenic acid (GLA).

The primary dietary source of Omega-3 fatty acids is alpha-linolenic acid (ALA) from seeds and seed oils that are derived from plants such as flax, walnuts, and canola. Fish and fish oils are the richest source of preformed long chain Omega-3 fatty acids, EPA and DHA.

Humans have evolved consuming a diet that contained approximately equal amounts of Omega-3 and Omega-6 fatty acids. About 100 years ago, the industrial revolution introduced technology that allowed for the refining of vegetable and seed oils, which led to a dramatic increase in the consumption of Omega-6 fatty acids among the industrialized countries. In addition, the introduction of animal feeds derived from grains rich in Omega-6 fats has resulted in the production of meat, fish, and eggs high in Omega-6 fats and virtually void of Omega-3 fats.

Today, in Western diets, the ratio of Omega-6 to Omega-3 fatty acids ranges from 20:1–30:1 instead of the pre-industrial range of 1:1–2:1.5. A large body of scientific evidence has established that a high intake of Omega-6 fatty acids shifts the physiological state to one that promotes thrombosis, vasoconstriction, inflammation, and poor cellular health. The physiologic changes that result from high intake of Omega-6 fats has been implicated in pathophysiology of heart disease, diabetes, autoimmune and inflammatory diseases (rheumatoid arthritis, colitis ulcerosa, multiple sclerosis, lupus, asthma, etc.), depression, dementia, and other chronic diseases.

The U.S. Food and Drug Administration (FDA) classified Omega-3 fatty acids from fish oil as "generally recognized as safe" (GRAS). In fact, The FDA has ruled that up to 3000 mg of EPA+DHA is safe to be included in the food supply of Americans without fear of adverse events. In addition, there are no known significant drug interactions with Omega-3 fatty acids.

The introduction of high-quality fish oil supplements that have been processed to remove environmental contaminants allows for supplementation of high levels of EPA and DHA for preventive and therapeutic clinical use without the risk of toxicity.

Omega-3 deficiency is extremely common among those in the United States; it's even been named the sixth biggest killer of Americans. So, it's not surprising that the researchers found all the service members had low Omega-3 levels, and suicide risk was greatest among those with the lowest DHA levels. There is speculation that PTSD should be considered to be a kind of traumatic brain injury due to a chronically stressed and adrenalized system. PTSD is a neuroplastic disorder in which an event overwhelms the mind and the brain gets rewired in the process.

According to Su et al. cited below: Omega-3 polyunsaturated fatty acids (PUFAs), such as EPA and DHA, are essential nutrients that have potential preventive and therapeutic effects on psychiatric disorders, such as anxiety and depression, as well as comorbid depression and anxiety in physically ill patient. Preclinical data support the effectiveness of Omega-3 PUFAs as treatment for anxiety disorders. A cohort study found that high serum EPA levels were associated with protection against PTSD. Su, K. P., Tseng, P. T., Lin, P. Y., Okubo, R., Chen, T. Y., Chen, Y. W., & Matsuoka, Y. J. (2018). Association of Use of Omega-3 Polyunsaturated Fatty Acids With Changes in Severity of Anxiety Symptoms: A Systematic Review and Meta-analysis. JAMA network open, 1(5), e182327. doi:10.1001/jamanetworkopen.2018.2327

As discussed by Matsuoka: Modulating adult hippocampal neurogenesis by Omega-3 fatty acid supplementation could be a target of choice to prevent PTSD. Such intervention would likely be acceptable in clinical practice in both mental health and critical care medicine because of its convenience, empirical results in animal studies and less frequent side effects. Matsuoka Y. (2011). Clearance of fear memory from the hippocampus through neurogenesis by omega-3 fatty acids: a novel preventive strategy for posttraumatic stress disorder? BioPsychoSocial medicine, 5, 3. doi:10.1186/1751-0759-5-3

While the causal mechanisms of TBI, referred to as the primary injury, encompass a spectrum from minor falls to sports-related head impacts to high-speed motor vehicle injuries, the secondary phase, which occurs immediately after trauma regardless of the cause, produces effects that continue to damage and kill brain cells over a period of hours or days following the initial traumatic assault.

Over the past decade, in large part to ingenuity and necessity of military surgeons, tremendous advances have been made in acute and surgical management of severe TBI. Unfortunately, the management of mild TBI and concussions hasn't changed in centuries! Management of headaches, pain, and sleep disturbances has not changed.

Every medical textbook, website, and healthcare provider is going to tell you the same thing:

Get plenty of rest;

Avoid physical activities and sports while you recover;

See your healthcare provider who may prescribe medicine if you have symptoms such as a headache, difficulty sleeping, or depression.

These things are important! However, no current therapies address either the secondary phase that continues to damage the brain over the hours and days following injury or the need to facilitate the early neuroregeneration process to help the brain repair any damage.

I am pioneering methods to rebuild the injured brain rather than masking of symptoms with pharmaceuticals. In addition, I advocate increasing the resilience of the brain to withstand injury so those at significant risk may be protected. That simple conclusion is the basis of why Omega-3s are important in concussion and TBI – both in prevention of injury and even more important when an injury does occur.

There is no cure for concussion and TBI. There are no magic medicines nor will there ever be. The brain has to heal itself. All we can do is optimize the conditions to help the brain do the healing. That is what using Omega-3's will do. It provides a tool, the basic building block, for the brain's healing.

30% of the brain is fat. Omega fatty acids are analogous to bricks in the wall of your brain. The balance between Omega-3 and Omega-6 fatty acids is important. Omega-6 fatty acids are more inflammatory and an overabundance of them in your body can prevent healing. The critical Omega-3 fatty acids seem to be **DHA** and **EPA** (EPA – eicosapentaenoic acid; DHA – docosahexaenoic acid), precursors of Resolvins and neuroprotectins, and EPA influence healthy blood flow, cell-to-cell communication, and mediate anti-inflammatory and antioxidant effects. Omega-3s have proven beneficial across the board in anecdotal cases for restoring brain function after traumas like concussions or car crashes, and all forms of age-related neurodegeneration.

For optimal brain health, at least 50% of the fatty acid content in the blood should be composed of Omega-3s.

The brain is made of fat and about 30% of that fat is what are called Omega-3 fatty acids. Omega-3s have many important, critical functions. The concept of The Omega Protocol is that, if we saturate the brain with what it is made of, and we help create the nutritional foundation for the brain to heal, it will heal.

Think again of that brick wall. If you have a brick wall that gets damaged, you probably want to use bricks to repair the wall. Omega-3s are, literally, the bricks of the brain. Omega-3s make up a significant part of every neuron cell membrane. There is no cure for concussion and TBI. There are no magic medicines nor will there ever be. The brain must heal itself. But, what we can do is optimize the conditions to help the brain do the healing. That is what using Omega-3s will do.

It would be great if we all ate enough foods high in Omega-3s, but we don't. The problem is that Omega-6 fatty acids are even more abundant in nature and in our food supply. While Omega-3s are anti-inflammatory, pro-resolving, increase blood flow, and enhance the immune system, Omega-6s promote inflammation, increase blood clotting, and depress the immune system.

Humans evolved consuming a diet that contained approximately equal amounts of Omega-3 and Omega-6 fatty acids. About a hundred years ago, the industrial revolution introduced technology that refined vegetable oils. At the same time, there was a meteoric rise in the production and consumption of processed foods. Both led to a dramatic increase in the consumption of Omega-6 fatty acids.

In addition, the introduction of animal feeds derived from grains rich in Omega-6 fats has resulted in the production of meat, fish, and eggs high in Omega-6 fatty acids and virtually devoid of Omega-3 fatty acids. Today, in Western diets, the ratio of Omega-6 to Omega-3 fatty acids ranges from 20:1–30:1 instead of the pre-industrial range of 1:1– 2:1. Research has shown this imbalanced intake of Omegas is a contributing factor to many chronic health conditions such as heart disease, diabetes, arthritis, depression, asthma, allergies, and obesity. This imbalance also makes the brain more susceptible to concussion and TBI and limits the biochemical ability of the brain to heal itself. As a friend of mine at the National Institute of Health (NIH) says, junk food equals junk brain.

Our bodies were meant to be in balance. It gets back to what you should have learned in kindergarten, and the concept is simple: You are what you eat.

Both the American diet and the American food supply have changed dramatically in the last fifty years. After World War II, we had saved the world from tyranny. In subsequent decades, we eliminated polio, developed vaccines and antibiotics, and even landed a man on the moon! There was nothing that couldn't be conquered, so how could we have starving children in America? The answer was found in farm subsidies and food programs that started in the 1960s and '70s. Soybean and corn are calorie dense, shelf stable, easy to grow crops that were subsidized by the government. As a result, the amount of soybean consumed by the United States population has grown by over 1200%.

The biggest source of Omega-6s in the American diet today is from soybean oil. Its consumption has gone up 1600% since 1970. Soybean oil is shelf-stable, so processed food is often rich in Omega-6s. In contrast, Omega-3s spoil very easily, so food additives rich in Omega-3s are not utilized by the food industry. The food industry isn't intentionally trying to harm people; rather, the industry is focused on making food more shelf-stable so it can be shipped cross-country and sit on grocery store shelves for long periods of time. The result, however, is that soy and Omega-6s are in everything, particularly processed foods.

The result has been a growing imbalance between Omega-6s and Omega-3s in the food chain and subsequently in our brains. Omega-6s are critical for brain development and function, but they are also very pro-inflammatory. Inflammation is a crucial process to fight infections and bring healing to an infected or injured part of the body. Omega-3s are equally critical, and serve as balance with anti-inflammatory and pro-resolving properties. But, in the last half a century, the foods we eat have set the balance between the pro and anti-inflammatory Omega-6 and Omega-3s off kilter. We have way too many Omega-6s in our diet and in our brains.

Now the preconditions are set for additional trauma when the brain is injured. If there is a head injury, the brain is flooded with inflammatory factors from Omega-6s, which is necessary, to a point. We need inflammatory responses to address the injury, but we also need the anti-inflammatory and pro-resolving Omega-3s to calm the brain and extinguish the fire of inflammation. If that doesn't occur, the acute injury can turn into a situation of chronic inflammation that continues to burn for weeks, months, or even years.

What the brain needs is, especially during and after trauma, is a balance between the Omega-6s and Omega-3s. Fish oil, filled with Omega-3s, can provide this protective armor and help feed the brain with what it needs to heal. To be clear, Omega-3s are not some miracle drug. They are a nutrition. When administered as a nutritional supplement in a protocol for TBI and concussion, they will only help heal the brain as much as it can be healed. Sometimes the damage is too great and nothing will help. Often, however, this healing far exceeds the expectations of doctors, parents, coaches, and patients. What we need to focus on is building that inner armor of Omega-3s in our soldiers and athletes.

If Omega-3s help with healing the brain and can be used to prevent or lessen the effects of concussion, do Omega-3s have any impact on brain trauma that occurred months or, in some cases, even years ago?

Daily routines of adding fish oil to the diet for maintenance and nutrition turn out to be different from post-concussion dosages. Dosing needs to be much higher for the recovery from brain trauma. I recommend starting with 9000 mg of EPA/DHA daily (3,000 mg of EPA/DHA fish oil three times daily) for at least the first week, sometimes as long as a month, and then decrease to 3000 mg once daily indefinitely to maintain healthy levels. I find people notice an improvement very quickly, often just a day or two after starting with such a high dose. This is encouraging, in and of itself, and makes patients more likely to continue to stay on the protocol. Concussion patients report clearer thinking, more energy, decreased headaches, less irritability, and a sense of calmness. Everyday life may have left them confused, headachy, forgetful, tired, and overwhelmed by the details of life. Their condition will improve quickly and they find they can return to normal activities and handle life and its challenges with a certain amount of grace.

Again, Omega-3s are not a miracle drug. Expectations must remain realistic when embarking on any treatment. What these fatty acids do is provide a nutritional foundation, what we all a neuro-permissive environment so healing of the brain can occur.

Different recovery outcomes from concussion have to do with many variables. I like to say that concussions are like snowflakes. Everyone person, every injury, every TBI is different — no two are alike. The extent of the injury is important, of course, but there are other variables as well. Who gleans the most benefit from fish oil and to what extent their brains can heal depends on age, gender, genetics, pre-existing conditions, and how long ago the primary injury occurred. All these variables have an influence on why patients can heal at varying rates.

Age is certainly a determining factor. The very young and very old may have a harder time recovering from a brain injury than a healthy, twenty-five-year-old man. A child's brain is still forming. All the connections between different parts of the brain are still developing as well, and sections relegated to certain responsibilities like the visual cortex, hearing, memory, spatial awareness, and risk assessment are all developing at different times. A child or teen's neck muscles are not as developed as well and leave the head more susceptible to brain injury. The head is large and heavy and needs a strong support. Without one, the head can be struck or strike an object, and a weak neck is left nearly useless to ameliorate the effects of the blow.

The brain also takes a while to mature. The last part of the brain to mature is the prefrontal cortex — the area of the brain that controls executive functioning, or how we control ourselves to make logical, good decisions. The male brain doesn't really finish this growth process until somewhere around twenty-five, believe it or not. Then, of course, as we get older, the brain becomes more fragile again. The neck weakens. The blood vessels become compromised and more susceptible to damage if an injury like a blow occurs.

Gender is another variable in concussion. Girls and women suffer concussion symptoms at a higher rate than boys and men. While a flood of attention has focused the spotlight on NFL players and helped create awareness of the health risks of concussion, girls' and women's sports are being overlooked. In many popular sports, boys are not the ones most likely afflicted by concussions, girls are too. Across all sports played by both male and female athletes such as soccer, ice hockey, basketball, lacrosse, baseball/softball, female players experience concussions at a much higher rate than male players. In some cases, the rate is doubled, or more. While football gets all the attention in high school and college, the sport that has the highest rate of concussion in youth sports is female ice hockey.

A lot of attention has been directed towards the head and neck size of girls and the musculature of girls. Researchers speculate that girls have smaller, weaker necks than boys of the same age, and this leaves them more susceptible to trauma. Hormones could also play a role. If a teen or woman suffers a concussion in the pre-menstrual phase when progesterone levels are high, the injury will cause an abrupt drop in the hormone. That kind of immediate drop in progesterone can contribute to, or worsen, symptoms like headache, nausea, and dizziness, and affect trouble concentrating.

There's still a lot of resistance for my Omega Protocol from the medical community; even the military community, too. There are times when I find myself questioning if I'm making a difference. After all, I couldn't get the U.S. Army to listen to me when I published a study with the NIH on how Omega-3s might reduce suicides in our soldiers. Julian Bailes and I published a paper in Military Medicine advocating for use of fish oil to increase the resilience of the brain to withstand injury in the first place. Then I had published a case report in a medical journal about a teenager I helped recover from a severe TBI and it was picked up as a great story by Sanjay Gupta for his CNN show, Sanjay Gupta, MD.

Starting in June 2014, Texas Christian University (TCU) began a concussion and nutrition study with their football team, the Horned Frogs. They enrolled their entire football team in a randomized, double blind, placebo controlled study, and looked at using a daily placebo versus Omega-3s. When the study was completed, they published their research as a medical journal article: "Effective Dose of Docosahexaenoic Acid on Biomarkers of Head Trauma in American Football." I did a bit of consulting with Jonathan Oliver, the lead investigator, to get the study up and running.

The study's duration was 189 days during the practice and football season. The TCU study was the first large-scale effort to: 1) examine the potential prophylactic use of Omega-3s in American football, and 2) identify the optimal dose of DHA to suggest a neuro-protective effect with supplementation. Additionally, they did a second study comparing baseline, pre-season blood measures of a possible biological marker of head trauma, and evaluated levels in players throughout the season. Published in the Journal of Neurotrauma, the TCU research team found substantial increases over the course of a football season of serum neuro-filament light polypeptide protein, particularly in starting players. As they reported, "These data suggest that a season of collegiate American football is associated with elevations in serum NFL (neuro-filament light), which is indicative of axonal injury, as a result of head impacts."

The results of the DHA were equally impressive. After reviewing past concussion rates and rates of concussions on teams of similar size, investigators expected, on average, fourteen concussions that year. Yet, only six concussions were documented in the 2014 season. We don't know if it was because of the Omega-3s or not, but a 50% drop in a single year is compelling even though the numbers are too small to really put a lot of scientific credence into it. More importantly, they found that DHA attenuated or decreased the amount of serum neuro-filament light. Basically, supplementation with DHA reduced this important biomarker associated with head injury.

This study, published in the journal, Medicine & Science in Sports & Exercise, makes clear that while American football athletes are exposed to sub-concussive impacts over the course of a season resulting in elevations of biomarkers of axonal injury, taking Omega-3s is imperative to help protect the brain from impacts. DHA clearly decreased the amount of this head trauma biomarker in these athletes.

Unfortunately, a huge setback occurred in 2017 when the NCAA came out and placed fish oil on their "Not Permissible" supplement list. When that happened, I started getting calls from university athletic trainers from around the country who were frustrated by this action. They were used to providing fish oil supplements every day to their athletes of all sports, they were using my Omega Protocol after an injury, and now were told they could not do either. I guess the backlash from the universities to the NCAA was influential. In January 2019, the NCAA changed its bylaws making Omega-3 fish oil "Permissible" so universities can provide the supplements at no cost to the athletes, stating in the rationale "Omega-3 fatty acids are essential for neurological development, resilience, and performance for student-athletes."

Concussions and TBI, with their diverse heterogeneity and prolonged secondary pathogenesis, remain a clinical challenge to clinician, patients, and their families. Current medical management of TBI patients appropriately focuses on specialized prehospital care, intensive acute clinical care, and long-term rehabilitation, but lacks clinically proven effective management with neuroprotective and neuroregenerative agents. Clinical studies thus far have failed to identify an effective treatment strategy as they typically have targeted single enzymatic factors in an attempt to identify a pharmacologic target rather than considering multiple mechanisms of injury with a more holistic approach. The concept of a 'magic bullet' focused on a single target is not helpful, and instead a combination of targets controlling aspects of neuroprotection, neuroinflammation, and regeneration is needed. Omega-3s offer the advantage of this anti-inflammation approach.

Although further clinical trial research is needed to establish the true advantage of using Omega-3s, there is a growing body of strong preclinical evidence and clinical experience that suggests benefits may be possible from aggressively adding substantial amounts of Omega-3s to optimize the nutritional foundation of concussion patients. Recovery from head injuries may be hindered by our modern, pro-inflammatory diet. An optimal nutritional regimen to overcome the Omega-6s dominance must be in place if the brain is to be given the best opportunity to repair itself.

Administration of substantial and optimal doses of Omega-3s earlier in the course of concussions, or better yet, prophylactically, has the potential to improve outcomes from this potentially devastating problem. With evidence of unsurpassed safety and tolerability, Omega-3s should be considered mainstream, conventional medicine, if conventional medicine can overcome its inherent bias against nutritional, non-pharmacologic therapies.

Visit: http://braincare.center/ for more information.

CHAPTER 26 - ONE WITH THE WATER

Kenneth Rippetoe (One with the Water®)

As a very young child, most kids are frequently asked, "What do you want to be when you grow up?" Although I initially dreamed of turning my engineering skills into those of a NASA astronaut, my service to the United States was not in the form of space travel or military duty. In August 2011, I took a leap of faith to implement a change to become more involved in the lives of Veterans – I help them to overcome their fears, anxiety, and Post-Traumatic Stress Disorder (PTSD), by coaching them in the pool. For some, that requires teaching them how to swim. For others, it's giving them a template to live a healthy lifestyle. Our program works for all levels and abilities. Whether a swimmer has PTSD from being in the military or having had a traumatic childhood experience, we can help them to overcome those fears.

OUR ORGANIZATION

Before starting One with the Water®, I lived in Bolivia, Venezuela, and Spain, working as a volunteer for "sponsor-a-child" programs which provide education to children in developing countries. The projects I participated in gave sponsored children and their families opportunities to participate in skills training or livelihood initiatives, so they could begin to rely less on sponsorship and more on their ability to provide for their families, creating an educated path out of poverty. This mission aligned with my personal philosophy and set the stage for the values integral to One with the Water.

Our organization, a 501(c)(3) school, was founded in 2011 with the mission of providing greater access to the lifesaving skill of swimming. We are a community of people united by our love of swimming. Together, we are working to share the wonders of swimming with everyone. We have a twofold approach to achieving our goals. We offer premium swimming lessons to children and adults and include specialty lessons for all special needs, service-disabled Veterans and adaptive athletes. Since our inception, we serve an average of twelve Veterans per year. We also offer need-based scholarships for premium swimming lessons to all regular and special needs students and low-income families. Donations, grants, and paid swimming lessons make these scholarships possible. We have helped thousands of people become 'One with the Water' and have provided over 1,000 scholarships, helping those with the highest needs and risks learn to swim.

Our students are our heroes! We especially admire our Veterans, our special needs swimmers, and adaptive athletes. Watching them face their fears and be courageous and resilient in the face of significant challenges is indeed an honor. Their grit, tenacity, and perseverance are a genuine inspiration to us.

We are staffed by professional swimmers, expert competitive swimmers, and former Olympians. I have worked as a swim instructor and lifeguard since 1986. I hold a Level 5 Disability Swim Coach certification and Level 3 USA Swimming Certification with the American Swimming Coaches Association. My additional certifications include U.S. Masters Certified Swim Coach Level 3 as well as the following American Red Cross: First Aid for Public Safety Personnel (Title 22), Lifeguarding & First Aid, Water Safety Instructor (WSI), CPR/AED for Lifeguards (Adult, Child, Infant), Administering Emergency Oxygen. Our Assistant Head Coach Mohammad Khadembashi currently assists the USA National/Olympic Team coaching staff, and has attended the USA Olympic Trials as a swim coach for multiple swimmers. He is an American Swimming Coaches Association (ASCA) Level 2 certified coach, a U.S. Masters Swimmer (USMS) Level 2 certified coach, and a certified USA Swimming coach with over ten years of experience.

Moving forward, we continue to passionately complete our core mission of providing access to the lifesaving skill of swimming to everyone, especially children and adults with high risk, high needs, and limited resources. We will continue to realize our vision of bringing One with the Water to communities across our nation.

Our swimming lessons are taught using growth-mindset techniques. I regularly witness transformational miracles in our Veterans, both in and out of the water, as they shift from a fixed mindset to a growth mindset. People with a growth mindset learn to love challenges, are intrigued by mistakes, and intentionally seek out new challenges. They have learned that their circumstances matter less than who they are.

SWIMMING AS A VIABLE PTSD THERAPY

Health benefits of swimming: The health benefits of swimming are well documented. Countless studies outline the many ways swimming has a positive impact on your health. Here are just a few, among many. Swimming improves cardio function without the stress of impact sports. Swimming helps maintain a healthy weight. Swimming improves endurance while toning muscle and building strength, and can help alleviate stress and reduce depression and anxiety.[1]

However, there are specific benefits for disabled Veterans and those suffering from PTSD. Water buoyancy allows movement-restricted individuals to move freely and helps build muscle in low muscle tone individuals. Additionally, self-regulation, speech, oral motor control, strength and coordination are just a few areas that can improve with therapy in the water. According to the Disabled Sports USA, swimming not only improves flexibility within the joints and muscles, but strengthens the cardiovascular system as well as the major muscle groups in the upper and lower body.[2] Finally, because the heart works harder when the body is submerged, swimmers benefit from decreased swelling, reduced blood pressure and improved joint position. This in turn improves the swimmers' proprioception, or body awareness.

Additionally, swimming boosts the blood flow to the brain. One 2014 study found that blood flow to the cerebral arteries increased between 9-14% depending on their location in the brain.[3] The benefits of increased blood flow to the brain are improved mood, better concentration and focus, and overall increased cognitive function. For Veterans suffering from combat wounds, reprogramming bodily awareness, and creating positive physiological change in the brain can be a life-changing experience.

Social/psychological benefits of swimming: Because PTSD is a stress-related disorder, engaging in activities that help reduce stress or provide an outlet for nervous energy can be very effective in helping PTSD sufferers cope with their condition. Many medical studies have shown that aerobic activity like swimming can play a pivotal role in a PTSD therapy program by helping those who suffer from PTSD battle depression and anxiety so they can achieve a healthy mind and body.

Swimming can potentially help reverse brain damage caused by stress and anxiety. It promotes the process known as hippocampal neurogenesis. In layman's terms, hippocampal neurogenesis is the regrowth of new brain cells in areas of the brain that atrophy under prolonged periods of stress. Moderate aerobic exercise three times a week actually increases the size of the hippocampus region in the brain, improving cognition, and helping with activities like planning, scheduling, multitasking, and memory.[4] In order to for it to be effective though, the swimming session must be prolonged and sustained.

Additionally, The National Sleep Foundation conducted a poll and found a strong correlation between proper sleep and exercise, discovering that exercise does improve sleep, vital for health, productivity, and overall happier life.[5] According to the Anxiety and Depression Association of America, stress and anxiety may cause sleeping problems or make existing problems worse. One of the more common symptoms of PTSD is difficulty falling or staying asleep or restless sleep.

Extended aerobic swimming workouts release the natural compound endorphins, the "feel-good" chemicals produced in your brain to combat those issues. Increased endorphin levels work to lower stress, increase pleasure, and reduce or manage pain. The release of endorphins do help to significantly lower anxiety and relieve depression. However, alongside the brain boost, swimming incorporates the same alternating stretches and regular breathing patterns of many yoga and other relaxation practices, creating a calming, meditative experience.

Application of such a meditative experience, in addition to providing opportunities for a safe and effective workout, can be of particular value for Veterans suffering with PTSD and the accompanying sleep issues that can occur.

Lastly, research shows that participation in swimming for individuals with disabilities afforded the participants heightened senses of self-concept, independence, ability and pride and an enhanced perceived quality of life.[6] Athletes found that they were able to redefine their physical capabilities, strengthen social connections and enhance acceptance among their peers. For Veterans suffering from PTSD and failure to reintegrate, this is a vital piece of the healing puzzle.

Our Aquatic Therapy Program/PTSD therapy swim program is custom-designed for each individual and does the following for physical and mental health:

Increases resistance
Improves stamina, strength and endurance
Encourages a wider range of movement
Reduces pain and tension in muscles and joints.
Improves cardiovascular conditioning since the heart pumps more blood per beat when body is submerged in water
Decreases post exercise discomfort
Range of movement increases and repetition, stretching and balancing is more sustainable
Develops and maintains physical control
Increases energy levels
Achieve your weight loss goals
Helps to develop discipline
Enhances self-concept and confidence
Increases independence and quality of life

Based on the above list, when in aquatic therapy, I expect to see the following benefits and changes in our clients: improved muscle tone, increased core strength and endurance, enhanced circulation, improved cardiovascular functioning, improved flexibility, extended range of motion, reduced muscle spasticity, elevated metabolism, reduced sleep disturbances, reduced joint stress, increased stability, decreased pain and discomfort, and an overall improved quality of life.

OUR APPROACH

Tony Robbins, a renowned coach and motivational speaker, teaches that there are six core human needs fundamental to our very existence, the needs of the spirit, and the needs of the personality. The needs of the spirit are growth and contribution, and the needs of the personality are made up of certainty, uncertainty or variety, significance, and love and connection. It's worth noting that the first two and last two are paradoxes, and yet, the simple, lifesaving act of learning to swim meets every single one.

For me, confidence and growth are key. Now that I have become so proficient in swimming, I always feel the most confident when I am swimming. I've been told in the past that I need to carry myself out of the pool as I do in the pool. Swimming creates a natural way to further develop your capacity to accomplish goals and to grow. When we accomplish impossible tasks in the water, it carries forward to us accomplishing anything on land!

These two core needs form the foundation of our approach using the growth mindset, pioneered by Dr. Carol Dweck. Dr. Dweck, one of the world's leading researchers in the fields of personality, social psychology, and developmental psychology, posits that we should be living life with a growth-centered mindset as opposed to a fixed mindset. In short: "In a growth mindset, people believe that their most basic abilities can be developed through dedication and hard work—brains and talent are just the starting point. This view creates a love of learning and a resilience that is essential for great accomplishment."

There are four key ways the growth mindset sets the foundation for healing and success, both in and out of the water. First, it helps us learn from setbacks. Individuals with a growth mindset accept challenges and continue to persevere in order to be successful. They face learning and challenges with an "I haven't mastered this yet" attitude. Second, it makes it easier to avoid distraction. When you know that productive effort equals more success, it is much easier to stay on task. Third, it forces you to look continuously for new opportunities. When you utilize the growth mindset, you take every chance to learn, change, and experiment with new ideas. Fear of failure ceases to hold you back. Finally, it helps to recognize and be inspired by the achievements of others. Instead of being competitive and jealous, let the success of others encourage you to work harder to improve your results.

FEAR OF THE WATER

This is of particular value when approaching Veterans with PTSD and anxiety who are unfamiliar with the water, and/or suffer from aquaphobia. To overcome aquaphobia or any other fear that paralyzes you, you must obtain competency and coping skills, both acquired by the proper application of the growth mindset.

Competency: The hard truth is that in order to conquer fear, you must face what you are afraid of. Avoiding your fear leads to a sense of failure, increased anxiety, and more belief in fixed abilities. Facing it, however, leads to confidence, empowerment, competency, and eventual mastery.[7] Physiologically, exposure creates nervous system habituation, the eventual subsiding of the physical fear response when exposed over time. Psychologically, confronting your fears creates a sense of empowerment and accomplishment. And finally, at the behaviorally, repeated exposure creates mastery, which helps reduce fear of failure. Find swim instructors that know precisely how to coach a person through the physical and emotional impact of anxiety using proven coaching methods and a firm understanding of the growth mindset. Exposure to your fear isn't natural or enjoyable, but neither is the eventual prison of fixed belief in your failure.

Coping: Momentary fear can strike even the most experienced swimmers. Learn coping mechanisms for fear, including the knowledge of your competency in the water, and the mastery of techniques that allow rest and recovery in a potentially dangerous situation. Understand that setbacks and failures during your journey only serve to drive you forward. Use your past negative interactions to fuel your determination to be at 'One with the Water' now.

A SAMPLE LESSON

Let me walk you through the first lesson for someone struggling with anxiety and fear of the water. I'll use the first 15 minutes teaching him or her how to blow bubbles through the nose, by humming favorite songs, breathing in through the mouth above water, and getting into a meditative state by bobbing, which, by slowing the heart rate, decreases anxiety. Sometimes, I have to use life-coaching techniques to help my clients become present with me.

Next, I'll have them continue breathing in this pattern while holding onto the side and starting to move the legs and feet, just to get a feel for what it's like to be in motion in the water, with support. We will work on technique and ankle flexibility later (to move the legs, the body must be in a prone position). Now we're getting to the balancing part, and by giving them something to think about, moving and breathing at the same time, they are now slightly distracted from doing something they are afraid of — letting go and letting the water support the body.

We take short breaks between activities as necessary. It is not a quick and easy process to face fears. Sometimes I start with floating without kicking, it just really depends on the spirit of the lesson. While kicking and holding on to the steps, or wall, I can now have my client quickly let go for a blink-of-an-eye moment and quickly return to holding on. "Wait! What! Oh, wow, did you feel that?" "How did that feel?" We repeat that with increasing the number of blinks per moment.

After this, we work on submerging. Some people think it's impossible to force themselves to submerge, and that's when they learn that the more force you exert on the water, the more force the water is going to exert on you. This pushes you up and keeps you afloat. Ideally, it raises your hips to the surface. This works best when your muscles are relaxed.

Having eliminated the fear and the reason for the fear, we move onto kicking, balanced on the water while breathing through the nose. I hold onto their hands the entire time until they are ready to let go. In just one lesson with this approach, I've taken clients from having intense fear of being in the water, to breathing, balancing, and kicking 25 yards across the pool, with the biggest smile you've ever seen.

OUR ORGANIZATION

It's important to note that at One with the Water, we are swimming experts. We teach the best and most efficient approach to the most pertinent skills of swimming: breathing, balance, kicking and pulling. We break it down to simple achievable goals to help everyone succeed. We get to know you as a person — your fears and your strengths. Instead of wasting time focused on your weaknesses, we work with your strengths to achieve your goals quickly. And we make you feel comfortable and secure. We are certified and accredited coaches with 10,000 plus hours of experience.

Our PTSD therapy in Los Angeles includes completely customized swim programs for individuals who suffer from post-traumatic stress. The program is specifically designed to help PTSD sufferers improve their swimming skills, increase their physical fitness and reduce their stress. One with the Water knows that each swimmer is different, and we are dedicated to working with Veterans to develop a PTSD therapy swim program that will meet unique, individual needs.

The science of swimming is important, but what I most want to tell Veterans with PTSD is what's truly possible in the water that can't be measured by studies, markers, or milestones. When I read the book Blue Mind by Wallace Nichols, a study of the emotional, behavioral, psychological, and physical connections between humans and this simple, life-giving compound, it affirmed my intuitive sense that water was a place of peace and happiness. He studies swim therapy and the neuroscience behind water's profound effects on the human race and explains why our bodies and souls are naturally drawn to water. Nichols' research fascinated me, because I could finally understand why humans possess deep emotional ties to being in water. The instinctual and emotional responses that people experience in aquatic environments can be directly linked to a calmer and more successful lifestyle. Nichols references the work of many scientists who have examined the brain's connection to water, and this research leads to a greater psychological understanding of how the human mind and emotions are shaped by interaction with the most prevalent substance on Earth.

Dr. Nichols writes, "Indeed, as a spiritual element of the natural world, there seems to be something particular about water that permeates humanity's consciousness."(235). The unique positioning of swimming as a PTSD therapy that works on a physical and spiritual way, while having a profound healing effect on the brain, cannot be ignored, or dismissed. Water has long been revered in all major world religions as a source of creative power, a giver and sustainer of life, and force of cleansing and purity. The thread woven throughout is clear. Water has the power to transform.

References

[1] https://www.cdc.gov/healthywater/swimming/swimmers/health_benefits_water_exercise.html
   https://www.medicalnewstoday.com/articles/321496.php
   https://www.sciencedaily.com/releases/2007/03/070320073101.htm
[2] https://www.disabledsportsusa.org/sport/swimming/
[3] https://www.psysiology.org/doi/full/10.1152/ajpregu.0516.2013
[4] Study finds aerobic exercise improves memory, brain function and physical fitness: https://medicalxpress.com/news/2013-11-aerobic-memory-brain-function-physical.html
[5] Exercisers say they sleep better: https://www.sleepfoundation.org/media-center/national-sleep-foundation-poll-finds-exercise-key
[6] "I think I became a swimmer rather than just someone with a disability swimming up and down:" paralympic athletes perceptions of self and identity development: https://www.tandfonline.com/doi/abs/10.1080/09638288.2016.1217074?src=recsys&journalCode=idre20
[7] Overcoming Fear: The Only Way Out is Through: https://www.psychologytoday.com/us/blog/insight-therapy/201009/overcoming-fear-the-only-way-out-is-through

Visit https://onewiththewater.org for more information.

CHAPTER 27 - ORGONOMY, PROGRESSION INTO TRAUMA AND MIND-BODY: OUR GUT-BRAIN CONNECTION

Patricia R. Frisch, Ph.D., MFT

With verbal therapies, the mind and emotions are engaged but not the body, therefore the mind-body split continues. Orgonomy embraces health with a functional mind-body approach that helps individual's access their naturally abundant free flowing energy, and couples it with capacity for lively contact and clarity of perception in an unarmored body. This approach is distinguished from other therapies by its energetic concept of functioning. When there is blockage in our mind and body, our capacity to function at our fullest is limited by both aspects. Our physicality is part and parcel of the health equation.

After 40 years in private practice, it is apparent to me that impressive and powerful mind-body alterations result from engaging an individual's body in treatment. Our lifelong memories are housed in our bodies; our physical structure reflect our genetics and our historical experiences. Our bodies are templates carved out of life situations and events. Many aspects of our physical health in maturity are directly related to our early psychological history.

With the Orgonomic biophysical treatment modality, the body is mobilized as a vehicle of expression for deeply held emotions. With strictly verbal work, physical expression is contained and inhibited by a seated upright position that relies exclusively on cognitive and verbal communications — leaving the defenses more intact. Many Veterans have difficulty expressing feelings — they have never cried as adults even when they desperately wanted and needed to. Others were warned not to raise their voices or get angry, and that inhibition has had deleterious effects on their own ability to be assertive and communicate openly in relationships. When a Veteran is given permission and instructions to express emotions new and old, and is able to actually feel and express those emotions, they feel liberated. Their awareness of self and what has occurred in their lifetime grows from the inside out. They experience deep release and relief as their physical tension and contraction gives way to energetic movement and expansion.

Historically, our survival depended on developing a coping style that resulted in the least amount of adversity; the character structure embeds in the psyche and becomes the individualized defensive style of the Veteran. That same defensive structure is the organizing template for all bodily processes and felt physical experiences of each individual. "Body armor" is the way character armor is expressed in the body — impacting the respiratory, nervous, hormonal, immune, circulatory, organ, and reproductive systems and the flexibility or rigidity and strength of the musculoskeletal system. Body armor affects all elements of basic functioning — sexual responsiveness and performance, digestion, elimination, and sleep regulation — and results in our felt sense of health. Our body-mind is one, and we can create improvements by working directly with both parts. Unfortunately, the majority of mental health therapies do not approach this obvious relationship. Focusing just on talk therapy leaves half of the equation ignored.

When we intervene directly with the body we reinstate natural breathing, unwind and release bound muscular tensions, and undo chronic blocks to the free flow of energy within the system. Most importantly, we realign the autonomic nervous system (ANS) so the sympathetic part of the ANS (stimulating activities of fight, flight, or freeze responses) balances with the parasympathetic functions ("rest-and-digest" and "feed and breed") relaxation responses. By balancing the ANS, which regulates the body's unconscious responses, we can gradually lower chronic stress reactions, resulting in reduced inflammation and overall better health. The ANS is an example of expansive and contractive systems within the body. As we impact the ANS therapeutically, we reinstate a balanced pulsation between the two parts of the nervous system that directly impact the functioning of the entire body. We are changing a Veteran's approach to life at its root — how they exist within their own body-mind.

Many individual's may suffer from a variety of symptoms that emanate from the lack of balanced expansion and contraction — pulsation in the body. They might feel edgy and irritable; suffer daily feelings of low energy, exhaustion, and fatigue; experience numbness, and lack of vitality; endure chronic pain in their gut with chronic bowel problems, or have pain in their joints, muscles, or head, and/or have endless back pain; have respiratory symptoms like asthma; and have chronic sleep problems. By balancing the ANS to allow for a natural pulsation, expansion, and contraction, the system can relax and unwind rather than sustain a state of contraction, tension, and hyper-vigilance — and many chronic symptoms can naturally get better.

The application of this method is quite precise, with a detailed protocol and contraindications. It necessitates an organized study of medicine and functional medicine.

If a Veteran still resides in the "old" body with its chronic conditioning, they still reside in an armored body and growth potential is limited. When a therapist helps them to loosen their breath, unwind their bound-up systems, and increase their available energetic flow; new behavioral coping strategies can be created. Sexual health can be improved as the Veteran overcomes difficulties relationally and in sexual performance due to various psychological and biophysical limitations.

Many have come to me because they want a mind-body approach. If they are open to including the biophysical component, bodywork can start once the relationship is firmly established.

Chronic pain is another way psychological symptoms manifest in the body. Painful sensations can occur throughout the body, from the tip of the head to the soles of the feet. If there is no organic cause that can be deciphered through thorough testing, then one has to look psychologically at the symptom. I have seen pain crisscross the body — a way the body screams "Help Me!" There are emotional issues to be untangled and new habits created that help, too. I have seen severe chronic musculoskeletal and neuropathic pain, previously treated with opioid painkillers, resolve with regular exercise, therapy, and an absence of medications.

Veterans who have had traumatic histories and exposure to chronic stress may have a heightened sensitivity to any inner perception of pain sensation. Working with the cognitive aspect is important so that catastrophic thinking is noted and minimized, as distorted assumptions contribute to subjective experiences of pain. Translating pain signals more neutrally helps, rather than identifying basic neurological signals as "serious and threatening." Fear engages the fight, flight, and freeze sympathetic nervous system response patterns and activates the hormone cortisol and other stress hormones known to increase pain sensations. Stress hormones have a negative impact on the immune system as well as the digestive and general nervous system and increase subjective experiences of pain as they cause contraction (hyper-vigilance) rather than expansion (relaxation) within the body.

Treatment Protocol: Trauma

Shocking tragedies at any time in one's life are traumatic events with a variety of consequences. Veterans who have served in combat duty situations have particular challenges. They can end up dealing with a condition called Post Traumatic Stress Disorder (PTSD) and this can, and does, impinge and overtake capacities for healthy functioning. Service in the military can become a traumatic series of events that results in serious consequences both mentally and physically. A condition of shock may result in a defensive disconnection in order to cope; a freezing up or freezing over mentally, emotionally, and physically. As time goes on, there can be prolonged anxiety with reoccurring memories — a sense that one's nervous system is chronically on edge and is producing a variety of symptoms such as irritability, anger, panic attacks, shakiness and trembling, sleep disturbances, hyper-vigilance, sensitivity to sounds (startle response) and sudden movements, recurring nightmares, flashbacks, constricted breathing, heart palpitations, and severe chronic tension. These symptoms result in exhaustion and can lead to serious depression with lethargy. After an accident someone might remember much of what happened; another might sleep for days as a way of responding to the trauma. Extended hours or days of sleeping can be a response that allows forgetting, yet oversleeping can become a habitual response to stress.

Case Study:

Erin accomplished her military service with two tours in Afghanistan. Although she was not in combat situations she witnessed both the injuries and deaths of her fellow soldiers in a visceral way. She could not forget the images. She was a sensitive woman, an introverted type and felt often barraged by the predominance of males who she found often intrusive, dominating and at times seductive. She became quite overwhelmed while on duty balancing all these factors yet tried to keep up and appear strong and competent. She learned to create distance from the men who were troubling.

Upon return she craved solitude and began instituting strict boundaries so that she didn't feel invaded or coopted. She became more and more isolated, not wanting to leave her apartment even to go to the market. She felt safer within her familiar walls but that resulted in reclusive behaviors as she was not building friendships and support structures. Her isolation resulted in anxiety and panic attacks when she went about to accomplish daily tasks. She was aware of her own furtive glances at others as well as her hyper-vigilance. She avoided people she knew. Over time she became more and more paranoid as she was feeling threatened even though there were no "rational" threats.

Therapy helped to establish gradual safety in the therapeutic relationship. Slowly she let her guard down and felt relief talking about her day-to-day feelings and concerns. We established a structure so she could begin to move out of her "safe space" and not be so intimidated. We established initial structure by having her find a Veteran to pair-up with to talk to and get together with.

Later, we set a further structure of support by finding a group of Veterans who were meeting with a trained leader. We found a qigong class she could attend regularly. As her nervous system began to relax we slowly discussed aspects of her traumatic experiences. We contained those experiences in the therapy room with strict instructions not to carry anything out the door. As we progressed, she could integrate memories without her nervous system going into flight, flight, freeze reactions.

After a year we could initiate bodywork and began very slowly having Erin breathe gently without initiating memories but rather working with her nervous system to tolerate the breath and my proximity of touch. Later we introduced expressive exercises as she began to tolerate the charge of the breath and sensation. We always stopped at the first sign of struggle. I always titrated the sessions carefully. Over time she could feel and express her outrage, her fear, her sadness, and her grief that included her history of trauma in her family as well as her military service related PTSD. This PTSD often compounds other traumatic historic issues and it becomes a one-two punch. All trauma can ultimately be worked.

Trauma and stress-related disorders are listed in the Diagnostic and Statistical Manual of Mental Disorders, fifth edition (DSM-5). Take a look at the following hyperlink available via online link here: https://dsm.psychiatryonline.org/doi/book/10.1176/appi.books.9780890425596.

The disorder is indicated when exposure to a traumatic or stressful event is listed as a diagnostic criterion. The entire picture of psychological responses and symptoms is defined as PTSD, although there are other disorders listed under the larger category. The essential features of PTSD are the development of symptoms following a psychologically traumatic event such as those I listed earlier. Additional characteristics of PTSD include reexperiencing the events repeatedly; numbing of responsiveness to, or reduced involvement with, normal or important activities; difficulty concentrating; self-destructive behaviors; and a variety of autonomic, mood-related, or cognitive symptoms.

Veterans may have persistent negative beliefs and expectations about themselves or others and the world at large; persistent negative emotions such as guilt, shame, horror, detachment, and estrangement; diminished interests; and difficulty feeling positive emotions. Dissociative symptoms can be part of the picture, including depersonalization (the experience of feeling detached from one's experience as if floating in a dream) and derealization (feeling as if everything is distant and unreal).

We use the term PTSD to describe the sequela from events in a person's life — such as neglect, deprivation, and physical, sexual, or emotional abuse — and from the variety of events that as a child, young adult, or adult cannot be metabolized and integrated in a way that allows the person to feel whole. The sympathetic half of the autonomic nervous system sustains a physiological/psychological state of fight, flight, or freeze. PTSD is frequently diagnosed in military personnel and Veterans originating in highly stressful combat situations. It can be diagnosed in first responders such as police officers and emergency responders. PTSD is a condition that will likely occur from the various examples described (American Psychiatric Publishing, 2013, 271–276). Personality or character disorders are often complicated by the presence of PTSD and the two diagnoses coexist.

Traumatic situations, although compartmentalized, will affect adaptation and development when trauma starts in youth. The brain's structural developmental progression is interrupted, and all levels of development can be arrested; biophysical, emotional, and cognitive — due to overwhelming strain on the significant developing brain structures. Normal development can be arrested by the consequences of trauma.

Although non-metabolized issues are compartmentalized and buried, they remain a major influence on development and adaptation.

Traumatic events and the resulting symptoms and character ramifications will surface in treatment; they can be notable or hidden and can be revealed or ferreted out as treatment deepens and the first phase hurdles have been cleared. Traumatic events can be retriggered by similar situations in one's current life, as there is residual, emotional/biophysical reactivity always available for re-stimulation. By working trauma through in therapy, a Veteran can develop a sense of what is being re-stimulated and triggered and can manage it better as integration is being worked on. Some events are so debilitating that they will always affect the individual, and the therapeutic work is to manage the reactions and lessen the charge.

Structures need to be in place so that life is well organized and structured, so that maintaining that, plus a healthy lifestyle, can help carry a Veteran as they confront the pain of difficult memories.

When I cover biophysical work, I explain how working directly with the body, the autonomic nervous system, and direct emotional expression helps get to the underbelly of the trauma and release effective amounts of charge so reactivity is diminished.

NOTE: (Frisch, P. R. (2018) Whole Therapist, Whole Patient – Integrating Reich, Masterson, and Jung in Modern Psychotherapy. New York, NY: Routledge; and Frisch, P. R. (2018) Whole Therapist, Whole Patient – Integrating Reich, Masterson and Jung in Modern Psychotherapy. Retrieved from https://www.routledge.com/Whole-Therapist-Whole-Patient-Integrating-Reich-Masterson-and-Jung/Frisch/p/book/9781138562363 — Chapter 16, Progression into Trauma)

Hardships can be integrated in treatment, illuminated in the conscious mind, parsed out cognitively with specificity, experienced emotionally and biophysically, and reworked repeatedly until situations are better integrated into the flow of the person's narrative without needing to be sequestered, partitioned off, hidden, and dissociated but rather absorbed, incorporated, and accepted.

Anyone who has been in therapy likely has their story to share, but it is likely the emotional effect is buried and the story line can become defensive in nature. For the Veteran to safely delve into the recesses of their mind and re-experience personal trauma, there needs to be a strong sense of safety in an environment that is stable, consistent, and regulated. Traumatic material captures the extreme vulnerability once felt and arouses physiological sensations once endured that are set off in the present. Traveling the traumatic minefield necessitates caution. Defenses must be softened and the parameters of the relationship established. Then deeper material will be able to unfold organically, in a safe environment.

With Veterans the protocol may change slightly as case management needs to be emphasized and in place right from the beginning. If there has been drug addiction to pain killers or extensive use of sleep medications or alcoholism then those acting out behaviors need to be translated into healthier habits so therapy can take hold. Recovery programs are suggested in parallel with therapy; possibly a new medication regime will be helpful. Likely a dysregulated lifestyle has taken hold, possibly sleeping too much (a sign of depression), high anxiety that defeats proper meals or routines. Instituting stable structures are critical: exercise, walks in nature, yoga or stretching, light classes like qigong or Tai Chi promote calming and arouse the parasympathetic side of the ANS.

Historic hardships can often manifest in current unhealthy behaviors. Therapy will create insights and understanding into those behaviors rather than the Veteran enduring unhealthy behaviors repeated over and over. As the reality ego is strengthened and one's functional aptitude has increased, life can become more adaptive, and activation can be established in a variety of spheres. A secure stage is set in the middle phase of treatment for an unfolding of a deeper level of feeling and subjective experience. The Veteran is able to feel more and may have more access to experiences, as defenses have been dismantled; and is more able to recognize character style when it reasserts itself.

More anxiety, panic attacks, or depression may emerge from a Veteran's mental and emotional recesses that are harbingers of the emergence of historic feelings and traumatic material. With Veterans, historic family heirlooms can also interact with current PTSD and all have to be included and worked. There may also be debilitating depression that does not relate to the present. As the Veteran's life is functionally sound, these symptoms represent historic shards that are surfacing from the recesses of the psyche as the defenses and acting out have been curtailed. Defensive behaviors were — and even can continue to function in — the service of blocking off anxiety, deeper experiences of pain, and traumatic remembering.

Therapy enables Veterans to have profound insights into what has driven many irrational behaviors and other symptoms; more introspection occurs coupled with a sincere assessment of earlier difficulties. Resistance lessens and trust deepens. As the Veteran weathers the pain of remembering, the therapist is a lifeline; the relationship protects the Veteran from falling too far into trauma alone.

Often there is amnesia around significant traumatic events. As traumatic material slowly unveils itself through clues in the present, traumatic elements emerge into consciousness. Many times only fragments reveal themselves; much of the time —

embedded material emerges through somatic sensory experiences; a felt sense in the body of an experience — a sheen of sweat, a feeling of suffocated breathing, a strong constriction in the chest that feels new and yet very old. There can be an urge to scream or cry out in the bodywork; as the consciousness deepens, experiences come to light through various physical sensations felt as if in a dream state.

In this process, new parts of the self are built through the Veteran healing the traumatized part by bringing it into consciousness. The newly built and recovered self can more adequately cope with the immense pain and abandonment feeling the Veteran has to face and grieve. So as more of the Veteran is recovered, it affords more confidence to explore other subjective experiences and at times, the amnesia is overcome. For others, amnesia will remain, but feelings and expression emerge in bodywork without cognitive anchors; healing occurs though expression of pure feeling. They will say, "I don't know why I am sobbing," "I feel terror, but I have no memory or image." "I have a faint sense of being strangled and I feel my throat closing up," and they may gag repeatedly until the sound releases.

Dissociation plays a critical role in trauma survival. Veteran's may demonstrate dissociative expressions through trance-like behavior, chronic daydreaming, and disconnectedness. Such dissociation can destroy swaths of memory. The Veteran may have a blotchy sense of history with missing chunks of significant memory within a narrative. The therapist always works to maintain solid eye contact in order to avoid issues with dissociation.

Reconnecting traumatic memories can be arduous for the Veteran. The extreme vulnerability and helplessness feels terrible yet there is relief in facing what has been driving the anxiety and depression. The Veteran may experience significant and vivid "flashbacks," flash memories, sensations, smells, and sounds of a traumatic event that can blur present consciousness. They may become disoriented or enter an altered state, as there is a liminal state between the present and the past that can disorient a person. Some Veterans may experience unexplainable body pain as a clue to something buried from the past. Memories are stored in the body and in the cells as well and those become retrievable as the Orgonomist works with the body.

The therapist gives words to trauma as a way to mediate the flood of experience. Resolution necessitates a process of going over and over an incident or experience such as a deadly accident where a family member died. Each time the Veteran tolerates the discussion better without being flooded with fear and anxiety. The details can be discussed repeatedly as the terror is felt until it finally softens its grip. The words ground the emotions until they are bearable. As the Veteran can bear the material, bodywork can offer release of pent-up feelings, allowing discharge of fear, rage, sorrow, and grief. The therapist and Veteran weave a clearer narrative of what happened and create and define a larger context in which incidents were embedded — a new family narrative, for example, that explains many of the perceived problems so they make sense and can be integrated. Horrible situations take on a newer, healthier perspective, that reassures the Veteran and supports a more resilient attitude and positive frame of reference.

As I stated earlier, it is important for Veterans with these somatic syndromes to keep active, if they are able to, with an exercise routine to thwart their overly protective tendencies that lead to chronic identification with being physically compromised or disabled. That faulty self-assessment results in a decline of healthy movement routines such as walking, hiking, or attending exercise classes — anything within their individual physical means. This attitude leads to further pain and symptoms exacerbated by stasis in the body-mind.

The biophysical work can create a deep bond between Veteran and therapist, as it exists in a context where defenses are confronted early on in treatment resulting in increased honesty and vulnerability as therapy proceeds.

Orgonomy is a mind-body analytic approach that understands the functional relationship between the two; it does not hold a dualistic conceptualization of mind as separate from body. Orgonomy treats the problematic character defenses and how those very character patterns translate as "body armor," and manifest in a variety of biophysical symptoms.

Selected excerpts herein (above) reprinted from Whole Therapist, Whole Patient: Integrating Reich, Masterson and Jung in Modern Psychotherapy as authorized by Dr. Patricia R. Frisch.

Mind-Body: Our Gut-Brain Connection [from my blog dated 2/23/2019, located at https://orgonomictherapy.com/2019/02/23/mind-body-our-gut-brain-connection/]

A relatively new area of research is making strides in the microbiome-brain connection and its relationship to mental health disorders. This research is illustrative of the profound interconnectedness of the mind and the body. The research into the microbiome-gut-brain axis, as it is referenced, is attempting to solve the riddles of how gut bacteria within the microbiota may affect our mental/physical states. Using fecal transplants and other research designs with both mice and human subjects, the edges of the puzzle are beginning to form. A decade ago, this idea was seen by scientists as hogwash and was emphatically rejected, but now international researchers are peering into the microbes within our microbiome to isolate specific ones that might correlate with certain diseases.

They do know that the microbiome-gut-brain axis is a circular process and can be impacted at either end, resulting in a variety of interesting hypotheses; it is bi-directional. Therefore, changes in attitude and mental states may affect the microbiome, just as the microbiome affects our psychological condition.

There are billions of microbes in the gastrointestinal tract. We once assumed that the blood-brain barrier limited access to the brain. Now we know that bacteria in the gut create metabolites that can circulate across the barrier. According to Bergland (2016) we understand that the barrier is penetrable, and the brain is highly impacted by microbes from the gut: the pathways are achieved through blood flow and through the vagus nerve, known as the "wandering nerve", the longest cranial nerve that travels from the brain stem through the neck and into the chest and abdomen, enervating the heart, major blood vessels, airways, lungs, esophagus, stomach and intestines. It controls the parasympathetic part of the nervous system that regulates among other things our ability to "rest and digest" as opposed to the sympathetic which drives the "fight-or-flight" response (Bergland, 2016).

So, you can see how this intertwined system cannot be separated into fragments. An overly aroused system of fight-flight responses and accompanying neurotransmitter activity is now seen as stimulating systemic inflammatory responses that are indicated in chronic pain responses (Bergland, 2016). OK, you get the picture of these profound connections: the revolving door of "mental states" becoming "physical states," and back around, while deeply embedded in our nervous system, influencing our neurotransmitters, hormones, pain responses, etc., all resulting in who we are, how we feel and how we live.

Inflammation is another probable connection that can impact the brain as immune stimulating molecules potentially cross the barrier effecting neural functioning. The microorganisms in our gut affect our immune system functioning, defend against infection, and create neurochemicals that impact the brain.

More research is needed on these various mechanisms and how they affect our mental/physical health. We do know these interactions directly affect our autonomic nervous system: the sympathetic and parasympathetic (Weir, 2018).

For many decades research has confirmed the existence of a "second brain" in our gut, as it houses a multitude of neurons and neurotransmitters (the enteric nervous system). Receptors in the enteric system are sensitive and set off hormonal changes throughout the body. We experience our emotions and our subliminal fears in automatic, habitual responses in our gut. When we are anxious or tense, our bellies clench and we experience roiling sensations and anxious feelings in our tummies.

This latest research is finding deeper connections between the quality of the microbiome and mental health disorders. As Orgonomists we make these connections as they are apparent in the way individuals feel, the way their breath flows into all regions of their body, the complaints of gastrointestinal pain, constipation, and Irritable Bowel Syndrome (IBS); all reflect a connection between the gut, the autonomic nervous system health, and the enteric nervous system that can initiate symptoms. More information is being collected with additional studies of the microbiome.

Through preliminary research there are fledgling connections being made between some mental illnesses and microbiome conditions. What are scientists finding in their preliminary investigations? According to Weir (2018), "People with gastrointestinal disorders have higher-than-average rates of neuropsychiatric problems such as bipolar disorder and depression," she notes, "while people with schizophrenia often have blood markers that are suggestive of gastrointestinal inflammation. People with autism spectrum disorder have higher rates of gastrointestinal problems than the general population."

Zimmer (2019) describes a current study on mice that creates dementia-like effects mimicking Alzheimer's by experimenting with changing the bacteria in the gut. This study has honed in on possibly one chemical in the microbiome that could alter how immune cells work in the brain thus affecting the buildup of clumps of proteins that indicate dementia.

As researchers study stress-related pathology in mice and its relationship to beneficial bacteria, they induce a state of stress by creating a colony with a dominant aggressor mouse and subordinate mice. Weir (2018) tells us "Normally, subordinate mice in this situation show signs of anxiety and develop colitis, an inflammation of the colon." These mice were injected with a bacterium shown to reduce inflammation. With this treatment, the mice showed lower levels of inflammation thus less submissive behaviors toward the dominant mouse, resulting in less anxiety and fear reactivity. The treatment prevented stress-induced colitis (Weir, 2018). Interestingly, one can see that when we feel subjectively or in reality that we are trapped in a situation where we are unable to express our aggression and instead, feel controlled, we develop serious symptoms of stress or PTSD.

As we know in Orgonomy, the in-utero environment has a critical effect on our development. Zimmer (2019) states: "It is likely that this influence begins before birth, as a pregnant mother's microbiome releases molecules that make their way into the fetal brain. Mothers seed their babies with microbes during childbirth and breast-feeding. During the first few years of life, both the brain and the microbiome rapidly mature." Studies of infant amygdalas, the emotional processing center of the brain, are analyzing the effect of diversity of species in the gut and their effect on an infant's developmental issues. The amygdala, part of the limbic system, controls our primitive reactions, predominantly fear and the memory of it and other emotions (Zimmer, 2019).

All this research is at a preliminary stage, so there are no real prescriptions for microbiome-based cures, and we have to be careful not to be seduced by promotional hype not founded on evidence-based research (Zimmer, 2019).

Weir (2018) suggests a top-down effect: "If you change the autonomic nervous system activity by decreasing anxiety and increasing coping skills, the signals get from the brain down to the microbes in the gut. It's not just the microbes talking to the brain. The brain has a big part in this conversation as well."

This is exciting research with great therapeutic potential. It reinforces the mind-body connection. As we change our mental processes we affect our microbiome. We should always review the factors of diet, exercise, sleep, self-care and self-regulation; as we know that all these habits directly influence our mental health.

References

Bergland, Christopher. (2016, July). Vagus nerve stimulation dramatically reduces inflammation. Psychology Today. Retrieved from: https://www.psychologytoday .com/us/blog/the-athletes-way/201607/vagus-nerve-stimulation-dramatically-reduces-inflammation

Weir, Kirsten. (2018, December). The future of psychobiotics. Monitor on Psychology, Volume 49, Issue 11.
Retrieved from: https://www.apa.org/monitor/2018/12/cover-psychobiotics

Zimmer, Carl. (2019, January 28). Germs in your gut are talking to your brain. Scientists want to know what they're saying. The New York Times, Science Times. Retrieved
from: https://www.nytimes.com/2019/01/28/health/microbiome-brain-behavior-dementia.html

See reviews for my book — *Whole Therapist, Whole Patient: Integrating Reich, Masterson and Jung in Modern Psychotherapy* — available online at the following link: https://www.amazon.com/Patricia-R.-Frisch/e/B079G7WN8R

CHAPTER 28 - PROFESSIONAL TRANSFORMATION SPORTS DEVELOPMENT (P.T.S.D.)

Russell Davies

The idea and mission of Professional Transformation Sports Development (P.T.S.D.) was conceived by me in 2012. It was originally started as an awareness campaign to help Veterans see the benefits of outdoor extreme sports by highlighting other Veterans who were elite athletes in various sports. I was honorably discharged from the military in 2011 and within a year I discovered kayaking to be a source of relief and rehabilitation in coping with post-military life and, at the same time, roughly two years later, I created my non-profit. In establishing myself as a recognized athlete in the extreme kayaking community, I learned that outdoor sporting is as reliant on its community as it is on the activities themselves.

Since coming to this realization, I shaped my passion and focus around sharing the benefits of outdoor recreation with Veterans of the U.S. Military also inflicted with Post-Traumatic Stress Disorder (PTSD) and Depression. The outdoors had a huge impact on my overall mental and physical health. I always thought there should be an easier way for more Veterans to get involved in extreme outdoor sports. I truly believe it speeds up the transition back into the civilian lifestyle.

It was, however, when one of my best friends (Chad Cook, who I served alongside when still in the military) unfortunately took his own life due to the effects of PTSD, and after losing him and several other close friends, that I decided, and I knew, that something had to be done. In 2017, with the help of some of my other best friends and some local funding, we put together a plan for the non-profit 501(c)(3) to help Veterans struggling with PTSD to provide them with an outlet through nature and outdoor sports. The Board of Directors for P.T.S.D. is composed of colleagues sharing similar interests and passion in the benefits of therapeutic sporting. Seeing the benefits of outdoor recreation on PTSD first-hand, I want to encourage Veterans to work towards discovering hope and possibility in post-military life. The outdoor sporting community holds a unique fellowship, similar to that which is experienced while serving in the military. We are confident that by reaching out to Veterans and showing them the possibilities of this lifestyle and community, we can make a tremendous impact on their lives.

We offer Veterans diagnosed with PTSD the opportunity to work with a caring instructor to improve their ability to develop a positive attitude toward their future. Our long-term goal is to empower Veterans to overcome personal struggles attained through the military to break the habits that hold them back from reintegrating back into a civilian lifestyle, ultimately utilizing outdoor sports to form a new connection with like-minded individuals who share a common passion in life. We help Veterans to discover a new outlook on their post-military lives. Not only do they get to go home with the gear and apparel they've been using, but we also provide resources to further support their ongoing growth in their sport once back home. This is mainly done through a website that connects Veterans with other Veterans who have already been involved with the organization. The more Veterans we can help, the bigger the community grows, the stronger it becomes.

I credit my proclivity for adventure sports to my untethered childhood. I was around 14 when my father taught me how to roll and I kayaked some pretty mellow rivers. My parents didn't hold me back. Anything I wanted to get involved in, they would support. It helped me to understand high-intensity situations and realize that I could operate under pressure. My family had me involved in all the team sports when I was a kid. I was about halfway into high school when I started branching away from team sports and getting into individual sports. My parents let me bull ride, box and fight MMA. The boxing was because I was in so many fights and my parents thought I could channel that rage into something constructive. Really, it just taught me to be a better fighter. I always loved challenging myself. It really helps you recognize your capabilities.

I knew right when I turned 18 that I needed to make the decision to kinda jump-start my life and so I decided that the military was the route that I was going to go. Getting boots on the ground was probably one of the most life-changing things the military did for me. I served five years Active Duty with the 101st Army Airborne, Charlie Company 3-187th Infantry Regiment Rakkasans (nickname in Japanese meaning parachute men) overseas in Iraq and Afghanistan. I saw heavy combat during my tours in Iraq and Afghanistan between 2007 and 2011. Just a few weeks into my first tour to Iraq my company lost five Soldiers in a single IED blast. My regiment ran mission's day and night, at an extremely high operational tempo, putting us in numerous fire-fights, ambushes, and bombings.

In Iraq our job was to get the Iraqi Army to handle their own issues. A lot of that was really complicated because we had our own Rules of Engagement (ROE) and they had theirs. They pretty much did whatever the hell they wanted and we had to be cool with it because it was their country. One time, we had a suicide bomber enter our base and they didn't even pat her down. She detonated the vest and killed a few of their commanders and Soldiers. Next thing you know the commander's brother took over for him since he was killed, and our first mission out was directly to this lady's house. The Iraqi Army took her brother and father out into the street and executed them in the middle of the road right in front of us. That was their form of justice. Another thing that made Iraq so difficult was families trying to help us out. There are people there who would leave Iraq in a heartbeat to come to the U.S. but it just wasn't an option for them. They would help us out and get tortured for that. I remember guys giving us intel and then the next day we'd see them completely dismembered. They were just trying to help us out. War is one thing but to torture people at that level is just about as insidious and evil as it gets.

I spent most of my time in Iraq bunking with Chris Bales, a heavy equipment operator from southern California who was 10 years my senior. We called Bales "Old Balls" because he was so much older than everyone else. We were tent mates for the duration of our 15 months in Iraq. When Bales' marriage went sideways while he was away, he leaned on me for support. Together we endured everything from the death of fellow Soldiers to monotonous nights on watch. We were reunited in Afghanistan with the 187th, but not as bunkmates. Bales was a specialist who often served forward duty on patrols, and he was critically injured on one mission. "I was hit twice," Bales said. "I took the first round in my lower back. I was still in the first and trying to go back and warn the others that it was an ambush. They were walking right into it. The second round went through my thigh and clipped a nerve under the femur. My leg did this weird chicken-leg thing, it stuck straight out and spasmed. There was all kinds of pain. Stabbing, burning and slicing...all at once. I don't think you can know pain like that unless you've been shot." I felt certain that Bales wouldn't make it, but they stabilized him, and an hour later he was on a helicopter. Bales eventually lost the use of the leg. I still take my friend out rafting and stand-up paddle boarding. "The balance is tricky," says Bales, "but the falls are safe!"

The major difference between the tour in Iraq and the tour in Afghanistan is that our units were spread so thin in Afghanistan. There were not enough boots on ground. A lot of things that would limit firefights to 10-15 minutes in Iraq weren't there in Afghanistan, so you were facing five or six hour firefights instead. Our enemy knew we didn't have back coming do they'd keep fighting. There were so many troops in Iraq that our that our responses were quick and we'd limit the damage by always having a backup reactionary force in the area. In Afghanistan that didn't exist. Afghanistan was far more chaotic than Iraq because of that. We were just constantly in contact with the enemy in firefights. I would say 50% of my unit had Purple Hearts by the end of our tour. We lost so many guys. The Taliban wasn't breaking contact because they knew we didn't have a division backing us up in the area. What we had was what we had. They had so many fighters available. We were fighting the Taliban, Pakistanis, Iranians and everything in between. I remember killing guys and realizing they weren't even Taliban. They were a part of some other fighting force just coming to kill Americans. They just crossed the border because they decided one day that they wanted to die some warrior's death.

Everybody is coming home from some pretty chaotic events that they don't fully know or recognize just how intense things really are over there. When I got out I didn't really have a plan. When I finally came home for good, something had changed inside me. We lost, you know, a good number of guys in Afghanistan. That was rough. Just for the fact of having that, and knowing that your brothers laid down their lives for you...and you would have done the same for them...it's kind of a huge motivation, once you are out of the military, to continue to pursue and push yourself and make life worth living. Like many Veterans, I struggled to find my place, and I felt aimless. I was drinking, partying and getting into fights. Eventually I found a healthier outlet through kayaking, mountain biking, rock climbing, skiing, and snowboarding. I was born and raised in Pocatello, Idaho and when I came home that is where I went back to before moving, at 23, to White Sacomp, WA where I started kayaking competitively. I've kayaked all over the U.S. as well as in Chile, New Zealand and Thailand.

When I returned home from service, I struggled from the chaos of war and trying to find what else life had in store for me. I happened to see a video of kayakers running waterfalls; something that I had no idea was even possible. After witnessing that, a fire was lit. I started charging hard and discovered a community which was very similar to that of the military. Everyone looked out for one another. You are required to place your life in another's hands. You must devise a plan, and similar to my experience in the military, even with a plan, things can turn to chaos in a moment.

I turned my attention toward the whitewater kayaking because it allowed me to move on with a new found passion in life. Kayaking allowed me to travel the world and let go of my past. After everything I experienced, it was difficult to transition back to the civilian lifestyle. In all honesty, if it wasn't for whitewater kayaking, it would have made the transition more difficult. Kayaking, for me, is how I escape. I love the heart pumping adventure of being in the middle of nowhere, locked into deep canyon walls with nothing but massive whitewater ahead and a small group of people who you can trust with your life. You get out of it what you put in, just like the military. The other paddlers become your brothers and the river becomes your battlefield. Plan your route, be on point, and stick your line. You are counting on your brothers and praying you make it out.

It all sounds good in theory, but just like in a combat zone, the situation can have you scrambling and holding on with everything you got. Counting on your buddies and praying you make it out. There is no greater feeling then coming out of such chaos with some of your closest friends, with your brothers, who without a doubt, become like your family, and overcoming something you didn't think you could. When we're running a huge waterfall, you're like, 'I don't know if I can do this, but I trust these people to do the utmost to make sure I get through it. I'm just going to trust my faith and abilities and work to make sure I was ready for this point.' You do, and you come up and you hit your roll and all your buddies are down there and stoked, and you're still alive. It gives you your life back. You know, you feel that pure rush of being lost in the moment. You're on the kind of high that can't ever be touched.

Talk to enough of my friends and a recurring theme emerges — that I derive a deep satisfaction from helping others. P.T.S.D. is funded primarily with private equity (by a local agriculture farmer by the name of Garn Theobold) while equipment is donated by gear companies. Thanks to that generosity, participants pay nothing for gear or other expenses. I want you to succeed. And once you have fun, if you start out in love with this stuff, it can only grow from there. You can't stay in love with this sitting on the couch. You can't stay in love with it when you're your own worst enemy. But if you step out for even a second, you'll find that love, that passion, again. I think the biggest challenge for young, active Veterans, when they return home, is that they feel like they aren't a part of something anymore. This feeling leaves them wondering what they are going to do next. You may go from holding such a high honor and having a sense of purpose, to working a nine to five job and barely getting by. I also believe that raw, uncertain adrenaline is something in which you become accustomed to and ultimately require, in order to feel normal. Nothing will ever compare to the chaos of war, but kayaking gives me that fix. I need to push myself and my boundaries.

I think having help when you get out of the military is massive. Everyone needs help in some way and why would we be any different? The transition back to civilian life is a tough one. I think it's safe to say that no Veteran is looking for a handout. We're not out there searching for handouts or thinking we're entitled to anything. It's just really tough because in the military, you're doing something that's so outside of most people's comprehension. I went from the closest bonds that I'd ever had in my life to civilian society where I didn't know where to turn. Brothers and sisters in and out of the community make the volunteer's choice to commit themselves to defense of our nation. It can also be a bad thing where you're constantly defined by the term "hero." Heroes don't typically get help and that can be detrimental to Veterans as a community. It's okay to ask for help.

When you get out of the military society kind of makes you feel bad or like you're different if you have a PTSD diagnosis. When you get out you're surrounded by people who don't know that kind of loyalty. The question then becomes, "Will I ever have bonds like I did while I was serving?" Having the assets that we have now is massive and it really helps with the trauma. As a Veteran, you just need to take that step to get off the couch and find those options. There are so many non-profits out there looking to help us know. It's okay to admit that you're not happy with where you're at. Our organization is really about helping bring Veterans out of their shell and teaching them a lifelong skill that will change their outlook forever. If it's not ours, then it could be another organization, but there are people out there trying to help you. Troublesome times will come no matter what in life, but being able to fully dive into something is what having an outlet is all about.

This is how my dream was born. I live for these moments, and they have become a part of my life. Similar to the way someone requires thirst, the desire can be quenched, but only for so long before they need their next fix. However, when I spoke to my friends who were struggling hard with PTSD and depression after getting out, I realized that a lot of my brothers didn't have this alternative passion. It has become apparent to me that I need to use my experiences to raise awareness to other Veterans; to everyone. A staggering 20 Veterans take their lives on a daily basis...and this is a statistic I was aware of but when I lost one of my best friends to PTSD I realized that I needed to get more involved and help to make a change. The reality is that one unnecessary death is one too many and something has to be done!

I started conducting research on why Veterans were struggling and the most common reason was that they felt like they didn't have a purpose anymore...and that they didn't have anything to look forward to. When I asked why they didn't participate in, for instance, extreme sports, I was told that the reason was a lack of financial stability and not knowing where or how to get involved to gain the necessary knowledge to try such sports.

P.T.S.D. is a non-profit organization established to bring Veterans out to Pocatello, Idaho and take them through a two-week introductory class in the following sports: kayaking (spring), rock-climbing (summer), mountain biking (fall), or skiing/snow-boarding (winter). We accept Veterans of all ages to participate in our program. We accept any Veterans with or without a diagnosis of PTSD. In basic terms, our acceptance policy is that our nonprofit offers a 2-week course for any and all Veterans seeking a change in their current life. All that is required is a DD-214 showing that you served in the U.S. military.

We help Veterans who are struggling with their transitions by immersing them in multi-week outdoor sports camps and personalized trips. Veterans register online at https://www.ptsdveteranatheletes.com once they complete the quick registration process. We then select Veterans based on a first come, first served basis. We pay for their flight from the nearest location and fly them directly to Pocatello, Idaho. Shortly after arriving we outfit each Veteran with all the necessary gear for his or her chosen sport. Over the two-week period we teach them the basic skills to be proficient in their newfound passion, utilizing highly experienced athletes to help guide the Veterans. There are always so many satisfying parts of each course we do. However, when our Veterans refuse to end the day without accomplishing a goal, it's an amazing thing to watch them dig deep, not quit for the day, and make it happen. During these two weeks our Veteran athletes have all expenses covered including but not limited to travel, food and drinks, accommodations, and all gear. Once the Veterans have completed the two-week course we then donate all of the gear to the Veterans so that they may continue to pursue therapy in the great outdoors and confidently continue their new found passion in life. My message, one articulated in a Facebook announcement of my nonprofit's ultimate goal, is to reduce the overwhelming amount of suicides that is currently plaguing our military men and women. We need to change the stigma surrounding Veterans returning from war. We need to turn tragedy into triumph.

POSSIBILITY - We want to expand the perspective of Veterans to make them aware of life's possibilities.

EDUCATION - We hope to educate Veterans on how to overcome PTSD and/or depression through engagement in outdoor sports of their choosing.

SUCCESS - Establish a strong network with both outdoor recreation industry and Veterans of the U.S. Military.

We engage Veterans in outdoor sports, using highly qualified instructors and coaches to assist Veterans in gaining the necessary skills to advance and progress in an outdoor sport of their interest and choosing. Our long-term goal is to empower Veterans to overcome personal struggles attained through the military and break the habits that hold them back from successfully reintegrating back into civilian life. This is accomplished by utilizing outdoor sports to form a new connection with like-minded individuals who share a common passion in life.

GEAR - Quality gear is essential to properly participating in extreme sports. It's yours to keep. Safety is important! All Safety gear is also provided. Pursue the sport and change your life.

PERSONAL - You're not alone. Meet other Veterans struggling with PTSD. Create a new sense of adventure in life! Develop a passion for extreme sports. Change your outlook!

NETWORKING - Develop a network of individuals with similar interests. Meet Veterans from all over the country. Create bonds with people who share your interests. After the retreat, we will continue to be there for you.

Myself and P.T.S.D. have appeared in Men's Health Magazine, Outside T.V., the Oscar Mike T.V. series, The Veterans Project, Canoe and Kayak Magazine, Kayak session, Veteran-ology Podcast, This is War Podcast, the Today Show, Blind Veterans Kayak the Grand Canyon short film, PTSD video, sender films, local news, and many outdoor industries helping us gain more exposure. Recognition and awards include: Congressional Award Idaho Hometown Hero, 20 Most Successful Under 40 award, Kind Community Award of Excellence and Progressive Change, JRM Foundation fundraiser, Summit of Island Peak Himalayas.

P.T.S.D. is a website that I created for all Veterans. The page is intended to showcase extreme Veterans around the U.S. who are still out there pushing the boundaries and raising the bar in sports. The goal is for more Veterans to get motivated, get engaged, and meet other athletes who are also passionate about their desired sports. We want to show these heroes that they can make positive changes in their lives and that they have the power to overcome PTSD. So, give this video a watch. This is my Life. This is my Adventure. This is my escape. What gives me clarity and helps me find a way to move on and move past. Nature and sports are my therapy. Share this message with everyone and lets raise awareness and get the word out to Veterans so that we can reduce the number of suicides. It takes just a moment and could help save a life.

I try to live a life that exemplifies all of the best characteristics of a Soldier. If my brothers I've lost are looking down on me, I want them to see the best possible example and that I'm living my life to the fullest. I want them to be proud of me and everything I'm accomplishing. I'm continuing to push the boundaries and trying to bring a new light to others' lives. I hope they see that I'm doing my best.

In regard to PTSD, you are probably trying to cope with a lot of things you went through and endured, and that's all right. It's all right to be struggling. And you should look outside the box for help. You don't have to do it by yourself. It's not weakness. As I said before, always remember that it's okay to ask for help.

Visit the website here: https://PTSDveteranathletes.com

CHAPTER 29 - PTSD AND NEURO-OPTOMETRIC REHABILITATION

Deborah Zelinsky, OD, FNORA, FCOVD

Why Is an Optometrist Writing About PTSD?

Traditionally, the role of an optometrist has been to prescribe glasses or contact lenses to help people see more clearly. However, many Soldiers have 20/20 eyesight and don't need any glasses, at least not for classic eyesight correction. Post-Traumatic Stress Disorder (PTSD) is an internal problem, isn't it? So why would they need glasses? Neuroscience research is continually discovering internal functions involving the eye. For instance, direct connections that the eye has (beneath a conscious level) with posture and emotional centers. These centers often remain in a stressed "fight-or-flight" state in people with PTSD and need to be calmed down. Recent research suggests that those with PTSD can benefit from neuro-optometric rehabilitation. That's where neuro-optometrists doing 21st Century eye examinations can help. The 20/20 classic eye testing was developed in the 1800s; it's time to modify the examination to encompass changes over the past 150 years.

When I was deciding on a career path, a wise man asked me two questions: "What interests you?" and "What do you have fun doing?" My answers were "Blindness and math puzzles". After considering those unrelated answers, his response was, "Why don't you consider being an eye doctor?" Before following through with his advice, I spent two years observing many types of ophthalmologists and optometrists, deciding on which path would be the most fun to spend the next few decades. I realized that ophthalmologists repaired damaged eyeballs, restored eyesight, and optometrists solved math puzzles allowing healthy eyeballs to process signals more efficiently. Both professions helped the patient, but one did it through structural repair and the other through functional skill development. The two professions work as a team, but one was more math based, so off I went to optometry school.

During school, optometry students were taught that the majority of light signals entering the eye were used for eyesight, and a minority of signals traveled "elsewhere". We spent four years after college learning how to put lenses on eyes to sharpen central eyesight and how to develop visual processing skills. At that time (1981), Illinois optometrists were not taught how to prescribe for peripheral retinal dysfunctions, nor were we allowed to dilate eyes or prescribe medication. Now, 42 years later, optometry has evolved from simple eyeglass prescribing to diagnosis and treatments of severe eye health conditions. In some states, minor eye surgery is allowed. A few years out of school and after seeing thousands of patients, it seemed as though the retinal signals that traveled "elsewhere" became more and more important in prescription choices.

Patients would say that they saw clearly but weren't comfortable. Since the retina is made of brain tissue and is considered (along with the rest of the brain and spinal cord) part of the central nervous system, it made sense to learn more about brain function in order to understand the effects of eyeglass prescriptions better. Joining the Society for Neuroscience and the Society for Brain Mapping achieved that goal. The lectures and posters presented at annual scientific meetings were filled with up-to-date research on retinal functions. Yet, there was a large gap between the neuroscience discoveries and their applications in eye-care. To help close that gap, the Mind-Eye Connection began.

Patients who have problems are viewed as a puzzle meant to be solved. The clues come from observations, patient reactions, and responses, as well as test results. Patterns emerge, indicating which treatment methods are most beneficial for each individual patient. There are relationships between what a person pays conscious attention to and what they are subconsciously aware of in their surrounding environment. One of my patients had experienced a weekend simulation at an Army training base where simulations of snipers were present, and she had to scan for them to avoid being shot. She told me that the "pretend" weekend of learning was so scary, that after the weekend when she went to her normal downtown store to buy groceries, she was STILL scanning for snipers and ANYTHING that moved in her periphery aroused a startle response. If a simulation can affect people's brains like that, even when they clearly know that no danger really exists, the actual battlefield must create a much larger stress on brain function and overall peripheral awareness. We needed some temporary glasses to get her nervous system back to her previous normal, where peripheral movement no longer frightened her to an extreme.

Brain glasses — "Brainwear" can be valuable as an adjunct to other approaches in patients' rehabilitation by offering new hope for patients with nervous system problems, neurodegenerative conditions, and injuries or conditions affecting motor skills and/or perception, including PTSD.

Brain Puzzle Solved: No More Depression

A case study regarding a Mind-Eye patient was published in 2017 in the Journal of Neurophotonics. It demonstrated that customized eyeglasses, along with other neuro-optometric treatments, can be useful as a therapeutic intervention to alter sensory signaling. The glasses normalized his brainwaves.

In this study, an 18-year-old volunteer underwent a thorough eye evaluation. Test results were used to prescribe a set of lenses to allow the patient to solidly integrate his visual and auditory signals. This type of lens was not for improving central eyesight but rather for peripheral retinal stimulation. In this volunteer's case, light was directed to the bottom portion of his retina. EEG tracings were recorded of the volunteer with and

250

without the customized glasses. Measurable changes were found normalizing his EEG findings, suggesting that specific lenses can be used as a safe, noninvasive approach to altering brain activity! After wearing these glasses, this patient's depression resolved, and he felt more like himself.

Brain Puzzle Solved: No More Nightmares

Another Mind-Eye patient was a Veteran diagnosed with PTSD at the age of 25 from horrific experiences. When stressed, his peripheral vision would go from hazy to black. He experienced nightmares, had bouts of irritability and anger, and had abnormal intolerance to visual perception of light(photophobia). After Mind-Eye testing, the patient was prescribed a set of therapeutic tinted lenses that angled light downwards on his retinas. Wearing the customized eyeglasses enabled the Veteran to better process environmental stimuli. His photophobia was gone, his nightmares stopped occurring and his temper tantrums significantly lessened. He stopped punching and lashing out at night. During the daytime, the lenses changed his spatial awareness through both auditory and visual sensory systems. Two years after his initial evaluation, the patient "graduated" to a different set of lenses to accommodate the positive alterations occurring in his brain signaling pathways.

Vision and The Military: Survival Depends On The Peripheral Sensory Systems

We have known for a long time that many mental disorders and learning disabilities involve abnormal brain activity and neurochemical imbalances. However, we continue to learn just how important retinal sensitivities in peripheral eyesight and the lack of integration between visual and auditory signals can be as well. Peripheral retinal dysfunction often plays a key role in patients suffering from symptoms of concussion, vertigo, stroke, and other brain injuries. It also has an effect on people who have learning disabilities that have not been resolved through standard therapies. When many of these patients are tested, they are found to lack synchronization between knowing where an object is located through their eyes and ears. This poor spatial awareness is also found in PTSD. Therapeutic eyeglasses can literally refocus their internal world and mitigate these brain-related symptoms.

Specific effects of PTSD vary by individual, but common symptoms including depression and anxiety, which can lead to changes in perception and cognition, causing abnormal reactions to various environments. For instance, seeing a car in a parking lot can trigger a memory of watching a fellow Soldier blow up in the same type of car. Sensory inputs link with emotional memories in an uncontrollable way. Awareness and attention are also adversely affected.

Some people with PTSD experience spatial dysfunction and disorientation. This phrasing means that the "Who am I" and "Where am I" pathways are disrupted. Those patients fail to pick up many surrounding environmental cues and expend more mental and physical energy to make sense of their perceived reality. They become exhausted or fatigued and eventually find it easier to "tune out" the peripheral surroundings. Their struggle to understand the environment can increase depression, anxiety, irritability, outbursts of anger, irrational behavior, and sleep problems, which can include vivid nightmares.

Biochemical changes also occur in response to disruptions in subconscious peripheral awareness. Stress chemicals reach higher levels, promoting a PTSD patient's chronic state of "Fight of Flight". Over time, this increase in stress chemicals can lead to adrenal fatigue, and a patient suffering from PTSD may actually lose the ability to produce adequate stress chemicals. Their "Fight or Flight" systems are activated by subconscious triggers, affecting them at an unconscious level. Some patients have actually undergone hormone testing as part of their treatment plans and have noticed a return to more normal functioning of their adrenal systems.

Eyeglasses can be designed to alter some of these pathways through a direct route between the retina and the hypothalamus. This chapter is intended as an introduction to neuro-optometric rehabilitation as one method of dealing with unresolved PTSD. For a more scientific viewpoint, please see the section at the end.

A patient with PTSD usually has a constricted visual world where the external peripheral eyesight becomes hyper-sensitized or tuned out and the internal thought processes often diminish. The overall experience is usually a more limited spatial environment. This spatial shrinkage is the opposite of normal human development, which includes larger and larger awareness of surroundings from birth to maturity. Eventually, an awareness is developed that we are simply residents of planet Earth and that Earth is just a tiny object in a seemingly infinite galaxy. This global awareness primarily occurs at the subconscious level. We do not constantly and consciously consider our existence as specks in the Universe. As part of normal awareness, we each develop our own "mental desktop" in space and time. The bigger the "desktop," the easier it becomes to move around in our environment. If we are feeling awake and energetic, for example, leaving home and driving to a restaurant can prove to be an easy, pleasurable task. If we have worked all day and arrive home exhausted, our "mental desktop" constricts. The thought of having to get back into the car and drive to another location to eat might be undesirable, even detestable.

For PTSD patients, the environment often remains chronically constricted. Sometimes it can be almost impossible to adapt to changes out of our control. Moving from one location to another can be almost too much to consider. Even doing things such as deciding what to eat can elicit strong physiological responses from patients with

PTSD. Awakened sensory systems are hyper-sensitized to "protect" those patients who are overly sensitive to both light and sound, but their perceptions of these stimuli are flawed, exacerbating the problem.

To combat these symptoms, Mind-Eye patients undergo a thorough examination with 21st Century testing techniques to measure their reactions and responses to light entering the retina. With this information, Patients are then provided prescriptive eyeglasses, contact lenses, or other optometric interventions to selectively stimulate light dispersed on the retina. Individualized lenses can:

Maximize visual performance and visual processing capabilities, as well as create a stable balance between eye and ear localization.

Enhance patient perception of the surrounding environment in order to increase comfort, which affects behavior and communication.

Help rebuild brain pathways or develop new pathways that enhance a person's ability to learn, understand, and interact more normally with others.

Of all the evaluation techniques used by the Mind-Eye team, the Z-Bell Test^{SM} is perhaps the most unique, most globally recognized. It is based on the fact that light affects retinas (and thus brain function) through closed eyelids and alters the mental map of target locations. It can be used for testing autistic patients, as mentioned in Patricia Lemer's 2019 book, "Outsmarting Autism".

The Z-Bell Test^{SM} has also become a direct method of checking a person's overall spatial awareness. It is one part of an answer to the question of what replaces the current standard for visual assessment. Patients whose sensory systems are out of balance due to neurological insufficiency, disorders, or brain injury are usually unable to pass the test.

Helping Others Learn

As the 21st century unfolds, optometrists are now in a position to be at the forefront of brain function, by using eyeglasses to alter the nervous system. By applying these new discoveries in neuroscience and neurophotonics to eye care, I've made the mission of my clinic, now called the Mind-Eye Institute, to transform the lives of children and adults who suffer from lingering symptoms caused by such problems as brain injuries and post-traumatic stress disorder, or those who have been labeled with diagnoses such as autism, learning disorders or neurodegenerative diseases.

My commitment to this goal began when as an apprentice to Albert Sutton, OD in Florida. He had spent decades devoted to having neuro-optometric techniques mainstreamed, having learned from the Father of Neuro-Optometry, A.M. Skeffington in the 1940s. After seven years of studying with him, my first private optometric practice was opening in 1992. Even then, as new studies emerged in neuro-optometry, neurophotonics, and neuro-optometric rehabilitation, I realized that standard optometric practices based on sharpening central eyesight were insufficient to meet all patient needs. A person can have sharp 20/20 central eyesight and perfect hearing, but if their eyes and ears are not integrated and their brain is impaired, the entire neurological system becomes analogous to an orchestra without a conductor. Each musician may be quite talented with his or her learned instrument, but they must play in synchronization with one another for the experience to occur as intended. If they are moving through the composition at different speeds, the result is noise, not music; they need a conductor to follow. Eye-ear co-ordination is developed as learning occurs. Standardized eye and ear tests check eyesight and hearing separately but fail to determine whether they are properly integrated. Testing of the brain's conductor is missing.

When working with Soldiers who had been in the Gulf War, they would tell me stories of how a flash of something in their peripheral eyesight could trigger a memory from their past. The relationship between the eye and other sensory systems, including body movement and coordination were fascinating. The Soldiers had emotional and visceral reactions to various sensory stimuli that other people showed no reaction to at all. How could I, as an optometrist, selectively activate their brains to mute the reaction? Each person had unique tolerance and stress levels; could my mathematical background be helpful?

Teaching other healthcare professionals about the crucial role the retina plays in comfort began in the early 2000s. Eventually, the Mind-Eye Connection as moved into a larger office in Northbrook, Illinois, to meet the different needs of patients. The décor was chosen to be relaxing and simple, exuding a feeling of home, rather than a sterile-looking doctors' office, and to be calming for the hypersensitive patients with anxiety. The newly established Mind-Eye Institute has a much broader goal of being able to treat more patients nationally and globally, training a worldwide network of optometrists to have neuro-optometric testing with the 21st Century viewpoint. Now, in 2019, we are expanding into yet a larger facility. The ability to help others is increasing!

Optometry alone isn't enough for all patient cases; for severe cases, the optometric interventions can synchronize sensory systems such as eye/ear connections and calm the nervous system, but it takes a village of various types of practitioners to address multiple imbalances. The Institute now consists of separate divisions including one section for research, another for creating clinical centers and training new doctors, a third on visual rehabilitation, and a fourth area focused on the development and acquisition of advanced patented technology.

Soldiers often have to deal with various levels of stress, grief, anger, and fear, which each take a toll on the overall body and mind. If some of these systems remain in a chronic hyper-sensitized mode due to a traumatic event or chronic exposure to severe discomfort or environmental stressors, a patient may develop PTSD.

Despite all the recent research and new understanding of the critical role of the retina, 20/20 central eyesight is still considered as the criteria for prescribing an eyeglass. Testing blocks off peripheral receptors, even though the heart rate and other body functions are connected to peripheral processing. Looking at an object clearly and directly is the slowest pathway for information processing and only activated when conscious attention is placed on a specific target. This classic, image-forming eyesight pathway is not even present in newborn infants; it develops later, within a few months of age, after other retinal pathways are already in place. Most eye examinations evaluate 20/20 eyesight capability by having a patient sit in a darkened room, looking straight ahead at a lighted, non-moving target. This testing method was developed in the 1862 as a way of standardizing eye exams. The 20/20 measurement isn't taking into account the relationship between attention and awareness, which are different and used as a team. When we are driving, we are subconsciously "aware" of vehicles around us but not necessarily focused on them. We may be reading highway signs or quickly checking the computer screen or the speedometer on our dashboard. In those moments, we are receiving signals from many directions, both subconsciously and consciously. Our brains are making sense of all of this information. The testing of visual fields during a typical eye examination seems to assess peripheral eyesight. However, that test is performed mainly at a conscious level. Someone asks if we "see" a flash in the periphery or not. To do the peripheral testing during the 20th century eye examination, conscious attention is shifted to the periphery. In life, most peripheral awareness occurs at a subconscious level while attention is on something else. Testing needs to be modified!

Prolonged stress, shock, injury, or disease can affect spatial awareness, thereby impacting a person's behavior, perceptions, and responses to environmental changes. For people suffering from PTSD, this shift in spatial awareness can be dramatic and oftentimes leads to abnormal brain and nerve activity. A common, compensatory mechanism to sensory overload is simply to ignore external environmental stimuli. The mind usually can tune out unwanted peripheral or background auditory and visual signals in a process called latent inhibition. This process disengages eye-aiming at targets in the surrounding environment, but this filtering capability is hindered when body systems are constantly in survival mode due to extreme stress, injury, or a neurological disorder. For a patient suffering from PTSD, sensory overload sets in far more quickly than it does for most, and its effects on the patient's basic agency are wide-reaching. Certain patients actually deteriorate so far as to experience panic attacks or seizures, and sensory overload can actually lead to flashbacks.

It is important to understand that each person has different acceptance and tolerance levels to changes in their environments based on experiences, temperaments, perceptions, motivations and organizational skills. How much change is required to push a person over the edge varies with that individual's "How am I" and "Who am I" pathways, which alters electrical and chemical signals in the retina. As we have established, these pathways are often damaged in those suffering from PTSD. Because sensory systems interact; each person has an optimal load and an upper threshold of tolerance before a breakdown occurs. In patients with PTSD, this threshold is far lower than it is for the general population. Most individuals have large ranges of comfort and tolerance and can readily adapt to change. However, such adaptation is oftentimes difficult for people who have sustained brain injuries or experienced shocking circumstances. Their protective mechanisms take over and hinder cognitive processing. The nervous system becomes hyper-sensitized.

External environmental signals affect a person's internal systems. Similarly, internal signals can influence the filtering abilities of external sensory systems. For example, exposure to noise impacts retinal sensitivity. Running with a peaceful water scene in the background elicits different stress chemicals than running while being chased by wild dogs. Sudden, unexpected movement caught out of the corner of one's eye can cause internal chemical and muscular systems to react. These internal systems, which are beyond conscious control, are triggered simply by a moving shadow on the peripheral retina. When we consider PTSD in this light, we can begin to see the solutions.

Humans have built-in protective mechanisms, and these mechanisms are stronger in patients with PTSD. When they pass their individualized comfort range and go into a tolerance range, some attention and mental energy are diverted to whatever is causing discomfort or an imbalance. Patients with fragile sensory integration or hypersensitive peripheral retinas, such as our patients with PTSD, may exhibit abnormal behavior by reacting internally, below conscious level, to the movement of normal, everyday objects in their environment.

Every system, external and internal, has its own comfort and stress levels as the mind and body react and respond to environmental changes. Constant interaction occurs between internal and external stimuli, involving shifts in eye movement. Shifting light influences the interplay between incoming signals from the outside environment and returning signals from a person's internal environment. Brain injury or undue stress can disrupt neurological systems and causes "comfort" ranges to be constricted. However, through the plasticity and malleability of the brain's wiring, new signaling pathways and connections can be established to bypass diseased or dysfunctional brain tissue. This results in balancing internal and external systems, returning normalcy to one's spatial awareness and awareness of self.

Neuro-Optometric Rehabilitation used for Neuromodulation

The term neuromodulation refers to a new science that looks at the ongoing process of signaling input and feedback that occurs beneath the conscious level and involves the retina and eye muscles. Even during sleep, chemical changes take place in the various cellular layers of the retina. For example, when a person falls asleep with the flickering light of a television on or with surrounding noise, the brain is unable to fall into a deep sleep, resulting in less-than-optimal restorative properties.

Retinal neuromodulation is the modification of neurological systems via retinal stimulation and an emerging area of Neuro-Optometric Rehabilitation. Mind-Eye examinations apply scientific principles in addressing issues related to a patient's neurological imbalances including abnormal responses and reactions to the environment.

Executive function skills, which develop by the time a person reaches 25 years of age and are based on "Who am I" experiences, can decline or disappear as a result of aging, disease, or injury. Other brain processes such as perception, emotion, and unconscious responses at the chemical and proprioceptive (sensory input and feedback that relates to body movement and positioning). Many skills can be rebuilt due to brain and retinal plasticity. Because it is part of the central nervous system, the eye, and more specifically the retina, is not isolated from other sensory, motor, emotional and cognitive systems.

As discussed earlier in this chapter, the eye plays a critical role in routing information through multiple brain pathways to the visual cortex. Much of this activity occurs beneath conscious awareness. What small portion reaches conscious awareness represents a conglomeration of inputs from a variety of senses, including the visual, auditory, and olfactory systems. The mind, body, and environment are continually shifting to achieve a comfortable balance, but this normal process is inhibited by neurological injury, disease, stress, or trauma.

Because of researchers' increased understanding of neuromodulation, the role of neuro-optometric rehabilitation as a non-invasive approach to brain function has grown in importance. The use of different lenses, prisms, mirrors, filters, and other optometric interventions to stimulate the retina is allowing eye professionals to evaluate possible hidden dysfunctions in mind-eye connections or neurologic disruptions that can impact a person's social, academic, and sports performances. By bending light in different ways across the retina, incoming visual signals are altered and informational pathways in the brain are changed, thereby enhancing spatial awareness, cognition, and perception.

Recent technological innovation supports neuro-optometric approaches. New instruments can quantify subtle changes in eye movements, such as video pupillometers and computerized testing batteries for brain-injured patients or individuals diagnosed as autistic.

Use of therapeutic Brainwear™ eyeglasses to modulate the frequency, amount, and direction of light on the retina allows neuro-optometric rehabilitation to accelerate recovery from brain injury or chronic stress levels. It can provide improvement in patient comfort and patient tolerance ranges to environmental changes. It can also decrease hypersensitivity to sensory stimuli as is demonstrated in patients with brain injury, developmental disabilities, mental illnesses, and PTSD.

The classic use of optometric techniques to sharpen central eyesight to 20/20 impacts a patient's attention at a conscious level, with high-contrast, non-moving targets. This approach is difficult in patients with neurodegenerative conditions or the fragile connections between external and internal systems as occurs in PTSD. To help these patients, it is important to understand the linkage between the eyes and ears and how the lenses are actually shrinking or expanding or distorting surrounding space, thus affecting behavior.

Neuro-optometric rehabilitation is different from classic visual therapy because it addresses the brainstem and unconscious, subcortical reactions to environmental stimuli. Therapeutic retinal stimulation to establish new pathways, and re-balance sensory systems can be readily and inexpensively applied using modern therapeutic eyeglasses. It works well as a singular approach or as an adjunct to other treatments to maximize outcomes, such as medication, behavioral, physical, and occupational therapies.

In the future, development of highly advanced eyeglasses that selectively stimulate specific retinal pathways may prove possible. Such a tool could be useful in treating patients with drug-resistant epileptic seizures, patients with autism, genetic disorders, mental illnesses, or neurodegenerative conditions like Alzheimer's disease or Parkinson's Disease. Future studies may also demonstrate the value of neuro-optometric rehabilitation for metabolic disorders or alteration of gene expression. Customized lenses may also be effective in developing brain plasticity or for attention training in brain-injured or PTSD patients using robotics.

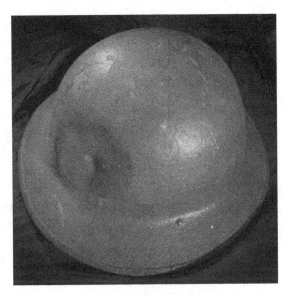

Above/Left: Bullet dented my grandfather's helmet during World War I.

Conclusion

This mission is personal for me. Each of my grandfather's fought in World War I. One was shot in the head, but his helmet absorbed the bullet impact and he survived. Each of them developed Parkinson's disease later in life. My father was drafted into the Korean War at a desk job, and I had an uncle who fought in the Vietnam War, but was never the same after.

Currently, I'm on the board of the Society for Brain Mapping and Therapeutics, which works with many aspects of the military. I'm also a Community Leader for the Society for Neuroscience, where a monthly blog allows 40,000 scientists to read about how new discoveries in retinal functions can be applied to eye care. As citizens of this country, it is our job to protect our Soldiers in any way we can. They are so important to every one of us in many ways. Try and imagine what our lives would be like without Soldiers. A simple, "Thank you for your service" is not enough to acknowledge their personal sacrifices. Using modern discoveries about the retina, neuromodulation, and neuro-optometric rehabilitation, neuro-optometry may be able to help many military members or Veterans who gave so much of themselves for us during their service to regain control of their mental abilities, resolve the adverse effects of brain injury or anxiety/depression due to PTSD, and live a normal life again with their families. They protect us, and we are developing new ways to protect them in return.

PTSD involves a host of neurological, chemical, and muscular reactions. The capabilities of modern optometric care are still growing rapidly. Brain function is affected by trauma from blast injuries that is different from whiplash or injuries with a blunt object. Most of those involve retinal dysfunction.

Mind-Eye examinations have been able to affect the lives of people who suffer from PTSD in many ways by calming the nervous system and muting the peripheral reactions from glimpsing or hearing something. People feel more like themselves.

The Retina's Role in PTSD Sensory Overload

Research has demonstrated the retina as being a piece of brain tissue that is part of our body's central nervous system. It not only sends the brain environmental signals obtained through eyesight, but also through luminance (external light) dispersed across the retina. Concurrently, the retina receives feedback signals from the body through informational pathways in the brain. This continuing process of feeding forward signals to the brain from the environment and receiving feedback signals from various brain structures makes the retina a two-way portal for influencing and monitoring body functions and thought processes, primarily below the level of consciousness.

Each eye contains approximately 126 million light-sensitive receptors. Input information from these receptors move through a sophisticated filtering system, resulting in some 1.2 million signals traveling across and radiating out from the optic nerve into electrical and chemical pathways inside the brain. In fact, the retina connects with many systems other than eyesight, including structures in the brain's cortex, cerebellum, and limbic system, as well as midbrain and brainstem. These structures affect the body's physiological, biochemical, behavioral, and emotional responses, including endocrine, respiratory, circulatory, circadian, digestive, and musculoskeletal systems.

As a result, the body's survival and the mind's executive functions are greatly influenced by changes in external sensory inputs. For example, if we are crossing a busy street and see or sense traffic speeding in our direction, we automatically, almost unconsciously, hasten our step or run. Conversely, external attention and awareness are altered by shifts in the body or mind. For example, if we are concerned or thinking we might be late for an important conference or a scheduled appointment we hasten to the meeting location with singular, focused attention on timely arrival. In those moments, we have limited spatial or environmental awareness of other people and activities around us, including busy traffic. Our only goal in that moment is to reach our desired destination on time. As such, selected stimuli is processed — those directly related to the goal of arriving on time. Environmental details that an individual would normally notice, and process are passed by obliviously. In patients with PTSD, this type of constriction is an everyday experience due to the hyper-vigilance and hypersensitivity the condition instills in the patient.

For simplicity, you can think of two main nervous systems -- an internal one that controls our organs, fluids, and rhythms, such as blood pressure or heart rate, and an external one that relates to our outside world. There are actually many smaller ones that work in harmony. When a person is involved in an activity, eventually other processes such as hunger and fatigue take over and thereby limit how long a person can function. The mind can override hunger and fatigue for a bit, but in the long run, the body signals are in control.

The eye is part of our external nervous system, yet heavily connected to the internal nervous system. When it becomes hyper-sensitized, as it does in PTSD, a person sometimes is unable to deal with the outside world, because he or she perceives external stimuli differently. The information passing through the retina into the brain evokes internal nervous system responses that do not occur for healthy individuals. Blood pressure rises; stress chemicals including adrenaline increase. A person's whole being is disrupted, placed in an abnormal "fight-or-flight" state. Developed skills can be lost and need to be regained.

By directing light onto different portions of the retina, environmental signals are routed through different cortical lobes on their way to the visual cortex. The balance of signaling pathways is affected and changeable. Such lobe activation can be verified during an EEG analysis by comparing EEG results with and without customized lenses. For instance, angling light downward stimulates temporal lobe activity. Some progressive new studies suggest a correlation between temporal lobe activity and PTSD, the ability to affect temporal lobe activity suggests a potential method of mitigating PTSD symptoms.

Neuroscientists are increasingly finding impaired brain communication in patients with PTSD. In order for the brain to function efficiently, both sides of the brain need to be sending signals to each other. NeuView Glasses were designed for PTSD to direct light to the retina from the side, in addition to the front. Depending on which side of the glasses is activated, they stimulate increased neuronal activity in either the right or left side of the brain thereby increasing the communication pathways in the brain. The concept of 20/20 as an endpoint is slowly being left in the 20th Century as neuro-optometry evolves.

Acknowledgments

Courtenay Nold had a wonderful idea for creating an avenue for people with PTSD to have help in one location with her book. James Smyth has been a great help in making Mind-Eye testing become globally known. Also, thanks to Mike Maggio, Robert Wilson, Julie Smith, and Matthew Kimball for their help with sentence structure, grammar and a military viewpoint.

I hope this information has piqued your curiosity about the role of optometry in treating PTSD.

If you would like to learn more about neuro-optometric rehabilitation and Neuview glasses, visit https://www.neuviewptsd.com and the Neuro-Optometric Association's website, https://www.noravisionrehab.org or the National Center for PTSD at https://www.ptsd.va.gov.

CHAPTER 30 - REBOOT COMBAT RECOVERY

John Dale, Operations Director

You may ask yourself "What is REBOOT Combat Recovery?" Basically, it is a 12-week combat trauma healing course that tackles the moral and spiritual wounds of war through a Christian faith lens. This course is available at no cost to participants, is peer-led by other Veterans and provides a meal and childcare so that the spouse/caregiver/family member can participate alongside their Veteran. They meet for two hours once a week in homes, churches, prisons, VA hospitals, community centers and military bases.

At REBOOT locations across the country and around the world, combat Veterans are healing, divorce rates are dropping, medication abuse is decreasing, and suicide numbers are being reduced. REBOOT is headquartered near Fort Campbell, KY (or in Pleasant View, TN to be exact) where it was founded in 2011 by Occupational Therapist Dr. Jenny Owens and her husband Evan. In what started as a small group in the Owens' home has expanded to over 150 course locations meeting in four countries and helping over 5,000 people since 2011.

I served in Iraq in 2005 with the Army National Guard leading a convoy team and supervising in a Communications Operations Center. A year later after my return, chronic pain from physical injuries got bad enough I sought medical attention and it got to the point where I had to let my chain-of-command know, which resulted in a medical discharge. A combination of loss of identity from no longer wearing the uniform, some moderate Post-Traumatic Stress Disorder (PTSD), and chronic physical pain put me in a bad place for too long. Not dealing with it well and choosing self-medication, I eventually created an environment of fear of my own, which deeply affected my wife and almost ended our marriage. Being desperate enough to try something as crazy as healing from soul wounds we got trained to lead a REBOOT Combat Recovery course that met in our living room in early 2015. Seeing the immense benefits it had on me and the others in the group it was clear that I needed to quit my job at the Department of Homeland Security and raise my salary to enable me to work full time for the non-profit to help it grow. In the last three years since myself and others came on staff, we've grown from five course locations to over 150. It's been amazing to have a front row seat to the healing that's occurred not only in my own life but in the thousands of other lives that have been positively affected by this course.

Here is the list of resources we share with all of our course participants. Out of those we have strong ties to the Might Oaks Warrior Program and the Warrior's Journey. Mighty Oaks is an organization based in California that does something similar to what we do, looking at healing from the soul wounds of combat trauma, but doing it in an week long outdoor retreat format. It's been very effective for the folks who have gone through it and are in areas where we have **REBOOT** courses because our program is often a next step for someone who has completed a Mighty Oaks retreat. Warrior's Journey is a resource of online content that's solely military related; from their site "it presents a message of faith as a path for military members, Veterans and their families to find wholeness in everyday life."

The list of organizations include:
Stop Soldier Suicide
Marriage Dynamics Institute
Mighty Oaks Retreat
Guardians for Heroes
Team Red White and Blue
Warriors Journey
The Joel Fund
Hidden Heroes
PsychArmor
New Rosie

Our course objectives/topics include the following:

WEEK 1: A WOUNDED SOUL
Introducing the concept of "soul wounds," showing the connection that exists between our damaged spiritual "roots" (due to trauma, poor choices, loss, guilt, etc.) and toxic "fruit" in our lives (anxiety, anger, hyper-vigilance, etc.).

WEEK 2: THE ROOTS OF TRAUMA
Recognizing that adversity is common in this world and its roots are found in trauma that has been imposed on us by others or trauma we have brought on ourselves and others; understanding that we have a spiritual adversary, and that God is our ally.

WEEK 3: A RESTORED SOUL
How one cooperates with God to experience a restored and healed soul, contrasting the humility of David and the pride of Samson in the Bible.

WEEK 4: STOP THE BLEEDING
Examines the consequences of wise and unwise choices we make seeking relief from trauma symptoms. Exposes the futility of our typical "go-to painkillers" (alcohol, drugs, self-isolation, sex, risk-taking, etc.).

WEEK 5: BE FREE

Understanding the therapeutic nature of conviction and true guilt, and the destructive nature of false guilt, and how we should respond to each when we recognize them in ourselves.

WEEK 6: THE COST OF UNFORGIVENESS

How harboring unforgiveness of ourselves or of those who have hurt us can lead to bitterness and unhealed soul wounds, hurting ourselves the most; participation in an exercise that will facilitate forgiving ourselves or others.

WEEK 7: WHEN YOU'VE LOVED AND LOST

How to deal positively with loss and grief, shifting our questions from Why? To Who? Study the example of how Jesus dealt with the loss of His good friend Lazarus; how it is that God can allow us to suffer if He loves us.

WEEK 8: DEPRESSION AND SUICIDE

Understanding how depression can generate destructive, false self-talk which can lead to thoughts of suicide, and how to counter the lies with God's truth.

WEEK 9: MADE ON PURPOSE

Traumatic events tend to shake our self-identity to the core and destroy it, producing a negative self-image and lack of confidence. But we can rebuild a positive self-image based on the truths from scripture, rather than the negative influences around us.

WEEK 10: GOING THROUGH THE VALLEY

Examines how fatigue, frustration, and failure can cause discouragement in a person even when they are making progress; uses the Biblical example of Nehemiah to show how to counter these debilitating factors.

WEEK 11: SHARE YOUR STORY

Each participant spends the week prior to this class preparing a personal narrative of "their story," describing some of the key stresses or traumas they have experienced in their lives; several members share their stories with the group.

WEEK 12: GRADUATION

A ceremony recognizing each of the graduates for the efforts they put into the course, and celebrating their accomplishment with their families, friends, and associates.

When we sampled a group of 155 REBOOT participants from 33 nationwide locations who had completed our 12-week combat trauma healing course, we utilized PROMIS 29, a National Institute of Health self-reporting tool that measures health-related quality for physical, mental and social well-being. When post-intervention measurements were compared to baseline measurements there was a statistically significant reduction in anxiety, depression, fatigue, sleep disturbance, and an improvement in the ability to participate in social roles and activities.

Additionally, the program had a positive effect in a selection of **PROMIS** 29 domains including Quality of Life and all domains of the Character Fitness Rating Scale (additional information is available via the website at: https://www.ncbi.nlm.nih.gov/pmc/articles/PMC4471856/).

Participants also reported high levels of satisfaction with the course and a majority reported a desire to stay involved with the program.

Five reasons you should try **REBOOT**:

REBOOT is led by fellow combat Veterans and spouses. Our leaders have lived it, learned from it, and want to help lift you out of it. Within our groups, every member is the same — no rank, no uniforms, no titles, and total privacy.

REBOOT is there for the whole family. Spouses and families are encouraged to participate. The course is designed to help married couples to reopen lines of communication and to heal together.

REBOOT approaches trauma from a different angle. If you mind and body can be wounded, doesn't it stand to reason that your soul can be wounded as well? What if that's the ingredient you've been missing in your healing?

REBOOT is a course, not a support group. Though we do provide support, and we are a group, we are much more than just a "support group." You won't find any rambling or whining in our groups — only productive conversations.

REBOOT is faith-based but not preachy. We don't hide the fact that it's a faith-based course. But we're not pushy about our worldview. No matter your beliefs, you'll learn proven methods to heal from trauma.

The following are stories about two Soldiers who have attended **REBOOT**, to give you a more personal view of what the program is all about and how it made a difference in their lives.

SGT Mitchell: "Through **REBOOT**, I learned that others felt the way I had felt and that I wasn't alone in my fight." I graduated from **REBOOT** Combat Recovery earlier this year and would like to congratulate everyone here today as you complete an important milestone and join me as a graduate.

I'd like to say that war was the only place in my life that I encountered trauma, but unfortunately that isn't the case. When I first began attending **REBOOT**, I attended due to the wounds I had encountered during combat. War is what led me to attend that night, but that was just the beginning.

During the first week of **REBOOT**, the instructor told us "You may experience healing from trauma that happen to you long before war." As the words came out of his mouth, it was as if he had hit a nerve. Through all of the struggling, the thought hadn't really occurred to me. Could my struggles have started prior to my military career?

As I sat there, I could feel my blood pressure rising as distant memories rushed to the front of my mind. I fought the return of the memories, but it was as if they were dying to escape the secret cave where they had been hiding.

When I was a child, for many years, I was sexually molested by my cousin. This is a secret I had kept from everyone, including my own wife. I had dealt with it. I was over it. I couldn't change it, so what was the point in reliving those dark moments? I simply stuffed it and moved on. Following this molestation, I in turn began to sexually abuse other members of my family. My sexual appetite grew out of control.

I began to wonder if perhaps I was gay. But I didn't think I was. I would try to get the attention of girls at school, but they didn't seem to notice me. Maybe I wasn't a real man?

I began to search for ways to prove my "manhood" to everyone around me. It is this search that led me into the Army recruiting station. I figured, if I join the Army and fight bad guys, surely that will make me a real man and prove to the world I have what it takes.

Looking back, the recruiter I met that day was full of lies — or maybe he just told me what I wanted to hear. As we discussed various job opportunities in the military, he informed me that mechanics never leave the shop and that I would be far away from combat. So I jumped at the chance. I would be a United States Soldier!

I learned quickly after getting deployed that this just isn't true as I was led to believe. In fact, I would see combat — often. In only the first few days of my deployment, I saw a little boy lose his life and an Iraqi Soldier with a portion of his head blown off.

Since I was new to the unit, the other guys thought they need to "toughen me up," so I was put on the recovery team that retrieved blown up trucks. This was a horrible job because of the things I had to see in the blown-up vehicles. Every door I opened was a new personalized horror movie complete with carnage and death.

The timing of my deployment wasn't ideal. You see, I was the new guy that arrived three months after everybody else had already deployed. This meant that they had already established their circle of friends — and I wasn't one of them.

But eventually, I actually did make a friend. His name was Jones, and he was the first person to show any real concern for me.

I remember very vividly one day as we were working near a checkpoint, Jones warned me to keep my head down because there had been snipers taking pop shots at people all day. I appreciated his genuine concern and felt a sense of protection as someone more senior was looking out for me. We said goodbye as I mounted my truck and we rolled out. Just moments later, I would hear on the radio a call for a nine-line medevac. Jones had been shot by a sniper. He passed away that day.

But the mission pressed on. I would continue to witness a series of events that no person should ever have to see. I struggled. I felt alone. I felt worried and sad all the time. And these struggles were only amplified during my second deployment.

Why was I struggling so bad when everyone around me seemed to be fine? Again, my insecurity as a man attacked. I began believing that I was a weak Soldier because of the way these events bothered me. After all, I was a Soldier, so these things shouldn't bother me, right?

I thought leaving the military would make things better. But when I left, my struggles only increased. I was filled with anxiety and depression and began searching for my identity. Suicide seemed like a logical option for peace.

I remember sitting with my mom at Thanksgiving. She looked at me directly in the eyes and, with a disapproving tone, asked me, "Where are you?" I didn't know. I knew I wasn't there. My body was present, but in every other way, I was dead.

I felt that I had died in Ramadi, Iraq. My body came home but my spirit stayed behind. I kept secrets. I isolated myself from the world. Life was happening, but I certainly wasn't living.

But before long, something changed. I heard a REBOOT outreach team member speak one weekend. He shared his struggles with suicide. He talked about three lies that people often believe about their identities — first, that we are what we do; second, that we are what others think of us; and third, that our best days are behind us.

As he spoke about his battles with false guilt and identity, it was as if he was reading my very soul. So I decided to attend an event for training REBOOT leaders. I assumed I could sneak in and put on a good face as a leader while I checked out the program.

Within only a few minutes of the training, I realized that I couldn't become a leader. In fact, I needed to be led. I needed help, so I registered for the upcoming **REBOOT** Combat Recovery course in Clarksville, Tennessee.

I remember walking into my **REBOOT** first meeting. Something struck me as strange. Everyone was smiling and seemed so freaking happy. What did they all have to smile about? Wasn't this a combat trauma healing group? Aren't we supposed to sit around and hear each other's war stories and complain about the VA? But everyone seemed to be happy. It didn't make sense!

Only a few weeks into the process, it started to dawn on me that I was healing. I was starting to address issues in my life that I had never exposed.

During Week 8, we discussed the cost of unforgiveness. For years, I had been carrying around a heart full of unforgiveness and bitterness. I was angry. I hated the enemy, I hated my cousin, and I hated myself. At the end of the lesson, we had the opportunity to come to the front and share the list of people we needed to forgive. I read through my list, which included my cousin and, most importantly, myself.

I took a pair of scissors and cut that card of names into pieces — and for the first time, I felt forgiveness. I felt joy. All of a sudden, I understood why everyone was smiling. They were free.

Coming to **REBOOT** Combat Recovery was the best decision of my life, after accepting Jesus and marrying my wife. Through **REBOOT**, I learned that others felt the way I had felt and that I wasn't alone in my fight.

REBOOT is much more than a program. I have made amazing friends here that let me share my story without trying to one-up me with their own stories. They listen and show me love and support. They have reaffirmed that I am a "real man" and that I do have what it takes to be a great husband, father, and friend.

I will forever be grateful to **REBOOT** Combat Recovery.

———

SGT Bradford: "I began to see that I was in a battle that wasn't against flesh and blood..."

I come from a long line of military men. There's been a "Bradford" in every war since America started fighting in wars. I always felt like it was my duty to step up when this war started. My story isn't much different from other soldiers in this war...but this is my story.

I grew up in Murphy, a small town in the mountains of North Carolina. In Murphy, guys love three things: women, beer, and guns. A good day is when all three are together. Now that's a good time.

So, there I was, five years old, hanging out at my Memaw's house, when life would forever change. The phone rang and I answered. On the other end of the line was my neighbor telling me to go get my mom. Instantly, I knew something was wrong. My dad had taken his own life. As I began to cry and tried to grasp the reality of the moment, my uncle walked up to me and said, "Don't cry, you have to be the man of the house now."

As life went on, I got into the normal thing's boys get into... in my case, mostly trouble. But my friends and I had a good time. As high school wrapped up, I decided it was time to enlist in the Army. I broke the family tradition of becoming an officer because I wanted to be "that" guy...the boots on the ground guy that hunted down the enemy.

While in the Army, I served in the 101st Airborne Division, 3rd Brigade, 3rd BLT, Iron Rakkasans. To any of you who don't know what that means, Iron Rakkasans are the most highly decorated battalion in the 101st Airborne.

My first day in the Iron Rakkasans, I was told that everyone in the Army is a dinosaur and that we were the meat-eating dinosaurs. We hunt our enemies down and kill them. And that's what I did. I had found my place in the Army. I was proud of what I had become. In fact, one of my proudest moments was when I was given a coin from COL Steele for my first kill. I would go on to eliminate numerous Taliban and Al Qaeda insurgents, including three high value targets. I spent a lot of my time in Iraq in an area known as the "Triangle of Death."

But during my deployment, I experienced one of the hardest moments of my life. I'd gone through having friends wounded and even killed in other companies, but nothing came close to what I would experience on this day.

On November 1, 2007, my commanding officer, Lieutenant Tracy Alger was killed in combat.

Our group of men was on a three day mission to push an insurgent stronghold out of our area of operation. We'd already not been able to cover the ground that we had expected to cover due to numerous IED attacks and sporadic arms fire, however, we had finally gotten to a place where we could set up a 360 degree perimeter and hunker down for the night. But that's when the first IED struck my vehicle and the vehicle behind me. The enemy was prepared for us, and we were ambushed.

The first thing I saw as I stood back up in my turret was my friend Lucia slumped over in his vehicle. I immediately told my driver to back up all the way to his vehicle. At that point, with no regard to my life, I hopped out of my gunner turret and began to bang on his windshield. After he finally came to his senses from being knocked out, we took incoming fire. I dove back into my turret and returned fire. As we pushed the enemy away from us, we were able to take Lucia and another friend, Bowden, out of their vehicle and move them to ours.

We thought that was going to be the worst part of the night. But as darkness set in, we decided that we were going to continue the mission, that it would not be a good idea to stay in this area. That's when all hell broke loose.

In the same area where we had just set up security, we swapped positions with my LT. A minute later, his vehicle was attacked by rocket-propelled grenades and small arms fire and was struck by a catastrophic IED. This was no ordinary IED. This was 500 pounds of explosive with 200 pounds of incendiary, which has the ability to melt metal and penetrate armor. Immediately, what you would consider a non-flammable armored vehicle erupted into flames.

As I looked back, I could no longer see their vehicle. The explosion was so powerful that the vehicle was now sitting in a crater. Nobody could completely understand what was going on. Our patrol's first reaction was to push forward, so they had left us. As we tried to call on the radio, the rest of our group was already too far away to return to our aid. We had driven into a trap, and I realized we were all alone.

Staff SGT Pennington (our platoon sergeant) and our medic were the first to respond, leaving me to set up security and call in our medevac. As we got closer to the IED site, I saw one of my best friends, Walley, crawl out of a hole with his leg beside him. At this point, I told the rest of the people in my vehicle to dismount and go care for the wounded. I watched them drag my best friend to the back of my truck. He had an injury that most people die from. As we provided care, my driver from my first deployment, Woodard, crawled out of the hole on fire. The first thing he asked was, "Is everybody out of the truck?" He had no regard for his own injury. Once I called in our medevac, I came to realize that we were missing one — our LT.

One of the most painful things that I've ever experienced was to call in that one of my family was KIA (Killed in Action).

After we medevacked our wounded, it still wasn't over. Because we were the only element on the ground that could retrieve the destroyed vehicle and its sensitive equipment, we had to sit there for 30 more hours waiting for the vehicle to cool down so that we could search for what was left of our LT. The only thing we could find was a piece of upper thigh and a necklace, which we placed in a bag and put into the back of my truck.

We would go on to clear 83 pieces of explosive ordinance in order for us to carry our LT home.

Amazingly, within 10 hours, we were back on mission to the same area. No tears, no time to grieve. We still had a mission to accomplish. There is no time to process emotion in the midst of war. The mission always comes before grieving.
But even after my deployments ended, a war raged on. This was a battle for my own mind and spirit.

The first time I walked into REBOOT, I had spent the previous six months struggling day in and day out. My marriage was ending. I was angry and had no fuse. Physically I had been injured in Afghanistan and was so frustrated with my medical care I was on the brink of giving up. Frustrated and not improving, I couldn't even sleep.

And that's just a few of the issues I was struggling with. Needless to say, life was not as I had envisioned it would be as a kid growing up in a little town in North Carolina.

So, as I walked into REBOOT for the first time, there stood a slightly chubby civilian and his do-gooder wife trying to help service members. Looking back, even as I stood up to introduce myself at the first group meeting, I can remember the anger that was still inside me. My identity still remained at war. I remember saying, "I'm SGT Bradford. I'm from the great southern state of North Carolina. I like to kill bad guys and look for IEDs."

But over time, the consistent support, encouragement, and teaching began to sink in. My insides had become calloused and hardened by combat but were slowly returning to their warm and gooey state. I could feel the holes in my heart being filled. I began to see that I was in a battle that wasn't against flesh and blood, and that I had the tools needed to regain my true identity. I was not sure that identity still existed.

I remember the first time I shared the story that I've shared just now, I felt like the world had been lifted off my shoulders and that I was loved. At that point I realized out of all the programs that I had been through; I had found one that worked.

Two years ago, I stood up and shared my story with a REBOOT group, full of anger, guilt, hate and despair. But today I share my testimony with you, full of hope, optimism, compassion and most of all, faith.

For the countless other service members struggling through government program after government program, I hope you know that hope and healing is out there. There is light that can shine into the darkness and through the support of people like you, REBOOT will be there to help.

———

We tell our course participants that we can't guarantee that their symptoms will go away but we can say that, after completing the course, they will experience some joy, peace and a renewed sense of purpose. If you've tried other things that haven't worked, give this a chance. For more information and to see if there's a course meeting in your community, please visit www.rebootrecovery.com.

CHAPTER 31 - REFOCUSING LIVES: SEEING THE WORLD THROUGH A DIFFERENT LENS

Josh Kuehl - Task Force ISO

"And that's when it 'clicked' for me. Behind a camera, I was invisible — even in a room full of people. Through the lens, I could see all of the action and even participate from a safe distance. My camera allowed me to be anonymous, while giving me a reason to be in the room and "mingling" with others. Gone was the awkwardness of conversation and networking. Gone was the struggle to fit in. Gone was that feeling of not belonging. I had a job to do and the means to do it and I was going to give it my best."

More than 200,000 U.S. service members return to civilian life each year. Military life can be challenging. Aside from the obvious physical demands — and the lack of privacy and personal freedom — for many military personnel there is the very real possibility of injury and death. It should come as no surprise, therefore, that many returning service men and women find the transition from military to civilian life difficult. In fact, researchers found more than 40 percent experience stress about the process. That difficulty is even more acute among Veterans from the post-9/11 era.

After living in the highly structured and demanding environment of the U.S. military, Veterans often find it difficult to re-engage with their families and communities. Adjusting to the normal pace of work and family life can be "boring" to someone used to the risks and intensity of life in a combat zone. And many Veterans crave the camaraderie and structure they experienced during their time in the service.

Traditional Veterans' programs focus on treating the physical issues returning military personnel face. Yet nearly a third of service members returning from Iraq and Afghanistan report symptoms of mental health or cognitive problems. These "invisible" disabilities, such as Traumatic Brain Injury (TBI) and Post-Traumatic Stress Disorder (PTSD), can lead to depression and self-destructive behaviors such as alcohol and substance abuse and even suicide.

Veterans like me who leave the military with a low level of PTSD may not recognize why they are struggling with relationships and dealing with boredom and depression. Used to being in an unsafe environment, the shift back to civilian life may cause them to relive that feeling through reckless and dangerous activities. Not knowing what they are dealing with, lack of access to mental health services, and the gaps in service for this level of need contribute to the high number of homeless Veterans, high rates of alcohol and drug dependency and high rates of suicide among Veterans.

Josh's Story
Josh Kuehl is the founder and executive director of Task Force: ISO.

I had an interest in the service from an early age, joining the civil air patrol in junior high. Though my sights were on academy attendance, I didn't have the grades to qualify. So, right after high school I enlisted in the Army as a light infantryman and ended up as a mortar man. During my tour, I heard about the West Point Prep School, which helps you get your grades up before applying to West Point. I got accepted and then applied to West Point as a soldier, with the help and support of my company commander.

After graduating from West Point, I knew I didn't want to return as an infantryman and through dumb luck was picked for the cavalry. Different from a regular Army unit, cavalry focuses on reconnaissance — spreading out and covering massive distances. Our most important weapon was the radio — reporting back on everything from enemy positions and geography and calling in air support. The tempo was intense. We were always leading and often with vague and incomplete instructions. On average, I moved every nine months. By the time I met my minimum service requirements, I was exhausted and had no life.

Even with a West Point degree and my military experience, the transition to a civilian job was tough. I struggled to find a position that offered development and advancement and was frustrated with the lack of opportunities. Looking back, my service experiences created challenges - I had difficulty communicating and developing relationships and hadn't developed the networking skills I needed to find professional positions within my field.

And then, I picked up a camera. Work and school had been too left-brain and I needed the release of something creative. Photography became both a hobby and an escape. I found I couldn't learn enough about it and it quickly became a passion. When a layoff spurred my disillusionment with corporate American, I decided to pursue photography as a profession.

I became involved with a non-profit called Project Wounded Ego, which focused on taking photos of Veterans engaged in activities. There, I began talking with other Veterans about using the camera in awkward social situations. Our experiences with the healing power of the camera — and the images it creates — were similar. We shared similar experiences, recognizing the need to tell Veterans' stories through positive images and understanding the value of photography in helping them transition from Active Duty.

When Project Wounded Ego shut down, there remained a demand for its services. Organizations wanted support in photographing Veterans. And, there was a clear need for tools that can connect and engage Veterans with other Veterans in similar situations. As a Veteran with a passion for photography, I knew that the camera can be a tool for coping with social anxiety and making connections. After talking with other Veterans about how they used photography in their own lives, I could see there was therapeutic potential in photography. Many of us had used our cameras as invisibility shields. Joining forces with a charismatic Veteran from Project Wounded Ego, I took the learnings from that organization to create a more robust program that focuses on education and the ability of photography to strengthen and heal.

Both of us had a passion to create images of Veterans that mattered and a desire to provide photography education.

In June 2016, we incorporated Task Force: ISO as a 501(c)(3) non-profit. Similar to Project Wounded Ego, we provide event photography for Veterans' organizations. However, we now focus on getting good images of every Veteran participant for their benefit, with the support of the organization as a secondary goal. Unlike our predecessor organization, we also teach Veterans photography and network with other Veterans' organizations to make connections for Veterans in need.

Early on, we understood that for Task Force: ISO to have any kind of value for Veterans, our program needed both technical rigor and professional credibility. Our training needed to go beyond "feels good" to having therapeutic value. With the guidance of the University of Denver's Sturm Center, which specializes in military psychology, we were able to add therapeutic value to our photography training curriculum. Our collaboration resulted in therapeutic metaphors that coincide with the technical training throughout the photography training classes.

Many Veterans don't seek help when they need it, so a program of "soft" self-discovery can lead them to professional mental healthcare, while giving them purpose after the classes are over. Once Veterans have completed the eight-week photography training course, we require them to photograph an event — using their craft to support fellow Veterans and using their new skills to show Veterans having fun and being vulnerable with each other in a very safe environment.

Low-lying PTSD symptoms — social anxiety, pulling back from community and family, and a lack of connection — can lead to depression and create a vicious cycle for returning Veterans. Many are reluctant to seek help due to the stigma of mental illness or the difficulty in connecting with the right services and care networks. Task Force: ISO focuses on Veterans who appear to be functioning just fine, but may be struggling as I was when I returned from combat. My journey through photography has led me to be more outgoing. The organization depends on networking — with individuals, with other Veterans and with Veterans' organizations. Not only have I engaged in the art and science of photography, but I have gained purpose by helping others refocus their lives through Task Force: ISO.

Marla's Story

Marla H. is a Veteran and student graduate of the Task Force: ISO SUPPORT: Photography Training program. She participates as a photographer in the IMAGING program and has served as a student assistant.

"I don't think of myself as broken; I just know my limitations."

At 15, I dropped out of high school because I was pregnant and married. I had always had a plan to get out of Midwest Illinois and get an education and the military was definitely in my sights. Both of my brothers served in the Army, and one was a lifer. My marriage wasn't in a good place and life wasn't working out as I had hoped. Looking around for a change, my husband and I both went into the Army's buddy enlistment program. This allows an enlistee and friends to attend the same Basic Combat Training and Advanced Individual Training together.

Though my husband didn't make it through basic, I went ahead and got stationed at a tech school. I ended up as a jet engine mechanic stationed at Petersen Air Force Base in Colorado. While I was there, I suffered an on-the-job injury — getting jet fuel in my eyes, which set off an allergic reaction. Since I couldn't continue in my current position, I cross-trained as a law enforcement officer. That got me sent to Duluth, Minnesota, where I worked hand-in-hand with men and learned to love the winters.

While I was there, I had an incident in the barracks that resulted in a hardship discharge (disability related to Military Sexual Trauma (MST). Back in civilian life, I struggled to find work and went into truck driving, which I then did on and off for 30 years. During that time, I was still experiencing health issues that started in the military. And I continued to have difficulties with relationships throughout my working life. After a series of issues — the deaths of my parents, moving, and continued health problems — depression derailed me.

I started to recognize that I had an issue with PTSD. Initially, I wrote it off to the type of jobs and lifestyle I was leading. Lots of dominos fell and I couldn't get my act together. I went into the VA and was getting counseling concentrated on the issues I was having at work. By then, I had blown out my ACL which made driving difficult. Finally, I was diagnosed with PTSD as a result of the MST. I had always felt that you just "pick up and keep going on." But all of this came to a head and I knew I had to do something different.

The VA wanted to medicate me, but that didn't get at the source of the problems. I had no alcohol or drug issues; however, I was diagnosed with fibromyalgia, depression, TMJ and hormone imbalance. Following a car accident, I also suffered from concussion syndrome, which is similar to Traumatic Brain Injury (TBI).

Josh's photography classes came at a time when I was transitioning out of the job market. "I've always worked and it was so scary to me not to have anything there." My key idea of retirement was to see the sights and enjoy the outdoors, so the classes were "a bit of a lifesaver." Photography was always something I had wanted to do and now I had a way to build my skills.

Photography has served me in a lot of ways. I grab the camera and it gets me out of the house and the group events get me engaged. "Like the old firehouses, I am used to the bell going off and all of that adrenaline - I gotta do something for someone else." So, it's important for me to serve others. Photography gets me out of the house and working with other people.

After I completed the photography training, I started working with Veterans' organization and Task Force: ISO partner River Deep Alliance as an event photographer. It was eye-opening seeing Veterans' faces when they first get to an event and then seeing the changes in their faces over the course of the day. It is awesome seeing what happens when Veterans are engaged in an event. And then there's the families — you see in their eyes that they are seeing hope they haven't seen in so long. "Seeing Veterans and their families enjoying themselves in an activity like catching fish is a wonderful thing."

"The photos allow vets to see themselves and have this permanent reminder that they enjoyed themselves. I just love seeing everyone's face and watching them experience the outdoors and the idea that they are appreciated."

My mind runs on two tracks — it's always working on something else — "cycling" while I am doing something. Taking photos — especially landscapes — is calming. And, working with Veterans is a good outlet and "pushes" me as a photographer. I have even been a teacher's assistant at the classes.

There's an interdependency when you're in the military. "A lot of what has served me is I don't know when to quit." I always had something in my life that I was really good at. As a retiree, now I have photography. It grounds me and gives me something to do. I need to get off my butt once in a while and out of the house with my Service Dog. Today, I am more outgoing and feel that I have purpose as a result of the Task Force: ISO classes. Being behind the camera, I can hide my own feelings and capture the emotions in other people.

About Task Force: ISO

There is documented value of creative arts in physical and emotional rehabilitation. Behavior change is accomplished when we engage both sides of the brain. Healthcare providers, mental health professionals, educators and Veterans' organizations have seen the positive impact of art, music, dance and creative writing in concert with more traditional therapies. These non-invasive and non-medication-based activities can reduce healthcare costs, promote improved cognition and concentration, improve communication skills and reduce depression. Overall, arts programming can reduce the time individuals spend in medical care and increase quality of life.

Task Force: ISO is a 501(c)(3) non-profit organization that engages and inspires Veterans through photography. Through our programs, Veterans gain purpose through activity and self-discovery and build community through continued mentorship and support. Expanding on the concept of its predecessor organization, Task Force has three program pillars – IMAGING: Event Photography, creating positive imagery of Veterans and showcasing their resilience; SUPPORT: Photography Training, using self-discovery through the creative arts to uncover and address issues that Veterans are coping with; and OUTREACH: Community Networking, engaging with other non-profits to foster connection and collaboration and ensure Veterans a pathway to success.

Today, while there are many Veterans' organizations working in the creative arts, Task Force: ISO is the only organization in the U.S. that uses education and photography to foster engagement and community. Through our IMAGING program, we support more than 20 non-profit organizations across the United States with professional imagery. In 2017, this resulted in positive images of over 2,000 individual Veterans at 34 events. Currently, Task Force: ISO has professional photographer volunteers in seven states (CO, WY, TX, NC, CA, MA, and VA). Each year our network grows, as does our outreach and impact.

References

JPMorgan Chase & Co. A Q&A with Former U.S. Army Chief of Staff, General Ray Odierno. https://www.jpmorganchase.com/corporate/news/stories/gen-odierno.htm. Accessed February 2019.
Orino, Brendan. Better understanding the challenges that service-members, military families and veterans face. November 2, 2015. https://www.brookings.edu/blog/up-front/2015/11/02/better-understanding-the-challenges-that-service-members-military-families-and-veterans-face/. Accessed February 2019.

US Veterans Magazine. Common challenges during readjustment to civilian life. https://www.usveteransmagazine.com/2017/02/common-challenges-during-readjustment-to-civilian-life/ Accessed February 2019.

American Psychological Association. The Mental Health Needs of Veterans, Service Members, and Their Families. https://www.apa.org/advocacy/military-veterans/mental-health-needs.pdf. Accessed March 2019.

Haeyen MAth, Suzanne, Susan van Hooren PhD and Giel Huchemakers PhD. Perceived effects of art therapy in the treatment of personality disorders, cluster B/C: A qualitative study. The Arts in Psychotherapy. Volume 45, September 2015, Pages 1-10. Elsevier Science Direct.

Examples of our work can be seen at https://taskforceiso.client.photos/galleries..

CHAPTER 32 - RELIEVING PTSD RELATED SYMPTOMS WITH THE TRAGER® APPROACH TO PSYCHO-PHYSICAL INTEGRATION

Michael Lear, Trager Instructor, E-RYT 500, YACEP

A few months after turning 22 in 1986, having a degree in finance and working in a management position, I was found to have impressively high blood pressure measuring 162/105 and elevated cholesterol levels. I also suffered from compromising chronic back pain which became acutely sharp at times. Being 40 pounds heavier than the average weight for my height didn't help the situation. Being allergic to many medications, including the most widely used array of prescription painkillers, I had to explore other alternatives to find relief. My body had rejected even muscle relaxants which left me with little latitude to journey comfortably forward.

Fortunately, through some serendipitous events, a unique method of psycho-physical integration or somatic movement re-education system called The Trager® Approach came onto my radar. Named after Dr. Milton Trager who developed the technique over his lifetime and professional career, it seemed like a good place to start. At that time, I had only the pain to lose. Though my symptoms were not Post-Traumatic Stress Disorder (PTSD) related, some are shared by those suffering from PTSD. Not being able to follow conventional paths for relief, I felt alone in my pursuit for an effective alternative. For those who may suffer from such symptoms, The Trager Approach may provide them relief.

Alternative approaches, including massage, were considered 'fringe' in the late '80s as they still lacked wide acceptance. Nearly a decade later, in 1995, hands-on therapies, including The Trager Approach, were cited as "Eye of the Newt Therapies" in the Market Place section of a Wall Street Journal issue. The Trager Approach has stood the test of time. My first experience with The Trager Approach was profound and would prove to be pivotal. Though I had arrived at the session with some discomfort, there was no time during the session that I experienced pain. In fact, most of what I felt was curiosity mixed with relaxation. I was feeling that most, if not all, of my body felt good, not heavy or restricted as it had an hour before. Often during the session, I wondered why the practitioner was working on a part of me seemingly not related to the pain I had been experiencing. Yet, when the session was over, all traces of functional limitation and discomfort were gone. "Where did they go," I thought to myself, "If they were not worked on directly?"

After my session I was given movement exploration exercises to do on my own, Trager® Mentastics® (mental gymnastics), to help me meet my world differently; to explore movement possibilities outside my default, habituated way of moving about my environments such as work and home. It was through these homework movement exercises that The Trager Approach got its traction within me.

I began receiving sessions monthly to ensure that the pain did not return. In other words, so I did not fall back in to old movement patterns that set up the painful conditions. Also, I had become a committed student of the Mentastics which are like Tai Chi or gentle yoga-type movements that leverage principles of autogenic training, a widely recognized method of biofeedback used to lower blood pressure as it elicits physiological change through silently repeated phrases. Mentastics also encourages memory of the session, of how it felt when I received the work, re-living the therapy in my mind. Every movement after a session is an opportunity to reprogram how one moves in their body and in relation to their world.

Mentastics requires mindfulness and, indeed, this was changing my relationship to the world around me. I even found that the underlying principles of The Trager Approach worked in dialogues, meetings, negotiations and in my relationships. They impacted all aspects of my life.

To note, The Trager Approach movement re-education process can be likened to piano lessons, where the student studies with a teacher and then practices in between each lesson so the next lesson can build upon the previous one. I discovered that each session was a lesson for my nervous system which then was reinforced by living differently through my body afterward. It was more than a treatment for my physical body as it worked on my mind as well which, in turn, affected my body's function.

The phrase "One doesn't have to feel bad to feel better," comes to mind as, although comfortable, I continued to receive the sessions regularly. Not only did I remain pain-free, but I also noted increasing fluidity, grace and lightness in my body, qualities that had been shut down through restricted habituated movement patterns which were compensatory responses to injuries and to surgeries which I had as a child.

That first Trager session was May 13, 1987, and my latest was just two days before beginning to write this chapter. Discovering The Trager Approach changed the course of my life significantly. It made me interested in, curious about, and aware of how I moved in my body; who I was towards myself as I lived in my body; and how all that impacted my movement experience, either by limiting it or by opening it up to new potential, like doing Yoga.

My body was feeling better and the deep relaxation fostered by the sessions facilitated the release of deeply seated muscle holding patterns that clearly had subconscious emotional counterparts. The insights I gained were game-changing. The work took me into foreign territory. Terrain that was inside of me, not outside, and which connected me to what was and what wasn't comfortable. The Trager Approach's capacity to provide a safe context for my body-mind to assess, re-organize and let go of dysfunctional muscle holding patterns that manifested as functional limitation and pain was extra-ordinary, comfortable, pleasurable. It facilitated a 'remembering' of my body's inherent coherence and, once it felt safe, my body naturally migrated toward more balance and harmony. I had let go of learned dysfunctional muscle patterns developed and valid at an earlier time which were now simply limiting.

The relaxation and release of stress promoted by the mindfulness of Trager Mentastics led to a controlling of my body's 'fight or flight' response. This produced a decrease in cortisol and adrenalin release, normalizing my blood pressure and leading to a lowering of my cholesterol levels. In addition, the decreased stress curbed my emotional eating and encouraged me to make better nutritional choices. As I was pain-free, I became more active which also contributed to a reduction in my body weight.

So, affected by the experiences that I continued to have, I began to wonder what education one needed to be able to impart such a feeling state to others. I then registered for the professional Trager Approach training and became a certified Trager Practitioner in 1991. Also, Trager had led me to Ashtanga Yoga and Vipassana meditation. Today, these three form the tripod of daily practices upon which my day's rest.

So, what is The Trager Approach and what are its applications for addressing PTSD related pain? Succinctly stated by Deane Juhan, Senior Trager Instructor and author of "Job's Body, A Handbook for Bodywork": "Unconsciously habituated muscular responses and adaptations to life's adverse circumstances, such as accidents, illness, surgery, emotional traumas, or high levels of daily stress, often develop into poor postures and patterns of movement that can become the silent accumulative context for further pain, injury or disease. And wasteful, ineffective muscular patterns can also frequently slow down, compromise, and even ultimately limit the process of recovery from physical or emotional breakdowns of many kinds. The Trager Approach is a rapid, effective, and painless, indeed pleasurable method of deprogramming these accumulated negative muscular patterns, and of restoring the positive body image and feeling, tone, and organized responses that are essential to healing and healthy development."

"The purpose of my work," Dr. Trager has said, "is to break up these sensory, motor, and mental patterns which inhibit free movement and cause pain and disruption of normal function."

The Trager Approach consists of the use of hands-on contact and movement re-education to influence deep-seated psycho-physiological patterns in the mind, and to interrupt their dysfunctional projection into the body's tissues. The method is to impart to the patient what it is like to feel right in the sense of a functionally integrated body-mind. Since the inhibiting patterns are affected at the source, the mind, the patient can experience long-lasting benefits.

Juhan continues, "During a Trager table-work session, the practitioner uses gentle, pleasuring rocking motions, compressions and elongations, gravity-assisted swings and hangs of the limbs, and shimmers of the tissues to facilitate a more and more painless and passive perception of movement throughout the patient's body. These manipulations are not perceived as intrusive because they do not work against the organism's basic reflexes and defenses, but rather simulate the normal ranges of elongation, compression, and jiggling of coordinated movement in the body. And the pleasuring aspect of each exploratory movement is not incidental to the treatment. On the contrary, it is of the essence, and any pain or discomfort is always an indication to modify the depth, range, or speed of the practitioner's imposed movements.

This pleasuring is important for three reasons: 1) Pain inevitably engages reflex muscular defensiveness, producing amplified, not reduced contractions and holding patterns; 2) Pleasuring is a potent biofeedback element which leads to deeper relaxation, softening, and increased ranges of motion within the limitations of the actual conditions in the body; 3) Trauma and pathology themselves have created pain and fear, frequently to the extent that the patient can no longer imagine any part of their body as a source of pleasure, comfort, or strength. The goal is to create in the session a sense of safety and ease in which new and better patterns can be learned, a delicate process that can be easily disturbed by any increase in pain or discomfort. "Every shimmer of the tissue," Dr. Trager has said, "is sending a message to the unconscious mind in the form of a positive feeling experience. It is the accumulation of these positive patterns that can offset the negative patterns so that the positive can take over."

The table-work portion of the session takes place on a massage table with the client draped and clothed to the degree they're most comfortable with. No oils or lotions are used. A typical session with Mentastics instruction lasts about ninety minutes, however time varies depending on the setting and the practitioner.

Some reported benefits from The Trager Approach include:

Increased mobility, vitality, clarity, capacity to relax and a sense of overall peace.
Improved sports performance without injury.
Quickened recovery from surgery or injury.
Relief from stress, joint pain, muscular pain, sciatica, chronic back/neck pain, headaches and temporomandibular joint (TMJ) pain.
Relief from fibromyalgia and chronic fatigue.
Improved neuro-muscular function in those with Parkinson's disease, cerebral palsy and multiple sclerosis.
Improvement in status with ankylosing spondylitis and post-stroke paralysis.

Please understand, this is not to claim that Trager is a cure for these or any other pathologies. "But in the absence of a cure, improved emotional balance, superior coping mechanisms, more effective compensations, and a measure of control over and active engagement in their own present and future will always be of extreme importance to these patients, and to anyone personally associated with them." - Deane Juhan.

Over the course of my career, I have successfully worked with clients with various painful or limiting physical conditions, stress-related symptoms, congenital neuromuscular disorders and survivors of various kinds of trauma as well as with clients who, although comfortable, wish to expand their range of motion and physical capabilities. During the time that I spent in post-tsunami Sri Lanka, I worked with numerous disaster survivors who still experienced pain and limited mobility long after the apparent healing of the initial injury. Self-medication, sometimes imprudent, did not help with their pain. The Trager Approach greatly improved their conditions, almost always decreasing or even eliminating pain and restoring greater degrees of function and enhancing ease in mobility.

One specific client experienced arm swelling a year out from the tsunami. She had been pinned down by that arm when a cabinet fell upon it, trapping her as the waves were rushing in. She nearly drowned before she was rescued. After her first Trager session, the swelling reduced by about 80% and subsequent sessions relieved the situation completely. In this particular case, it was the artifact, the memory of the experience that had remained frozen in her mind and body and produced a physical expression long after the original incident. Through the gentle touch and inquiring movements of Trager, her mind was able to experience safety and eventually release the pattern holding the physical expression.

Similarly, the effects of sexual abuse are present long after the trauma takes place, sometimes producing a fear of physical contact altogether or a dissociation with bodily identity. Through The Trager Approach I have been able to help such clients to acknowledge their physicality and reset their level of comfort with healthy normal contact with others.

The touch dialogue that The Trager Approach sets up can be compared to the approach of "Non-Violent Communication" as described by Marshall Rosenberg in his book of the same name. For example, if you were yelled at, how long would you listen? In the same way, to force the body to do something that it is not ready to do sets up a similar resistance-push back. It's important to emphasize that Trager is not a form of psychotherapy or "talk" therapy and references made to the "touch as a language" or "touch dialogue" pertain to the use of hands to engage in a conversation with the unconscious mind.

Trager practitioners feel/listen for resistance patterns and honor their set points. They do not attempt to move into muscular resistance or change what is true for the body-mind. Instead, the Trager Practitioner will emphasize ranges of motion that are acceptable, safe and comfortable so as to invite the client's letting go of such patterns that may be no longer relevant. As the body feels safe and 'heard,' it can choose to let go of valid but outmoded patterns that may have projected into the tissue as pain or limitation. For Veterans experiencing pain, this non-intrusive process may be of particular benefit. Like any learning process, success requires repetition and continuity of practice for a new pattern to establish itself.

The restoration of optimal sensorimotor patterns through neuromuscular re-learning, or through the choice of the body-mind or on the nervous system's terms, contributes greatly to the health of the body by improving joint mobility, circulation, and reducing pain and functional limitation.

Trager's gentle and subtle approach may also serve those suffering with phantom limb pain associated with amputations. The initial trauma to the body usually produces a variety of protective bracing patterns and subsequent compensatory patterns to aid the body in healing. If these patterns persist after the healing is completed, the potential exists for there to be excessive limitation and sensitivity near the point of amputation. The Trager Approach in general, helps the body to experience greater integration, helping it release such patterns. This may also assist the nervous system at its subtlest level to decrease the triggering and sensitivity of the portion of the nerve fibers associated with the lost limb.

Painful muscle spasms may be reduced using The Trager Approach. It was shown that 20-minute sessions of Trager Therapy three times per week had a significant impact on the level of spasticity within Parkinson's patients in a study published in the Journal of Manipulative and Physiological Therapeutics, September 2002 (The Effect of Trager Therapy on the Level of Evoked Stretch Responses in Patients with Parkinson's Disease and Rigidity by Christian Duval, Denis Lafontaine, Jacques Hebert, Alain Leroux, PhD, Michael Panisset, MD, and Jean P. Boucher, PhD).

The relaxation response of The Trager Approach is also profound. The practitioner him/herself cultivates a state of deep relaxation from which to do the hands-on table work so that the relaxed state can be imparted to the client. This relaxed state after only ten minutes of Mentastics is measurable in Heart Rate Variability studies (Dr Gebhard Breuss, Heidi Stieg-Breuss, Dr Alfred Lohinger, www.autonomhealth.com). The Heart Rate Variability of the client is also measurably changed. Heart rate variability is a well-known measure of emotional resilience and relaxation/stress measurement. Shifts in mind states to enhance relaxation increase levels of comfort whereas stress is known to exacerbate pre-existing painful conditions.

Dr. David Hubbard, formerly Medical Director at Sharp Pain Rehabilitation Services, Sharp Health Care, San Diego, CA, published studies in Spine, (18, 13, 1803-1807, 1993) that showed that intrafusal muscle fibers that figure prominently in fibromyalgia were innervated by the sympathetic nervous system. It was found that painful muscular conditions were exacerbated by sympathetic nervous system arousal. Dr. Hubbard used The Trager Approach in his clinic to facilitate the release of these sympathetically stimulated mechanisms that were causing pain. He found that The Trager Approach, with its invitatory touch dialogue which includes compressions and elongations of the muscle spindles, elicited relaxation responses.

Muscular changes may also be elicited through the mental movement explorations, Mentastics, of The Trager Approach. Utilizing self-inquiry, Mentastics helps to keep a moment-by-moment awareness of what is occurring within the framework of the body, the mind in relationship to the environment and how that is feeling to us. An important component of these movement explorations is to stay within pain-free ranges of motion to reinforce movement without painful consequence. The range of motion expansion should remain acceptable and comfortable. Much like the table-work explorations performed by Trager Practitioners, who move the body while maintaining the body's comfort, Trager Mentastics help the nervous system drop anticipatory contraction patterns that can exacerbate painful conditions. Once anxiety over possible discomfort is relieved, the body mind can make a truer assessment of what is happening.

Much like the success of autogenic training in biofeedback, Mentastics mindful movement utilizing self-inquiry can elicit new and more comfortable shifts in the musculature. Self-inquiries such as "What would feel lighter or freer, more fluid here?" or the visualization of something that embodies these qualities, can invite the body to follow the mind. This process is much like how a dancer or actor will take on the characteristics of the role they're playing and, by getting in to character, they initiate change in their carriage, deportment, and gestures, even tone of voice. Our bodies are designed to get good at what we practice, even when we practice in our thoughts. All of us have been able to call on a memory and bring forth a physiological response with a recalling of the feeling. Perhaps too often we reflect on negative experiences rather than recalling and re-living positive, relaxing, or soothing ones with the enjoyable feelings that accompanied them. We can go there too, but only through practice. By recalling the Trager session where lightness and fluidity are experienced, one can begin to elicit similar muscular changes and comfort. For those suffering from trauma, this may present some challenges, but the Mentastics process is gentle and patient. When practiced properly, Mentastics does not re-traumatize the body mind but rather provides a safe movement experience.

The efficacy of Mindfulness practices, such as Mentastics, is supported by the growing body of evidence-based research regarding the benefits of Mindfulness practices and Trauma-informed Yoga. Mindfulness implies keeping a moment-by-moment awareness of what is occurring within the framework of the body, our feelings, bodily sensations, surrounding environment, and even our thoughts. An important component of this state of awareness is being equanimous with, or accepting of, what we observe as it is in particular physical sensations. In doing so we are in the present moment, not ruminating over the past or being anxious about the future and experiencing their associated emotional states. Coupled with curiosity, self-inquiry, these mindful movements have a capacity to reprogram our motor function to be more efficient, comfortable and easy.

In addition to controlling heart rate variability, Mindfulness has been shown to result in a decrease of the grey matter of the brain's amygdala, the region known for its flight or fight role in stress. This decrease of the amygdala allows for increased self-control as it decreases impulsivity allowing for more emotional resilience. These studies have also shown a beneficial thickening of the grey matter in the pre-frontal cortex, the area of the brain responsible for emotional control, awareness, concentration, problem-solving and planning. The hippocampus of the brain, which helps with memory and learning as well as emotion, also has been shown to have increased amounts of grey matter with mindfulness practices. This is especially important for those suffering with depression or PTSD as the hippocampus is covered with receptors for the stress hormone cortisol which can be damaged by chronic stress such as those conditions may cause.

Additional evidence that Mindfulness and Trauma-informed Yoga can reduce symptoms of anxiety and depression was reported in a research study found in the February 2018 Journal of Alternative and Complementary Medicine. The study, "Mind-Body Therapy for Military Veterans with Post-Traumatic Stress Disorder: A Systematic Review" was co-authored by Kathryn Braun, professor at University of Hawaii at Manoa and Robin Cushing, Army Physician Assistant. Braun and Cushing researched the effects of Mindfulness, mind-body therapy and Yoga on Veterans diagnosed with PTSD and found a significant reduction in symptoms for all the Veterans studied who had participated in the Mindfulness, mind-body therapy, and Yoga practices.

My own personal experience teaching Trauma-informed Yoga in prison and residential juvenile justice settings demonstrated the benefits of mindful movement practices with a breath awareness component. In these settings, many within the populations suffered from unresolved abuse trauma and PTSD that led them to engage in behaviors that resulted their incarceration. Trauma-informed yoga, like The Trager Approach and its Mentastics mindful movement component, focuses on greater body awareness, development of enhanced psycho-physical integration. Ensuring safety, predictability, consistency, and choice, coupled with non-violent communication as well as meta-cognition techniques also facilitates favorable results. Gains were noted in the empowerment of survivors by increasing emotional resilience, decreasing impulsivity, and de-escalating hyper-vigilant nervous systems.

Over the course of my career, whether as a Trager Practitioner, a Trauma-informed Yoga Instructor or working with international relief efforts in disaster areas such as Sri Lanka and Haiti or in post-conflict regions such as South Sudan and Uganda, the creation of a safe environment for those affected by PTSD has been a priority as its benefits cannot be overstated. Until they can safely experience what is true for them in the moment, with a high degree of equanimity fostered by mindful breathing and movement practices, the potential exists for persons with PTSD to be governed by their symptoms, physical or emotional.

This holds true for everyone. Safety is paramount for the body to let go of protective and limiting patterns, whatever they may be. Both The Trager Approach and Trauma-Informed Yoga with Mindfulness provide a safe context for the body to migrate back to balance and harmony, the place where it is designed to rest when given the proper support.

"There is a something on the other side of relaxation. And, that is peace."
- Dr. Milton Trager

Biography:

Since 1992 I have been working both domestically and internationally as a Trager Practitioner/Instructor and as an Ashtanga Yoga Instructor. My client base spans five continents and includes refugees, incarcerated adults and youth, homemakers and businesspersons, medical professionals, corporate leaders and entertainers, some of whom are Academy Award and Grammy winners.

In addition to international service, I contribute locally in my home town as a founding board member, Trauma Recovery Yoga Instructor and lead trainer with The Shanthi Project, a non-profit organization which conducts Trauma-Informed Yoga and Mindfulness classes at the county prison, juvenile justice center, Boys and Girls Club, and area school districts for grades K-12.

I was fortunate to have studied with Dr. Milton Trager, the founder of The Trager Approach, who passed away in 1997. Further study with outstanding Trager Instructors has provided me with professional expertise for which I am very grateful. Studying Yoga with Sri K. Pattbhi Jois, who introduced the West to Ashtanga Yoga as well as with many of Ashtanga's foremost instructors enriched my life immeasurably. Of additional benefit to my endeavors is the knowledge received while obtaining Plant

Based Nutrition Certification through Cornell University, the classes being taught by Dr. T. Colin Campbell, author of "The China Study" and "Whole."

My passion for service found me engaged as Director of International Relations for Real Medicine Foundation and working closely with UN Agencies and foreign governments. It was a privilege to participate in so many international relief programs to improve primary health care service in disadvantaged areas of post-conflict, disaster affected and poverty-stricken countries, including Sri Lanka, South Sudan, Uganda, Kenya, Nigeria, Pakistan, Armenia and post-earthquake Haiti.

It was humbling to be honored by mention in South Sudan's Medical Journal/JubaLink as a principal in establishing the country's first College of Nursing and Midwifery. The work I conducted to introduce Trager to physical therapists in post-tsunami Sri Lanka, which I also did in Japan, was recognized with a cover article in the Massage Therapy Journal in 2007.

To maintain balance in my personal life, I play drums professionally in my band • ITO •. As a life-long drummer, I have played professionally in a variety of genres. To contribute to the drumming community, I developed an entirely on-line yoga and mindfulness program specifically for drummers, www.yoga4drummers.com, to help them access their full potential.

Though my professional journey began with a Bachelor's Degree in Finance and International Management from Rider University in Lawrenceville, New Jersey and was followed by extensive work in the corporate field, I'm grateful that my path led to mind-body, somatic education, and a career improving the physical and emotional well-being of others. I make home is in Easton, Pennsylvania, where having frequent opportunities to spend time with family, friends, and my cat Sayagyi is an ongoing blessing.

I can be reached at michael@pangea-yoga.com. For more information please visit www.pangea-yoga.com.

For more information about The Trager® Approach, or to find a Practitioner in your area, please contact The United States Trager® Association. United States Trager Association, 3755 Attucks Drive, Powell, Ohio 43065. #440-834-0308. www.tragerapproach.us.

Additional information can be found at: http://www.tragerfordailylife.com*

Books on The Trager® Approach:

Trager for Self-Healing: A Practical Guide for Living in the Present Moment - Audrey Mair
Mentastics: Movement As A Way to Agelessness - Dr. Milton Trager and Cathy Guadagno
Moving Medicine, The Life and Work of Dr. Milton Trager - Jack Liskin

Other Books - For more information on Trauma-informed Yoga and Veterans PTSD, the following books and organizations may be helpful. It has been reported that Veterans tend to prefer Yoga teachers who are also Veterans as they better identify with those who have shared experiences. It is always best to find a Yoga teacher with whom you resonate, one who is interested in empowering the student to perform on his or her own.

The Body Keeps the Score: Mind, Brain, and Body in the Transformation of Trauma - Bessel Van Der Folk
Trauma-Sensitive Yoga in Therapy: Bringing the Body into Treatment - David Emmerson
Best Practices for Yoga with Veterans - Editor: Carol Horton, Ph.D. - Yoga Service Council Publication
Non-Violent Communication - Marshall Rosenberg
The Pocket Guide to Polyvagal Theory: The Transformative Power of Feeling Safe - Dr. Stephen Porges, (Norton Series on Interpersonal Neurobiology)

Organizations:

Veterans Healing Veterans from the Inside Out - http://veteranshealingveterans.com/index.html
Veterans Yoga Project - www.veteransyogaproject.org
Warriors at Ease

For more information, please feel free to visit www.tragerapproach.us/pennsylvania/michael-lear.

CHAPTER 33 - SHADOWLAND FOUNDATION: WOLVES AND WARRIORS

Paul and Colette Pondella

My husband Paul Pondella is a man among wolves. That is what he was when I met him. Today, by his side I am his mate and Wolf-mom to 12 Alaskan Timberwolves in the 10 years we have been together. Since his first encounter with a Wolf-dog, he fell in love with the Wolf...powerful, wise, intense, loyal, fierce with an overabundance of gentle lovingness. Wolves have an unmistakable grasp on unconditional love. This inspired him to raise a pack of Wolves himself, socialize them to meet people and let the Wolves touch their hearts as they had touched his.

Together, we founded an Educational Non-Profit Organization called Shadowland Foundation whose mission is to "Educate not Eradicate." To be honest with you, I did not know Wolves or anything about them until we met and raised these wild creatures as our own. It has been the single greatest contribution I have made in my life and started a healing process so deep I could never have dreamt it to be possible.

Mind you, I was never in the armed forces nor was my husband Paul. Although we do not believe anyone escapes the ravages of war, the wounds of the warrior leave a legacy behind; affecting all those who have suffered those wounds, their families, their communities and all the rest of us too. For both Paul and I, our programs had to include our Wolves with Veterans and Active Duty service members.

Paul's father had two Purple Hearts from his time fighting in Korea. Apparently, after escaping death once, he healed and got sent back into battle again. This time his entire platoon was killed. He was the lone survivor saved only because his fellow soldiers fell on top of him when they died. As with all Soldiers at the time, they sent him home to his family with his life without acknowledging or talking about his unseen wounds.

"Shell Shock" I believe is what they called it when they would talk about it at all. Paul's grandfather told him little except that they had to watch his father carefully, especially at night. He would wake up thinking he was back in Korea, in battle; and he grabbed a weapon once and went to battle in the quiet and quaint neighborhood of Glendale, California one evening. The only treatment back then for what we now know as Post-Traumatic Stress Disorder (PTSD), was self-medication through alcohol abuse. He died of it, but it took more than 60 years to kill him.

There is probably no one in his whole life who could have possibly known what was in his heart, his mind, his soul...and how he tortured himself with survivor guilt. How it may have led to his tumultuous and often violent marriage to Paul's mother who ended up despising her husband most of her life. When you live into your 80's, that's a long time to hold a grudge. Paul knows first-hand how his Dad's perfectionism and need to control everything created competition and rifts between his four children; hurt feelings that have never healed to this day. Paul's father and mother divorced when he was 12 years old. He never recovered from that separation. Not knowing how to talk to him, his mother sent him away to live with his father when he couldn't cope with the separation. He grew up on the streets and hiding in the woods while his father ran a local gas station. At night his father remained drunk and unavailable.

This legacy of addiction was passed down to Paul. Even though he has been sober for 18 years from drugs and alcohol, the ramifications of his actions still haunt him today. From what he has shared with me, I know he is lucky to be alive. From what Paul has shared about his father; I don't think he felt lucky to have survived Korea. Paul found his healing with the wild ones hiding in the woods. He will tell you today that he relates better to animals than people. It was animals, and a dog with Wolf in it that saved his life.

Other than Paul, I am certain his father's service and what he suffered in Korea was never given a first thought much less a second one by his other siblings. There is a special place in his heart for Veterans so he can honor his dad and his service. Paul has addressed in therapy why his dad drank so much and could not find little if any satisfaction in the life he lived. Today, because of science and advances in psychotherapy we now know better how to help. We also know that access to help is still wholly inadequate. As wild animals, Wolves can never be registered as Service Animals, but that does not mean that their value and therapeutic nature is irrelevant.

I am a little older than Paul and remember Vietnam. I only knew survivors and their stories. They were a little more eager to share their stories and for some reason they trusted me enough to tell me. Of course we all know they were not honored for their service; on the contrary, they were blamed for it. One friend of mine spoke about "never having gotten off the plane." He was here. It was the 80's so he had been home from Vietnam for almost a decade. He was walking about, living his life, carrying on as if he was home, but for him...he never "got off the plane" when he landed back in the United States.

The men I met over the years, even the ones who evaded the draft...all had issues with some form of substance abuse, multiple marriages, isolation, detachment, or were adrenaline junkies. I am not a professional nor do I wish to seem judgmental about them, it was my observation and my heart broke for them. The Vietnam War was on TV every evening, on the news, just in time for dinner. Bloody soldiers, half naked children with burnt bodies, tanks and more were our dinner companions when I was growing up. We were all there together.

Today, this is still true I believe. Even though we do not see Iraq, Afghanistan, Syria, etc., on the nightly news, we are never far from one degree of separation from those that serve or have served. There are movies and television shows about the wars of today and what it might be like; we watch them in support. I lived in New York just blocks from Chelsea Piers on 9/11. The day this world was traumatized irrevocably and we all went to war with terror. That's why I say, the effects touch all of us. None of us however in any way like those who have risked life and limb in service to our country and live with it. These are the brave, fearless, honorable, survivors I believe Courtenay is writing this book for.

Because of my own experience with childhood abuses, I suffer from PTSD. I didn't know or understand it or even what was happening to me until I was well into my 30's. I now know my own personal symptoms when I have been triggered, but for most of my life, I was just unable to fathom "what was wrong with me." The level of shame and lack of confidence was unbearable. It kept me from fulfilling my dreams of a career in acting that I dreamed of, and the children I wanted to have. Luckily I found the help I needed and was treated with brilliant techniques like Neural Linguistic Programming and Eye Movement Desensitization and Reprocessing (EMDR) Therapy.

In 2004 I found a spiritual practice that suited me and put a shiny button on my carefully woven cloak of recovery. It taught me that I was one in all of creation with gifts no one else can give and that I have a divine purpose to fulfill here in my lifetime. There was nothing "wrong with me." In other words, I matter...no matter what came before.

I met my first Wolf in 2008 by way of a shiny blue special construction motorcycle parked along the curb. It caught my eye and like a tractor beam I was drawn to it and met Paul, my two legged Wolf. At home he had two four legged Wolves, one an exquisite tricolor Alaskan Timberwolf named Alaska and an imposing, superior black beauty named Shadow. I can safely say without equivocation that seeing myself in the eyes of these three, felt like the first time I had ever really been seen. Those golden eyes looked into me, not at me and saw me...whole. It was then hard not to see myself that way too.

A wash of acceptance, an initiation if you will, took my heart and I have never been the same since. They chose me as special enough for their pack family and fated to meet. Wolves however, do not discriminate. After ten years and the thousands of individuals who have met them and the rest of the pack we raised, everyone gets initiated into the pack. When they look into you, they share who they are. There is no other experience like it. This is what they do.

As the original dog, (God spelled backwards) man has known now for over 15,000 years that they are our kindred species. After centuries of near eradication Wolf recovery and studying Wolf behavior is teaching us more about our original nature, our authentic nature and the loyal, tribal, families we are; meeting the emotional bonding necessary for healthy, thriving, sustainable communities.

While studying the Wolves and Wolf pack dynamics to develop our educational programs, I was pleasantly surprised to know that many squadrons throughout the armed forces had named themselves and model the Wolf pack. Very early after establishing Shadowland Foundation we got a call from the Space Superiority Systems Wing stationed at Ft. McArthur Air force Base in El Segundo, California. They called themselves The Wolf Pack.

We were asked if we could bring our Wolf pack to honor their Wolf pack for a ceremony and picnic afterwards. At this time, we had not only Shadow and Alaska, but Takoda, our Alpha male and their seven three-month-old puppies.

We packed up all ten with a handful of volunteers and made our way to the base. If you could just imagine wrangling three-month-old puppies who are the size of medium size dogs and that get car sick just looking at a truck. One of the puppies was recovering from a very tricky back surgery so he had his own very special volunteer. Leaving him at home was not an option. No wolf gets left behind.

The Ft. MacArthur "SYSW Wolf Pack was in the middle of a ceremony. They were hidden in a meeting room without windows so we could set up as a surprise. Paul and I were sent in with Shadow, Alaska and Takoda in tow, but they let us in too early. The Colonel leading the meeting made a comment that seemed to suggest that he did not intend to be upstaged by the wolves and turned the microphone over to me. I had prepared something to say to honor the squadron.

"Like the wild Wolf pack, our service men and women epitomize the best of our nature...ensuring the safety and survival of all. What wolves and warriors have in common is:

Loyalty and devotion is routine, not the exception.
Strict discipline and exemplary leadership ensures the survival of the pack.
The Wolf pack is unsurpassed by its unity of purpose and diversity of skills that make each member invaluable and indispensable.
What they lack in size, they outperform in solidarity and endurance.
In the Wolf pack...everyone eats...no one is left behind.

With pride, we honor all of you for demonstrating these qualities and the sacrifices you have made in the name of honor and country; from the bottom of our hearts, we thank you. Today we wish to share our gratitude with a bunch of big ole sloppy unforgettable licks of appreciation from the Shadowland Foundation wolves."

After the ceremony, they surprised and honored us right back with a beautiful plaque we will always treasure.

Everyone joined us outside by this beautiful ocean setting where they enjoyed a picnic with their families and helped us initiate our puppies to their first public event. Many photo opportunities for all and a memorable day for us and we hope for the Wolf pack too. Soon afterwards we were invited back to surprise the Colonel at his retirement party. This officer comes often to our Wolves and Warriors Veterans Day open house. He gifted us his favorite picture and it hangs in our educational center. We are touched by our relationship with such a vital aspect of the armed forces.

We would and will always do whatever we can for a service member or a Veteran. Over the years, we have had many visits from many Veterans from many wars come meet the wolves at our yearly Veterans Day Open Houses. A Native American Vet came to sit with the pack for hours. He has become a friend of our pack. He showed up to help us through the Powerhouse Fire in June of 2013. His expertise knew the fire would get to us and when. We survived the fire intact. He made sure we were protected.

A Vietnam Air Force Vet with a crush on one of our males named Cochise. She has become a regular here. Cochise is a MacKenzie wolf with red fur and she is a red head too. She is prone to sitting alone meditating until she mingles with the Wolves. Her face lights up, her eyes sparkle and she becomes more conversational with other visitors. Her son and daughter survived the shooter in Las Vegas in 2018, but they had friends who did not. Even though her daughter is deathly afraid of dogs, she asked her mom to call us and see if she and her friend could come and sit with the wolves. Of course and always, would be our answer.

An Iraqi Vet and our neighbor shared with us that he had PTSD and a Traumatic Brain Injury (TBI). He also lost his hearing in one ear. He said his job was to detect and dismantle land mines and that he "messed up." I could tell by the sound of his voice that he blamed himself for his injuries. He was so sensitive to loud sounds it was impossible for him to keep and hold a job. After visiting us we learned he adopted a puppy and talked about it like he had a newborn child. It's when you see the eyes light up and get goose bumps all over when you know a healing has had a moment.

A 92-year-old World War II Veteran came one day to visit the Wolves. It was too cold a day to meet them outside as we usually do so we brought him and his wife into our home. We have Indoor/Outdoor Wolves. When he met our Alpha male and father of our pack, Takoda, they really connected. Takoda a huge 116 pound Arctic/MacKenzie curled up at his feet. Within a minute this tall warrior climbed onto our living room floor, face-to-face with Takoda. They lay there staring into each other's eyes for nearly an hour. Every once in a while, Takoda would reach out to him and touch him with his paw. They had an in-depth secret conversation while we were in their presence. What we wouldn't give to know what they found out from each other...the Vet got up and joined in conversation with us two-legged folks. He wasn't offering any details and we felt it intrusive to ask.

Recently an enlisted Marine came to spend the night in a Cottage we make available to the public for Thanksgiving weekend. He was part of several teams during his long career that called themselves Wolf packs. He had a Wolf that looked like our wolf Tehya tattooed on his arm. He had done several tours overseas. Forgive me for not being able to share much about their experience. It is theirs after all. Most don't speak about it. We try not to pry, but what we witness is kind of indescribable. It is not a simple thing, it is just extraordinary. The best he could do is to say he slept better here than he had slept in years. The sound of the Wolves howling in the night was what he loved the most.

I did ask why he came to see Wolves. He said in his leadership roles he embraces the Wolves for their success as a pack. He was not specific, but my knowledge is that these creatures survived the ice age because of the respect and loyalty for the leaders and utilizing the talents of the other members of the pack. Most wildlife biologists will tell you that they are the most unlikely species to survive based on the fact that they cannot eviscerate their prey which can weigh up to 700 pounds or more. They have endurance, jaw pressure and each other...that's it. Those aspects seem to be enough. Their main form of death in the wild is getting kicked and gored by their prey and at the hand of men with guns. Like us, they will fight to death for territory, but we have evidence that they are very respectful of each other's boundaries. They will invade when resources are not at levels the pack can survive on. When invaded, the leaders sacrifice themselves for the pack. When the Alphas are killed the rest of the pack sometimes fall apart and they do not survive. They are physically vulnerable to knee and head injuries as well as loss of limbs to traps set by hunters. We are similar species in so many ways.

I wish I could measure the healing that happens with an experience with the Wolves. Then there would be data that would be helpful as a method of healing...but alas, only the Wolves and the people who are changed forever know. They looked into each other's eyes, touched each other literally, emotionally, energetically and spiritually. We have been given a gift and we are honored to share these amazing creatures who intuitively know when you are hurting and want to help.

We also have a program called "Wolves and Wellness." This includes but is not limited to those recovering from Drugs and Alcohol which usually uncovers deep traumas of abuse, injury, loss, grief, abandonment, and PTSD. We bring our Wolf, Freedom mostly; he is like a magnet for whatever ails you and he can love it all away. Shielded by his fur, he doesn't mind looking acceptingly into your eyes, rubbing his healing, energetic scent on you and then rolling over to let you pet his belly with all of the trust the universe has to offer. They are all healers, but I believe his destiny is to be with us to bring wellness and peace to the hearts of those who suffer and are in need of healing and recognition.

We here at Shadowland Foundation are dedicated to saving Wolves in the wild and we do it by introducing Wolves as they really are, as sentient beings. As I said as I started this writing, we have had the honor of living with and being unconditionally loved by them and letting them teach us every day the meaning of life. Abandoned by our families' years ago, we have been adopted and are treasured by a pack family that takes care of us in every way that's meaningful. They serve our hearts and souls desires. Our emotional needs are met, and the Wolves think we deserve it. We are still working to believe that to be true. We do know that they are probably right about us. Our pack doesn't just give these vital life necessities to me and Paul; they give it to you too.

Please visit us at: http://www.shadowlandfoundation.org

CHAPTER 34 - SHAMANIC HEALING IN THE TREATMENT OF PTSD

Susan Mokelke, JD; Narrye Caldwell, MTCM, L.Ac; Alexandra Solomon, MSW, LCSW; Scott Williams, MA

Susan Mokelke, JD, president of the Foundation for Shamanic Studies (FSS) and director of the FSS faculty, explains how core shamanism offers time-tested and effective methods to help heal Veterans experiencing Post-Traumatic Stress Disorder (PTSD). Biographies for Susan and her co-authors can be found at the end of this chapter.

The following example of shamanic healing for a combat Veteran was reported by FSS faculty member Scott Williams. It is one illustration of how "core shamanism" methods can be used to treat Veterans suffering from PTSD. Shamanic healing derives from the practitioner's relationship with evolved, wise, and compassionate helping spirits existing in what is referred to as "non-ordinary" reality. Shamanic healers develop their relationships with these spirits over a long period of time, becoming skilled at bringing the power and wisdom of these helping spirits to our "ordinary" reality dimension. These spirits work through an experienced practitioner to do the actual healing work for the client. Since every practitioner of shamanism is unique, individual variations on the basic shamanic healing methods are common, so not every session will closely resemble the one described in the case study below. The case report is followed by a description of some of the principles and methods of shamanic healing, along with resources if you want to learn more.

Shamanic Healing PTSD Case Study: Combat Veteran "Dan" — by Scott Williams, MA

I first met Dan when he started work at my place of employment six years ago. He was in the National Guard, and still is. I did not know at the time that he suffered from PTSD, or the depth of his issues. Gradually, as I got to know him, I learned more about his life: he was married, had volunteered for the military, had served three combat tours in Iraq and Afghanistan, and was suffering from PTSD. Additionally, he had problems both with his marriage and with anger.

After working with Dan for about six months, we were talking and I mentioned that I had a healing to do for a client. He inquired about what that was so I briefly explained shamanic healing to him. He commented that he could really use some spiritual healing. He also mentioned that he was feeling particularly stressed that day as he had just talked to a lawyer about divorcing his wife (she had opioid/alcohol addiction issues). I asked if he would like me to do healing work for him to which he answered, "Can you do it now?"

I explained to him that I could not do it right then but I would see if there was anything I could do for him that day. We both work at a large manufacturing facility where it is possible to find a "quiet" space to vanish into for short periods of time. So, I did a shamanic journey to my spirits to see if there was something I could do for Dan that day. I was told I could give him power. I talked to Dan and let him know that I could pass power to him then. I also told him there were other things I could do for him, just not at work.

We found a spot where we would not be bothered for at least fifteen minutes and we went to work. I called on my spirits to come and fill me with their spiritual power. They came relatively instantly, filled me with power, which I then passed to Dan. After receiving the power, Dan started to slump so I caught him and helped him into a chair. Within a minute he was doing well and in his own words, "Holy shit, what the hell was that! That was amazing!" The passing of power helped Dan recover enough that he could continue on the rest of the day without feeling the draining effects of his PTSD. I reminded him that there was more work to be done, just not at the workplace. He thanked me and we set up a date to do more work.

Several days later Dan arrived where I did my healing work. We chatted for a bit, reviewed what types of healing could happen, and then got to work. I journeyed to my spirits to see what could be done for Dan. I was told he needed extraction (removal of spiritual "intrusions" that do not belong there) and a soul retrieval (restoration of a person's vital spiritual essence), but not necessarily both that day. I asked Dan if he was ready for this; he was, so I proceeded with the extraction.

That extraction session was the longest I had ever done. Dan had many intrusions in various parts of his body but the most stubborn, and the largest number, were in his chest and head. After spending a long time, I finished with the extraction healing. Dan said he felt a little spent, but also invigorated after the healing. He really wanted to jump right into the soul retrieval but at my suggestion we did not do the soul retrieval. Instead I had Dan sit with the extraction for a week to see how things went.

All during the week up until his next session, Dan kept telling me how great he felt after the extraction. He said he had not felt that good in a long time. At the next session I again journeyed to my spirits to see what to do and was told that he needed more extraction done. I told him and he was a little disappointed that we would not be doing the soul retrieval. I again found a number of intrusions in his chest and head and removed them. This session did not take as long as the first. Prior to the extraction I had done a special shamanic healing drumming practice referred to as "Tuvan

Drumming" for him; he had injured his knee on his first deployment and it was bothering him.

Dan's next session was three weeks later; he had his National Guard two-week training and then a week's vacation. When he returned to work, he asked me if I could give him power again. I said I could but it would have to wait a while, I was working on a hot job that needed to be finished first. He kept coming over to talk while I worked, discussing how his two weeks had been. Then he told me his week of vacation was for filing for divorce and also getting his wife into a treatment program. He definitely needed a boost but the most important thing is that he was not having anger issues around his wife. After having the extraction work done, he was able to work with and for his wife calmly, even though their marriage was ending.

One thing that had not changed for Dan was that he still had problems sleeping due to the PTSD. Routinely, he only got two to four hours of sleep per day. He said he got used to that while in Iraq. At the beginning of working with Dan I had asked him if he had seen a doctor for his issues. He said he talked with a therapist in the military but did not tell him about the extent of his issues. He was afraid that, if he did, he would be discharged from service. I had expressed that I would do healing work for him, but that he should continue seeing the therapist, which he did.

The week he came back to work Dan asked for power twice, which I did for him. At his next session I did a soul retrieval for him. As you might expect from someone who had done three combat tours and was ending a marriage, there were a number of "soul portions" that had left Dan.

After checking with my spirits, I proceeded with the soul retrieval. I brought back four soul portions for Dan. There were a number of others that were not ready to return at this time. I also did a "power animal retrieval" for him at the time of the soul retrieval. After it was done Dan opened his eyes and inhaled a giant breath — it almost sounded like a small jet engine it was so intense. He then dropped his head and sobbed and cried for about ten minutes or so. It was a very humbling experience to be in the presence of this man who had fought for his country, being so emotionally present and raw.

Since I worked with Dan, I saw him every day. I could see the change in him happen on a small, daily basis. His rapid, intense, anger slowed noticeably. He seemed happier and smiled more. He told me he was sleeping more. He told me he felt more like himself than he had in a number of years.

Since then, I still work with Dan, but on a much lesser scale. I did more extraction work for him and two more soul retrievals over the next few years. He now sleeps at least five or six hours a night. He still has some anger issues, but it takes a lot more to get it started. As Dan said, "I don't even get mad at other drivers anymore." In this process I taught Dan how to do shamanic journeying, which he still does even though he says he does not believe in this stuff! What he does believe is that it has helped him. It has allowed him to regain himself, to stay in the military, and as he stated, not to become another Veteran suicide statistic.

Shamanic Healing and Core Shamanism: Some Background

Shamanism is the world's oldest spiritual practice, dating back tens of thousands of years. Our ancient ancestors used shamanic methods to alter their consciousness and travel to other realms to interact with helping spirits for the purposes of healing and gaining practical knowledge to help themselves and their peoples. Shamanism has been found on every inhabited continent. For Westerners, our shamanic traditions were lost centuries ago due to religious and political oppression. But beginning in the fifties, anthropologist Michael Harner (1929–2018) began his decades of pioneering work, originating, researching, and developing authentic methods of shamanic practice in order to restore this highly effective spiritual heritage to the West. In 1980, his classic book, The Way of the Shaman, launched a worldwide reawakening of interest in shamanism. Today these methods form a complete knowledge and healing system called "core shamanism." Core shamanism consists of the "universal, near-universal, and common features of shamanism, together with journeys to other worlds, a distinguishing feature of shamanism."

Training in core shamanism is particularly suited to contemporary society, as it does not focus on ceremonies, rituals, or other culture-specific practices of shamanic peoples. Rather, it addresses the underlying methods of shamanic practice worldwide. Students of core shamanism learn to alter their consciousness through classic shamanic non-drug techniques, primarily repetitive drumming, in order to activate their own spiritual resources and learn directly from their own helping spirits how to heal and help others. Core shamanism is very much an independent spirituality, a system of personal knowledge, not of faith. Shamanic practitioners are trained in methods, particularly the shamanic journey, so that they can travel directly to the compassionate helping spirits and discover and know truth for themselves.

Methods of Healing

Shamanism is a holistic healing practice. As noted in the above case study, it works very well with other forms of healing, including physical medicine and psychotherapy. Shamanism works at the level of the soul. It is a basic principle in shamanism that all forms in creation have a soul, and that in order to be healthy and function optimally in life, the soul must be vital and empowered, and fully present within the body.

Otherwise, even the best physical and/or emotional medicine cannot be completely effective.

In addition to a fully empowered soul, from a shamanic view, everyone needs a connection with at least one guardian spirit, commonly referred to as a "power animal," to help and protect them. These two things—an empowered soul and a helping spirit connection — form what is sometimes called our "spiritual immune system." If this system is weakened, which can happen due to trauma or neglect, we may fall prey to illness, depression, bad luck and accidents, loss of vitality and purpose, and a general decline in body, mind, and spirit.

Trauma can occur to a person in a myriad of ways. The obvious trauma of exposure to violence and conflict, as is the case with combat Veterans, is of course a major source of what is called "soul loss." But soul loss can also occur through emotional pain and shock, accidents, long term illness, constant stress, overwork and even the loss of connection with nature. The shamanic healing method needed for soul loss is called "soul retrieval."

Soul retrieval is a shamanic methodology in which the practitioner, with the assistance of their helping spirits, in an altered state using rhythmic drumming, makes a shamanic journey to locate and return missing portions of a client's soul, which have been lost due to some form of trauma. The missing soul portions can be thought of as part of a person's vitality and essence that they can no longer access, leaving them diminished and lacking in power. The shamanic healer is guided by their helping spirits in finding and identifying soul portions that are ready to be returned to the client and re-integrated. When found, the practitioner is trained to gently return them to the client, by blowing them into the chest and top of the head. The work can be quite moving for both practitioner and client. The client may experience an immediate healing effect, though often things shift over a period of time as the soul portion re-integrates.

Another form of restoring power to a client is the return of a guardian spirit, which appears most often in the form of a power animal. Power animal retrieval is done in a similar way to soul retrieval. Power animals are a treasured and crucial aspect of our spiritual immune system, providing spiritual power, help, protection, and advice. It is important, in maintaining one's connection and relationship to a power animal, to learn ways of working with the animal spirit in ordinary reality. The shamanic practitioner, after returning a power animal, can advise the client on how to nurture this important relationship.

Sometimes, if a person is lacking in power due to soul loss from trauma, as with combat Veterans, they can become vulnerable to spiritual "intrusions," such as "spiritual darts" resulting from people's hostile thoughts or other small non-physical influences, which can lodge in the non-corporeal aspect of the physical body and cause localized pain and illness. The shamanic healing method for removal of these intrusions is called Extraction Healing. This process is done while the practitioner is in an altered state, using drumming or rattling, so they can work closely with their helping spirits to do the work. After these intrusions are removed, power is restored to the client with soul retrieval and/or power animal retrieval, so they are no longer vulnerable to such non-physical influences.

All of these methods are facilitated by the shamanic healer, who brings the spirits' power here, but it is the practitioner's own helping spirits that do the work. Before every healing session, the practitioner will journey to ask the spirits what healing is needed — as Scott did for Dan in the case study above — and then proceed accordingly, as directed. This practice, of asking the spirits for information and answers to questions, is called Shamanic Divination. In addition to direct healing, with the client's permission, the shamanic practitioner can also ask the spirits to provide information and knowledge about the client's situation that can help them on their path.

An essential ethical consideration before any shamanic healing can be performed is obtaining the expressed permission (informed consent) of the client to do shamanic work. Shamanic healing deals with the soul. Each person has the right to decide what to do in matters of their own soul and to choose their path without interference or undue influence.

What is a shamanic healing session like?

Since shamanism is an independent spirituality, each shamanic healer develops their own specific ways of setting up their practice and working with clients. But if you go to a well-trained practitioner of core shamanism you will find common themes and methodologies.

In general, initially the practitioner will ask some general questions about what is going on for the client, briefly explain shamanic healing and obtain permission for shamanic work, and then set an appointment.

When the client arrives for the session, the practitioner will settle the client comfortably, fully clothed, on the floor, in a chair, or on a treatment table, like a massage table. The practitioner will then use rattling, drumming, and sometimes singing to connect with their helping spirits and "power up" in preparation for the healing work. Typically, the practitioner does a short divination journey to determine what methods will be used in the current session. Some practitioners use a special shamanic drumming recording (rhythmic drumming at three to seven beats per second) to support their shift in consciousness; others drum for themselves. Some practitioners may even have a drumming assistant. Any of these methods are effective to alter consciousness.

Once the healing methods to be done are determined, various things may happen, depending upon which method is to be offered. The practitioner may rattle and drum a lot more, may dance/move around the client, and may use hand motions near the client's body, with some light touching involved (permission to touch is usually requested in advance). There may also be singing or chanting, and at some point during the treatment power may be restored by blowing gently over the chest and at the top of the head.

At the end of the session, the client may choose to share their experience of the work with the practitioner. The practitioner may also offer a few directions or follow up suggestions, if guided to do so by the spirits. It is not usually necessary to talk a lot, since the work is accomplished spiritually at the level of the soul, and a quiet peaceful space can facilitate the client's integration of the experience. The practitioner may recommend that more than one session is needed, as was described in Dan's case story above, or sometimes a single session is all that is required at this time. The timing and number of sessions is directed by the practitioner's helping spirits.

How does someone become a shaman? How do I find one? Can shamanic training be helpful for Veterans with PTSD?

"How do I know if someone is a shaman?" Michael Harner was asked. "It's simple," he said. "Do they journey to other worlds? And do they perform miracles?" When a person starts to perform miracles of healing, consistently getting good results, then that person might be named a shaman by his or her community.

In indigenous cultures, people became shamans in various ways. They might survive a life-threatening illness, undergo initiations or physical challenges, inherit the role, pay a master shaman for the knowledge, or be apprenticed to an elder shaman. In contemporary society, though these processes may still be a factor, people may feel drawn to shamanism as a healing practice, often after receiving a miraculous healing themselves, or perhaps have a transformative experience that they discover is shamanic in nature. This may lead them to investigate contemporary shamanic training.

In 1985, Michael and Sandra Harner established the FSS, a public nonprofit educational and charitable organization "dedicated to the preservation, study, and teaching of shamanic knowledge for the welfare of the Planet and its inhabitants." The FSS offers an integrated program of weekend workshops and advanced residential training that guides students through progressively advanced methods, practices, and initiatory experiences. The program includes workshops for gaining shamanic knowledge, such as Shamanic Dreamwork, Divination, and Spirits of Nature, as well as the primary shamanic healing methodologies. The ethical use of shamanic methods and power is emphasized.

In addition to receiving healing, shamanic training can often be useful for Veterans who have suffered from PTSD. The shamanic journey, particularly, offers the journeyer the opportunity to experience personally the realms of the helping spirits, an expansive dimension of compassion, wisdom, healing, and oneness. In addition to being able to contact the spirits for personal knowledge and help with daily life, shamanic journeying can provide a cosmic perspective of our place in the universe, resulting in a hopeful and inspired orientation toward one's life. Altering consciousness through non-drug methods using rhythmic drumming is time-tested, effective, and safe. Most people can learn the shamanic journey fairly readily. The steps of the practice are set forth in Michael Harner's book Cave and Cosmos: Shamanic Encounters with Another Reality(see Appendices A & B); or one can take the FSS introductory weekend The Way of the Shaman® under the guidance of an experienced faculty member.

To find a shamanic practitioner to work with, it is important to do your own research, just as you would when seeking any other healthcare professional. Sometimes you can find someone who has had a good healing experience with a practitioner, and you can start with their referral. Be sure to talk with the practitioner and find out how they work, what they charge for their work, and what training and experience they have. Find a practitioner you feel comfortable with and avoid those who charge excessive fees, promise healing miracles, or boast of their skills.

The FSS provides a practitioner list, searchable by location, of people who have participated in Foundation advanced trainings such as the Three Year Program in Advanced Shamanism and the Two Week Shamanic Healing Intensive, and how many years they have practiced. All practitioners work independently of the Foundation and no endorsement can be made since it is the connection with the helping spirits that makes an effective shaman. But high-quality training and practical experience are good places to start looking. You will find resources for finding practitioners at the end of this article.

Summary

Shamanic healing is finding a well-deserved place as an effective complementary healing modality for people who struggle with the disabling effects of trauma in general, and for Veterans with combat related PTSD in particular. The methods reviewed in this chapter are time-tested, authentic, and effective non-drug practices for addressing trauma and illness. Though they may be considered "alternative" in contemporary society, they have a track record of success that dates back tens of thousands of years. Shamanic methods can be an important part of the recovery process for many who suffer with serious medical conditions and traumatic life experiences. We hope this brief introduction will help demystify shamanic healing for those who might benefit from this ancient therapeutic methodology.

Resources:

Visit the Foundation for Shamanic Studies website, shamanism.org
   About Core Shamanism: https://shamanism.org/workshops/coreshamanism.html
   Shamanic Healing, We Are Not Alone by Michael Harner: https://shamanism.org/articles/article01/.html
   Introductory Workshop, The Way of the Shaman®: https://shamanism.org/workshops/calendar.php?Wkshp_ID=10
   Finding a Practitioner: https://shamanism.org/resources/services.php
   Shamanic Training: https://shamanism.org/workshops/index.php
   Cave and Cosmos: Shamanic Encounters with Another Reality by Michael Harner, © 2013 The Foundation for Shamanic Studies (North Atlantic Books, Berkeley, CA), Appendix D, Core Shamanism and Healing: Information for Physicians and Health Professionals; Appendices A and B, Shamanic Journey instructions
   The Way of the Shaman by Michael Harner © 1980, 1990 Michael Harner (HarperCollins, New York, NY)

FSS Faculty Member Contributors:

Susan Mokelke, JD, is the president of the Foundation for Shamanic Studies (FSS) and the director of the FSS faculty. She has worked with non-profit educational organizations her entire adult life. Susan has a Bachelor of Science degree from the University of Southern California and a Juris Doctorate from Loyola Law School of Los Angeles. She has practiced shamanic healing since 1999 and has been an FSS faculty member since 2006. More about Susan: https://shamanism.org/fssinfo/mokelke.html

Narrye Caldwell, MCTM, L.Ac, is a shamanic practitioner, martial artist, and teacher of traditional Chinese healing arts. She is a graduate of the FSS Two Week Shamanic Healing Intensive, Three Year Program of Advanced Initiations in Shamanism and Shamanic Healing, Harner Shamanic Counseling Training, and an FSS faculty member. She also teaches at Five Branches University and at the Academy of Martial Arts in Santa Cruz, CA. More about Narrye: https://shamanism.org/fssinfo/caldwellbio.html

Alexandra Solomon, MS, LCSW, is a shamanic practitioner and licensed clinical social worker. She is a graduate of the FSS Two Week Shamanic Healing Intensive, Three Year Program of Advanced Initiations in Shamanism and Shamanic Healing, and Harner Shamanic Counseling Training, and an FSS faculty member. Alexandra has a master's degree from the University of Connecticut School of Social Work. More about Alexandra: https://shamanism.org/fssinfo/solomonbio.php

Scott Williams, MA, is a shamanic practitioner and an archaeologist. He is an FSS faculty member and a graduate of the FSS Three Year Program of Advanced Initiations in Shamanism and Shamanic Healing and the Two Week Shamanic Healing Intensive. Scott works for a major aerospace manufacturing corporation and has an MA in anthropology from the University of Connecticut. More about Scott: https://shamanism.org/fssinfo/williamsbio.php

Visit the FSS faculty directory for biographical information: https://shamanism.org/fssinfo/directory.html

CHAPTER 36 - TAI CHI, QIGONG, SPIRAL ANATOMY AND PTSD

Susan A. Matthews, MS, ND

Tai Chi is a Movement Art for the Brain. Practicing Tai Chi and Qigong benefits Veterans with PTSD through several mechanisms and this chapter will identify important components of a robust practice. Tai Chi is a great therapeutic exercise for PTSD for several reasons. To me, the most profound reason is how it acts on the brain and nervous system. For example, the popular technique referred to as 'mindfulness,' has been well-documented as effectively helping the body respond to stress.

But that concept is not so new. Long before the term mindfulness was ever coined, Tai Chi practitioners had advanced meditative movement far beyond mindfulness as a practice to cultivate awareness of energy in movement. This may sound abstract, but how one focuses one's attention on movement can create a powerful response in the brain and nervous system that can help to heal such ailments as PTSD.

So, what is Tai Chi and what is Qigong?

First of all, Tai Chi (and its historical name, taijiquan), is evolved from Chinese martial arts and is more popularly practiced as an exercise to promote overall health and longevity. Translated it means "supreme ultimate fist" and is often referred to as Taiji boxing. Practitioners do a variety of styles traditionally named after the family who developed their own particular style: Yang, Chen, Wu, Sun. As an exercise, Tai Chi is basically a sequence, or choreography, of postures and movements known as forms. Forms have martial applications; thus, it is a fighting art, as well as health exercise.

Qigong, which is much older than Tai Chi, is primarily performed for the purpose of health, but with one great difference — to build vital energy called 'qi' (pronounced "chee"). Characteristically, Qigong movements are performed repeatedly in a stationary position, either standing or seated. Tai Chi usually requires stepping and changing position and directions.

Tai Chi and the Brain

Tai Chi and Qigong mind-movement practice can profoundly affect mental states, including PTSD and attendant anxiety, depression, chronic stress, chronic depression and sleep disorders. Tai Chi and Qigong practice affects every system in the body and is considered whole-body, or mind-body-spirit exercise. The movements of Tai Chi and Qigong, which are very precise in nature, nurture precise mental focus, which directly affects brain and nervous system function. Later on, I will give some examples how this can happen in practical terms and which can be implemented.

Scientific discoveries about the brain and nervous system have revealed the brain's capability of plasticity — the intrinsic ability to change and grow—to adapt to environmental, physiological and behavioral cues. All physical and mental health are dependent primarily on a fine-tuned nervous system, yet rarely does conventional physical exercise take into account this understanding. Most of what we see these days is "muscle exercise" with secondary effects on the cardiovascular system and internal organs. This direct stressing of the cardiovascular system is promoted by western practitioners. In contrast, practitioners of Chinese internal martial arts, such as Tai Chi, have consistently used various forms of "meditative" movement as exercise to promote the ability of the brain to change and adapt to conditions experienced by the body.

Plasticity, reprogramming, and making new neural pathways can be accomplished by practicing Tai Chi, because it contains a multilevel approach that activates the brain for health, healing and even higher consciousness. Indeed, practitioners have cultivated the dynamic qualities found in Tai Chi to enhance physical and mental abilities well-beyond normal, and to further their learning paths. In terms of rehabilitation, these same qualities make it the "supreme ultimate" exercise to access the brain and to activate the nervous system to change, to even heal itself, through movement.

Similar benefits can be achieved in many other types of exercise if they contain certain mind-movement principles. Running, walking, ballroom dancing (highly recommended, goes well with Tai Chi), tennis, golf, and everyday activities can be enhanced.

I remember loving the idea of the old 1960s TV series "Kung Fu" with David Carradine. I needed his peaceful heart amidst conflict and confrontation — yet I also needed to be a fierce warrior who could protect myself. I experienced my own PTSD after being serially abused as a child. I can truly say I have accomplished a sense of peace, strength and well-being far beyond my dreams since starting Tai Chi nearly 40 years ago. Rest assured, however, that benefits can be experienced immediately with the right practice, plus they build up over time. Knowledge, ability and skill are cumulative with time and effort. This is known as one's "gong Fu."

Six ways Tai Chi and Qigong Effect Brain Function

Rhythmic and synchronous movements train the brain:

The first two, rhythmicity, and second, synchronicity, have been linked to brain activation during memory acquisition and learning, as well as neural information coding, growth and development, states of consciousness, perception and awareness, locomotion, autonomic function, neural repair, and rehabilitation. That's a long list, but all you really need to know in order to begin is Tai Chi and Qigong movements are repetitive and rhythmic and slow motion. Slow, precise motion trains the brain for fast motion.

One of the hallmarks of Tai Chi is the practice of "silk reeling" which is a training where all the joints of the body are coordinated to perform in a spiraling synchrony. The biomechanics at each joint are integrated with all other joints, and the force is generated from the ground. Practice trains the bone, tendon, ligaments, joints to be "connected" like a single snake. And through a special form of stretching in Tai Chi, the combined muscle force/activation patterns produce whole-body superior power without muscle.

Communication between distant brain areas is important for integration of complex information to adapt to changes in the environment and to generate appropriate responses necessary for successful behavior in daily life. Through numerous experiments, it has been established that cortical neurons strengthen their connections by repeated stimulation and synchronous activation — this is called 'Hebb's Rule,' commonly stated as "neurons that fire together, wire together."

On the basis of this, it has been assumed that perceptions or actions are represented in the brain by large numbers of distributed neurons firing in synchrony. Synchronous activity is often associated with oscillatory firing patterns, rhythms, in discrete frequency bands that represent certain aspects of behavior, learning, common motion, direction and velocity, or coordination. These rhythmic activities are synchronous over relatively large areas of the cortex and even deeper brain structures, between the left and right cerebral hemispheres, between the visual and motor (movement command) centers of the brain, and between the motor and somatosensory (what the body feels) centers. They are also enhanced in amplitude when performing new and complicated motor acts.

Mental practice and movement imagery trains the brain:

Third, mental practice, mind training including visualization and movement imagery, are receiving greater significance for training and for treatment potential. For example, new imaging techniques have shown that imagery, or mental practice, causes neuronal (nerve cell) activity that mirrors actual movement. We also know that movement, respiration, and heart rate can be synchronized with training. This capacity of the nervous system is just beginning to be explored in brain injury research and treatment.

Mind training that includes meditation, mindfulness, and visualization is an important component of Tai Chi and Qigong. Unique to practicing these arts is that the mind is not just trained to relax, but it is trained to build a sense of awareness of energy or qi inside the body, thus it is an 'internal art.' Further, the mind is trained to direct movement of qi with mind intention...and that movement of qi is what directs the physical body. The result is that the brain strives to create the mental image, not an isolated arm or leg movement.

Merged PET-MRI brain section illustrating changes in cerebral blood flow during movement visualization. From: Lafleur, M. F., et al., 2002. Motor learning produces parallel dynamic functional changes during the execution and imagination of sequential foot movements. Neuroimage. 16, 142-157.

Tai Chi training tools greatly enhance mental agility by tapping into the mind connection between visualization of internal energy (qi) and movement. For example, the simplest meditation is done at night before going to sleep. The meditation that I teach guides you to fill the brain and body with energy, light and love. This practice brings spiritual energy and earth energy to the heart, profoundly affects your sense of well-being, calms the nervous system, reduces fear and anger, and trains the mind to bring healing energy to specific affected areas of the body. This practice benefits sleep and reduces stress, anxiety and depression.

Balanced left-right movement balances left-right brain activity:

Fourth, balanced, integrated, left- and right-sided movement, as found in Tai Chi, must be accompanied by balanced brain activity; i.e., accessing the brain's neural circuitry is a direct approach to enhancing function or to healing physical and mental dysfunction resulting from mental trauma, mechanical injury or biochemical imbalance. I often think of Tai Chi as **EMDR** (Eye Movement Desensitization and Reprocessing Therapy) using the whole body. Balance is accomplished by using four major components of Tai Chi training: 1) central equilibrium training, the concept of maintaining a straight spine with an energetic central "plumb line"; 2) the biomechanics of spiraling in the joints, called silk reeling training mentioned above; 3) cultivation of a powerful physical and energetic connection to the ground called 'root'; and 4) synchronization of right/left or bilateral (opposite sided) and ipsilateral (same sided) movement. Moving left and right sides together becomes linked in the nervous system, requiring tight inter-hemispheric coupling, plus synchronization binds movement into functional synergies: synergies in energy movement, brain and spinal cord rhythms, muscle activation, breathing, heart rate, and so on. Such movement activates the motor and sensory neural circuitry of the whole brain.

To take balanced, rhythmic, left/right movement even further, we can add the movement model presented in Spiral Anatomy™ Training which describes and trains a specific backwards bicycle or reverse cycling rotational movement in all the joints. This movement facilitates spiraling in the joints, which allows for maximum fluid motion, so that the body flows like water.

The practical application of this information is that slow rhythmic movement (1 Hz or one beat per second) may entrain, control, or balance a vast neuronal network. Thus, the slow-motion movements of Tai Chi forms may result in this kind of neural control. The comfort imparted by rocking and walking my daughter's new baby, or the incessant kneading and purring of my cat, or the well-known benefits of therapeutic riding for developmental disorders, suggests the power of rhythmic movement. It also suggests that imbalanced activity results in imbalanced mental/emotional states, tremors and epileptic seizures, and could be a result of the loss of the superimposed slower rhythms.

The graphs below show altered brain rhythms after performing a 1 Hz backwards bicycling movement.

EEG — Quiet standing

Backwards Bicycle Punching

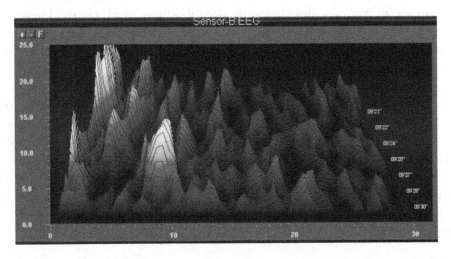

Tai Chi engages multiple sensory systems to practice being in the present moment:

Fifth, just as the motor system is trained in many ways, fast progress can be made by engaging multiple sensory systems (visual, kinesthetic, and sensory for gravity and position; muscle stretch and load; skin sensations, bone and joint stress, left/right weighting; rhythmicity; the sensation of qi, both physically and with mind intention.

For example: simply visualizing sand filling the feet and legs causes greater stability, heaviness and a downward 'root'. Next, just turning your attention to the top of the head and visualizing an upward motion along a center line establishes a plumb line around which all movement and thought is balanced and focused. Mentally shifting sand from left to right, along with weight, sets up a rhythmic movement that can affect brain rhythms. Engaging the brain with attention on numerous positive sensations, thoughts, intentions, at the very least helps distract one from thinking about negative emotions.

Tai Chi trains the mind to harmonize movement of energy and physical movement:

Sixth, in Tai Chi we are training the mind to: 1) increase awareness of the sensation of internal energy (qi) in the body; 2) direct the internal energy to flow in harmony with the physical movement; 3) allow the physical movement to follow the mentally directed energy flow, and; 4) ultimately cultivate awareness of the energetic movement in the space (universe) surrounding the movement. A person who trains mind-body-spirit on this level is learning to live as a spiritual/energy being. We are tapping into a direct internal experience of energy, light and love.

An example of this training begins with practicing Qi Circles (pronounced 'chee' circles) which are Qigong movements that include something like rolling an imaginary ball in circles in various directions in the abdomen and chest. These circular movements improve blood circulation to the digestive organs, kidneys, and other abdominal organs directly and can be practiced sitting in a chair or incorporated into other movements.

Qi Circles specifically increase blood circulation to reproductive organs, bladder, prostate and change the state (tone) of the pelvic floor. These exercises can relieve incontinence and greatly improve sexual function. This is ancient training from Wu Style Tai Chi for cultivating energy in the middle and lower dantian (energy centers located in the heart and abdomen) and kidneys. The exercises open and balance energy flow in the meridians which are the channels in the body and limbs in which energy flows. Likewise, they improve bone, blood and lymph circulation which boosts the immune system.

Finding a great training program

To recap, practicing Tai Chi and Qigong can benefit Veterans with PTSD and the most important components of a robust practice include: 1) Practicing relaxation and mindfulness training which is probably the most important thing a person can do to relieve symptoms of stress and chronic pain on many levels; 2) Practicing Qigong to increase circulation of qi, blood and lymph, and; 3) practicing gentle movement, meditative walking, Tai Chi form and gentle stretching.

I recommend searching and trying many teachers and styles. Some have more levels of internal experience than others. I am grateful and very lucky to have trained with one of the best Chinese masters, George Xu, who exposed his students to the finest masters in China. Through this training, along with graduate education in neuroscience and anatomy, I have designed a program to supplement those who are learning and teaching the internal arts.

A Spiral Anatomy™ Training Course is presented as a series of videos and supplemental materials that are available for download. Module 1 - Cultivating an Energy Body contains an extremely robust visualization, meditation program and Qigong. Module 2 - Balance plus Brain Workshop™ contains materials to help you understand the physical and energetic principles of balance and to activate neuro-rehabilitation and repair. Module 3 - Connect the Body Physically as One Unit with Power Stretching is essential for whole-body or one-unit, connected, loose, relaxed, spiraling power in all styles of martial arts.

Power stretching is the next step essential for understanding how to repair posture to alleviate chronic health issues including chronic musculoskeletal pain. I invite you to visit www.SpiralAnatomy.com for more information.

I am a Master of Chinese Internal Martial Arts, founder of the Shanti School of Taijiquan in Durango, Colorado, co-founder of Masters From China Video Productions, and have been a practitioner of Tai Chi and Qigong for nearly 40 years. I am also a Neuroscientist, anatomist, biomechanist, and researcher in neural networks and neuroplasticity, spinal cord development, stroke rehabilitation, Parkinson's and pineal neurophysiology and I integrate Western scholarship and research in neuroscience with Chinese Internal Martial Arts training. I study and teach various internal martial arts styles, including Wu and Chen styles of Tai Chi, Xing Yi, Bagua, and the Lan Shou System. I am certified in the Mi Zong School of Medical Qigong.

Books:

The Art of Changing the Brain: Enriching the Practice of Teaching by Exploring the Biology of Learning, James E. Zull –
https://www.goodreads.com/book/show/210204.
The_Art_of_Changing_the_Brain
Practicing Tai Chi: Ways to Enrich Learning for Beginners and Intermediate Practitioners, Paul T. Richard –
https://www.goodreads.com/book/show/40735525-practicing-tai-chi?ac=1&from

Contact course@susanamatthews.com to join the 'Tai Chi for Vets with PTSD Club' for free access to supplement your training.

CHAPTER 36 - THE IREST PROGRAM OF MEDITATION FOR PTSD

Dr. Richard C. Miller, Integrative Restoration Institute

There are an estimated one in three military combat personnel who experience Post-Traumatic Stress (PTS) or Post-Traumatic Stress Disorder (PTSD). This equals over 300,000 Veterans who served in the Middle East, and 1.7 million Veterans from the Vietnam era. While some of these individuals will be able to manage their symptoms and recover a sense of normalcy, there are still a large number of individuals who end up experiencing PTSD.

The symptoms of PTSD include hyper-arousal, numbing, avoidance, flashbacks, and vigilance. While not everyone will have the same physical symptoms or issues that accompanies PTSD, other related issues include depression, anxiety, panic disorders, dependency on drugs or alcohol, impulsive or dangerous behavior (i.e., driving aggressively), and a variety of other ailments. It is important that a sense of trust be established between providers and Veterans who are experiencing PTSD. A failure to do so can seriously hamper effective communication, care, and successful treatment. iRest

Integrative Restoration, or iRest, is a modern-day adaptation of the ancient meditation practice of Yoga Nidra (yoga = our interconnectedness within ourselves and the world around us; nidra = during all states of consciousness), that dates back thousands of years. The practice focuses on helping individuals develop attention and concentration skills, a strong inner resource of unchanging peace and well-being, the recognition, acceptance, and engaged responsiveness to feelings, emotions, thoughts, and bodily sensations, and the development of an unchanging inner sense of joy amidst daily life. iRest practices also help individuals acquire perspective of themselves and what they are experiencing — something that is difficult for those experiencing PTSD. This enables them to reclaim a sense of control and connection within themselves, and with others.

When I first learned the practice of Yoga Nidra, over 48 years ago, I was teaching primarily those who attending my yoga classes, who wanted to learn meditation. Back then, I made adaptations to the classical forms of Yoga Nidra that I learned through my studies of yoga, in order to make the program secular in nature. My intention in doing so was to make the program available, so that everyone — irrespective of their lifestyle, background, or philosophical or religious orientation — could easily and comfortably engage the practice. Instead of imposing archetypal images, colors, or sounds that were particular to ancient India, from which the practices of Yoga Nidra were derived, I instead asked my students to inquire as to what they were experiencing within themselves, as they brought their attention to the various sensations, emotions, thoughts, images, and memories that were present within their body and mind. I taught Yoga Nidra as a form of self-inquiry, to help people deeply connect to their own experience of themselves and the world around.

Along the way, as I started working with populations that included Active Duty and Veterans who had experienced trauma and were exhibiting symptoms of PTS/PTSD, I began enhancing aspects of the practice to best suit my work with this population. For example, on recommendations from the military, I stopped using the name, Yoga Nidra, to refer to the practice. Instead, I called it, 'Integrative Restoration,' or 'iRest'. I also added to and enhanced various components of the practice. For instance, I split the first step, Intention, into three parts.

1. Intention: Find your intention(s) for a particular practice of Yoga Nidra.

2. Heartfelt Mission: Find your intention(s) for your overall life.

3. Inner Resource: Find your intention(s) that represents an inner felt sense of security, safety, peace, ease, and well-being.

I found this third aspect, the Inner Resource, to be particularly helpful for those who had experienced trauma and its subsequent symptoms of PTS/PTSD. The addition of the Inner Resource to the classical practice allowed participants the ability to better relate, accept, respond, resolve, and heal disturbing thoughts, emotions, and memories that they associated with the trauma that they had experienced.

Research

Research on meditation, has revealed many important discoveries that are pertinent for people who have experienced trauma. For instance, meditation stimulates the production of natural opiates, such as serotonin, oxytocin, and endorphins in the brain and body; generating natural feelings of safety, ease, well-being, joy, and interconnectedness with self and others. During meditation, the Default Network (DN) in the brain, which gives rise to negative thinking and self-criticism, calms down, and self-referential negative thinking diminishes, or even stops altogether. The Present Centered Network (PCN), which is involved with creative thinking, insight, and producing feelings of peace, equanimity, and connectedness with self, others, and the world, comes more 'online'. And limbic structures within the brain that have either enlarged — such as the amygdala (which is associated with emotional regulation, fear, anxiety, and depression) — or decreased in size — such as the hippocampus (which is associated with the ability to maintain context, perspective and consequences of actions) — increase to normal size. These structural changes are critical for people navigating symptoms associated with PTS/PTSD.

Without our ability to maintain context, perspective, and understanding of the consequences of our actions (hippocampus), and when we are held hostage by our emotions (amygdala), we lose our ability to navigate the circumstances of our life. When people with PTS/PTSD are able to manage their symptoms — through therapy, or alternative methods like yoga and meditation — they regain control over their emotional and cognitive faculties, which they had previously lost. These large-scale brain and body transformations are the ultimate goal of iRest Meditation, which I have dedicated my professional life to developing.

Through the iRest Program, people suffering from PTS/PTSD, depression, anxiety, chronic pain, and/or insomnia are able to break free of the ways they have been held hostage by their thoughts, emotions, and memories. They begin to regain perspective. Anxiety, fear, depression, and feelings of helplessness, and being out of control begin to lessen or entirely resolve. PTS/PTSD symptoms diminish. They regain their ability to navigate their life, work, and relationships in more authentic and responsive ways. And they feel a sense of joy, well-being, and peace return to their lives.

Through engaging iRest Meditation, negative self-talk diminishes. Creativity and insight come alive. Your brain and body turn on reparative and restorative processes that boost your immune system, increase your overall sense of well-being and joy, reduce stress-related symptoms of PTS/PTSD, and support you to enjoy restful sleep at night.

Military and iRest

In 2004, the U.S. military approached me with a request to conduct research on iRest with Active Duty and Veterans who were experiencing PTSD. The research was so successful that iRest immediately became a permanent program offered by the Walter Reed Deployment Health Clinical Center, providing every wounded warrior the opportunity to take part in a three-week healing regimen of what became known as 'Integrative Restoration' or 'iRest Meditation'.

When I first started the research at Walter Reed, I called the program, Yoga Nidra. But I was quickly informed by the military that soldiers in the program couldn't relate to the word, Yoga Nidra. With this realization, I subsequently changed the name of my program to Integrative Restoration, or iRest for short. 'Integrative' because the program teaches us how to self-regulate our emotions, thoughts, and body sensations. It enables us to become fully integrated human beings. And 'Restorative,' because the program nourishes and restores our body and mind to its intrinsic essential nature of well-being, wholeness, and interconnectedness, with ourselves, others, and the universe.

Regardless of its name, the research, and program that was instituted at Walter Reed, was hugely successful. As a result, research has continued, with over 35 studies completed to date (2018), and more on the way. Research has proven the ability of iRest to address symptoms of PTSD, TBI, depression, pain, and sleep related issues, as well people undergoing treatment for cancer and MS. iRest is currently supporting Active Duty, Veterans, and families of service members in over 85 VA and military settings across the United States, as well as in Canada, Australia, Germany, and the UK. With now over 4,000 trained iRest teachers, the current number of facilities offering iRest include military hospitals and bases, Veterans' hospitals and facilities, and non-military organizations throughout the world. And in 2010, as a result of the research with iRest, the U.S. Army Surgeon General, and Defense Centers of Excellence declared Yoga Nidra a complementary Alternative Medicine (CAM) in the treatment of PTSD and chronic pain.

The 10 Tools of iRest

Trauma can leave you feeling disconnected — from yourself, from your friends and family, and from the world around you. iRest helps reestablish your connectedness — with yourself, with your partner, and with your children, friends, and workmates. And for those returning from war, it enables healing to take place so that you can finally feel that you've come home. iRest allows you to heal the sensations, emotions, thoughts, memories, and images that underlie the symptoms of PTS and PTSD. It provides you with the self-care tools you need to navigate your daily life, and restore your inner sense of ease and well-being. As one Veteran from an iRest study at the Miami VA so beautifully said when asked for his reflections, "Every program I'd been in before finding iRest emphasized what was wrong about me. iRest showed me what's right about me. Knowing what was right about me helped me the face what needed healing. Through my practice of iRest, I feel I finally came home."

The 10 tools that form the iRest Program can be incorporated into every part of your daily life. These are 'tools for life,' that foster health, healing, and wellness at all levels of your body, mind, and spirit. To produce true healing, treatment must reach and heal the deepest nooks and crannies within your body and mind. The iRest toolkit has been designed to do just that. The 10 tools include:

1. Affirming Your Heartfelt Mission. Being in touch with what it is that you truly want in life, so that you feel in harmony with yourself, and with life.

2. Affirming Your Intention. Establishing why you want to practice iRest today, and tomorrow. Intentions support you living your Heartfelt Mission.

3. Affirming Your Inner Resource. Finding an inner felt-sense where you feel secure, to which you can return at any time during iRest, or whenever you feel the need to feel grounded and at ease.

4. Practicing Bodysensing. Welcoming and being present with what you are experiencing in your body. Learning to feel, welcome, observe, and respond to sensation.

5. Practicing Breathsensing. Tuning into, observing, and actively engaging in the natural rhythm of your breath.

6. Welcoming Opposites of Feeling and Emotion. Observing and proactively engaging and responding to feelings and emotions that are present.

7. Welcoming Opposites of Thought. Observing, proactively engaging, and responding to thoughts, beliefs, images, and memories that are present.

8. Welcoming Joy and Well-Being. Experiencing, engaging, and responding to feelings of joy, love, well-being, pleasure, happiness, and bliss.

9. Experiencing your innate Wholeness of Being and Awareness. Experiencing yourself as the witness or observer of all that present in your body, mind, and the world around you. Your ability to be unchanging witnessing presence, that is always at peace and ease.

10. Integration of iRest into Daily life. Integrate the tools of iRest into your daily life.

The power of iRest rests in a variety of core principles. These core principles are foundation stones that underlie the iRest Program, and each of its 10 steps. The core principles are what make iRest such a powerful program for healing PTSD. They include:

Learning to be welcoming.
Accepting what is.
Stopping self-judgment.
Recognizing that everything is a messenger.
Knowing that you're always doing your best.
Understanding the law of awareness.
Feeling safe with yourself.
Engaging ongoing self-inquiry.
Embracing right attitudes of body, mind, and speech.
Discovering your innate, non-separate wholeness.
Practicing little and often.

As you gain skill in iRest, you can engage any of the 10 tools of iRest in as little as a minute or less. By consistently practicing the 10 tools of iRest, little and often, you gain trust in their ability to help you respond, heal your symptoms of PTS or PTSD, and thrive in your life and relationships.

The iRest Program teaches you how to respond to each and every situation, emotion, and thought you experience as you navigate your life, so that you can:

Experience inner peace and the feeling of being grounded, no matter your circumstance.

Experience the core aspects that provide purpose, value, and meaning to your life.

Depend on your inner resource of safety, security, and well-being.

Dissolve guilt, blame, and shame.

End self-judgment.

Heal your PTSD.

Enjoy restful sleep.

Restore inner harmony, peace, joy, and well-being in your daily life.

Thrive, not just survive.

Joy is in the Journey.

Healing PTSD is a journey. It takes time. Learn to welcome patience, persistence, and perseverance into your daily routines. Be gentle with yourself. Go slowly. Millions have walked this path. They did it. So can you. iRest teaches that there can be joy in the journey of healing. With this in mind, take a moment and welcome the following statements into yourself:

"Just as others have healed their PTSD, I can heal my PTSD."

As you heal, you become a light for those who follow in your footsteps. We are all brothers and sisters on our healing journey, supporting one another as we travel this path. May you be a light unto yourself, so that those who follow in your footsteps can also affirm:

"If he or she healed his or her PTSD, I can heal my PTSD."

iRest restores, nourishes, and enhances unshakable, indestructible well-being, joy, love, and interconnectedness — with ourselves, in our relationships, and in how we relate to the world around us. iRest teaches you how to interweave each iRest tool into every circumstance and relationship you encounter — every day of your life — for the rest of your life. iRest teaches you a way of living your life so that you can heal your PTSD, and feel fully alive and joyful — wherever you are, however you are, no matter who you're with. So, welcome to the iRest Program. Engage it. Then pass on what you've learned, so others may benefit, as you have.

Visit https://www.irest.org for more information on this topic.

CHAPTER 37 - THE RESILIENCY PROGRAM: AN EFFECTIVE ALTERNATIVE FOR PTSD

Dr. Steven M. Zodkoy, DC, CNS, DACBN

The Resiliency Program is one of the most unique and successful programs to help Veterans and service members overcome Post-Traumatic Stress Disorder (PTSD). What makes the program different is that it utilizes clinical nutrition and hands-on emotional desensitization techniques to restore normal function to the mind and body. The program focuses on restoring balance and control to the fight-or-flight pathway (HPA-axis, sympathetic nervous system) to improve both the physical and mental health of the participant. The added benefits of the program are that participants starts to feel results almost immediately and are completed in 180 days. This approach is dramatically different from using medications which control the nervous system and may require a lifetime drug use or talk therapy which slowly works through traumas and stressors that often takes years to complete. The personal strength and fortitude to accept, process and move forward from traumas offers a much deeper healing and greater long-term success rate, and The Resiliency Program does all that!

The Resiliency Program's History: The Resiliency Program was initiated by my encounter with a mother who was concerned with her daughter's abnormal gait. During a routine chiropractic exam, I noticed that this teenager did not walk normally but rather swung her leg out and around. Her physical exam indicated no muscle weakness nor any joint limitations, so why was her gait so strange? This question had been baffling orthopedists, physical therapists and other healthcare providers for nearly a year. Talking with the mother and daughter revealed that the mother had been on active duty, a Colonel in the USMC, and that the daughter had been stressed over her safety. I switched my examination to look for hidden emotional traumas and stresses. I quickly found several hidden emotional issues that were weakening her whole musculoskeletal system and exacerbated her gait issue. The key reason for her gait issues had been found, it was not physical but rather trapped emotional trauma. Her care for the next several weeks focused on nutritional supplements to help her deal better with stress and Neuro Emotional Technique (NET), I will explain this in detail later) to quickly and effectively relieve the trapped emotional trauma. Her gait, which has been abnormal for years, was restored to normal within weeks and her overall health was greatly improved.

The Colonel quickly understood the magnitude of the work that had been done to her daughter and enquired if her Marines with PTSD would benefit from this type of care. I explained that PTSD with the associated symptoms of; anger, anxiety, burnout, confusion, fatigue, depression, insomnia and pain are all caused by the mind and body inability to accept, process and move on from traumas and stressors. Supporting PTSD patients with nutritional supplements and emotional desensitization techniques (like NET) would definitely help to resolve many aspects of their problem and thus The Resiliency Program was born.

The first few years of the program were fueled by word of mouth, with one successful case sending in several others until the buzz was all around. Request for meetings by the Department of Veterans Affairs (VA), Navy and Marines lead to an even greater buzz and an urgency to expand the program. Those in command of troops and responsible for their well-being were quick to accept and promote the program, but government red-tape and the lack of vision by military medicine looked like the end for the program. A chance encounter with Jack Downing, the CEO of Soldier ON a Veterans' service organization, led to the exponential growth of the program. Jack Downing saw the vision of restoring emotional and physical health back to Veteran so that they would have a high quality of life. He realized that The Resiliency Program could do that quickly, effectively, and cost efficiently.

The Resiliency Program in conjunction with Soldier On has been able to help 100s of Veterans achieve a higher quality of life, greater than what was ever thought possible after being diagnosed with PTSD. The program is loved by Veterans for its quick and long-term results. Their families love that the program restored their loved one to an active part of the family again. The key to the program's success comes from understanding how the mind-body processes and heals from trauma and restoring those normal pathways through clinical nutrition and hands-on work.

"In one word, 'AWESOME,' I still can't believe the results. This is exactly what I needed and have been searching for. Thanks to the Resiliency Program. I am living a life with balance and finally have a regular sleep routine. This is a must for anyone living with mental health issues." - John C.

How The Resiliency Program works:

The success of The Resiliency Program comes from the understanding that emotional and physical stress will abnormally affect the biochemistry of the mind-body. Chronic emotional and physical stress will often wear down a person's ability to deal with even the most minimal stressor and often lead to overcompensation reactions including anger, fatigue, panic attacks, and physical complaints. PTSD causes the mind and body to lose its ability to maintain homeostasis thus leading to both physical and emotional symptoms. Proper care for PTSD requires a two-prong approach including a method to deal with emotional triggers and past traumas plus support for the biochemical pathways that have been worn out. Relieving the trauma and rebuilding the system allows for true healing, balance and restores homeostasis to the mind and body.

Traditional PTSD treatments fail because they focus on controlling the mind and body. Medications will push a biochemical pathway in only one direction, but health and happiness require that these pathways be able to fluctuate as life's situations change. Traditional talk therapy often stresses the participant to an even higher level leaving them feeling worse, agitated and unwilling to work through the painful memories. Healing a Veteran with PTSD requires protocols to gently relieve the emotional traumas that cause stress and support to restore normal fluctuation in biochemical pathways to achieve homeostasis. The Resiliency Program does both of these.

"You don't have to go through life angry". That's what a friend of mine said when he told me about Dr. Zodkoy's Resiliency Program and the use of the Neuro Emotional Technique. Within hours of treatment, I called my wife in a state of euphoria. I had emotions I hadn't felt for years and definitely not since commanding a combat brigade during Surge Operations in Iraq. I'm able to be happy again and, as my wife put it, "You finally came home,"" - Colonel Dave S.

Nutritional Support for PTSD:

The idea that nutritional supplementation could change the outcome of PTSD is completely beyond the realm of traditional medicine. The common thinking in the medical field is, that if a drug isn't strong enough to help with PTSD...how can nutritional supplements. The reason nutritional supplements are more effective than medications in PTSD is because drugs push a biochemical pathway in only on direction, but our moods need to fluctuate with the changing events throughout the day. Nutritional supplements by nature bring the mind-body into homeostasis or balance so that it can adapt to life's daily changes. It is nutritional supplements ability to restore homeostasis to the mind-body that restores a PTSD sufferer's sense of well-being and happiness.

Military medicine wanted no part of nutritional supplements or natural approaches to helping with PTSD. The strongest argument was that there were no studies to prove that nutritional supplements would help in any way with the mental or physical complaints of active duty personnel. To prove that nutritional supplements can improve the emotional and physical complaints of active duty Marines I did a study, with the support of command officers looking for a way to help their Marines. I lectured to 100s of Marines on the signs and symptoms of Burnout, a less threatening term than PTSD, and had a group of volunteers ready and willing to be helped.

The participants were recommended nutritional supplements based on clinical lab testing that measured how well their biochemical pathways dealt with stress. These clinical lab results were correlated with questionnaires about their physical and mental complaints and a questionnaire about whether they felt burnout. This process was repeated at 90 days and changes to their nutritional supplements were made. The study was completed at 180 days.

The results of this study proved to be amazing and was the basis for The Resiliency Program. When the study began all participants were rated at "extremely to moderately" burnout. 180 days of nutritional supplements had made a remarkable change. A remarkable 95% of the participants had moved up at least two levels and the group were now rated at only "moderate to no" burnout. There was also an average 80% drop in the groups emotional and physical complaints from the start to the finish. This small study clearly showed that nutritional supplementation can effectively improve physical and emotional complaints in a short period of time.

The study showed that by focusing in on how the mind and body's biochemical pathways deal with stress we can effectively use nutritional supplements to help those with burnout. The relationship between burnout and PTSD is well documented, the common link is an abnormal response to the fight-or-flight (stress response) pathway. The key to successfully utilizing nutritional supplements to improve the physical and emotional complaints of Veterans with PTSD is to focus on the same fight-or-fight pathway. The fight-or-flight pathway is an ancient biochemical pathway that was designed to give humans a short burst of adrenaline to deal with an imminent danger. The problem is that today's stressors are not short lived but long and drawn out which burnout the fight-or-flight pathway leading to PTSD. This is even more evident in the military where warriors are doing more with less and for a lot longer. Basically, we are wearing out our fight-or-flight mechanism which causes us to be unable to deal everyday stressors. This pathway is controlled by the Hypothalamus-Pituitary-Adrenal axis or HPA-axis which links the mind to the body. If we want to help rebuild the pathway we need to give nutritional support to the HPA-axis.

"I think it's a great program with an innovative approach to Veteran Care. For the first time, I am sleeping better, feeling less anxious and calmer. Through a combination of supplements and NET, I found that I could be myself again." – Belinda

What does the HPA-axis control:

The HPA-axis is the link between the endocrine and nervous systems and the mind and body. Every physical and emotional event involves the HPA-axis so even a small imbalance can have a large effect on our health. HPA-axis systems help us protect ourselves from danger and stress. The problem is that this system was designed for short term use and today's stressors are nearly constant and often excessive.
While, in the past, our ancestors may have had to run from a tiger, today we have a lot of constant low-grade stressors; phones, emails, TV, etc, that wear us down and leave us venerable to any major events. The simplest way to understand the system is that

when the brain perceives a stressor it releases hormones through the HPA-axis, that at the end, releases adrenaline to fight the danger. Veterans with PTSD have been proven to have a compromised HPA-axis pathway which is no longer in balance. A compromised and imbalanced HPA-axis often will trigger an abnormal response to stress. Examples of an over response from the HPA-axis include; getting enraged or panicked over a minor incident, a muted response to a major stress or being unable to motivate themselves to do the basic things. Resetting a normal and appropriate response to a stressor is key to restoring emotional and physical health to a PTSD sufferer and nutritional supplements are key to rebalancing the HPA-axis so that can happen.

Symptoms from HPA-Axis Dysfunction

Low Energy	Insomnia	Wired & Tired
Anxiety and/or Irritability	Auto-Immunity	Depression
Inability to Lose Weight	Inability to Gain Weight	Accelerated Aging
Sexual Dysfunction	Menstrual Irregularities	Chronic Pain
Digestive Problems	Menopausal Symptoms	Hypertension
Chronic Inflammation	Heart Disease	ADHD
Feeling Overwhelmed	Cravings for Sugar and Salt	Muscle Tension
Bone Loss	Lowered Immunity	Hypoglycemia

"...referred to Dr. Zodkoy and The Resiliency Program – one week into the program, I cannot believe how much better I feel, how much better I sleep, and my mood is much better." – Eric

Nutritional supplements that help restore normal HPA-axis function:

The HPA axis, Hypothalamus-Pituitary-Adrenal axis, has been accepted by healthcare professionals as the main biochemical pathway involved with how we deal with stress or rather do not deal with stress. A person's HPA axis is highly influenced by their genetics, personality traits, race, age, lifestyle, and their physical and emotional environment from childhood to adulthood. These variables make it difficult to test the HPA axis with standardized lab tests and limit the effectiveness of mono-directional medication to correct any dysfunction. Nutritional supplements are extremely effective at restoring balance and control to the HPA-axis and thus relieving stress and PTSD.

There are numerous nutritional supplements to address the HPA-axis biochemical pathways, which provides excellent flexibility to adapt this approach to a patient's individual needs. Supplement protocols can be adapted to address genetics, allergies, lifestyle habits, and medical history. The goal of the nutritional supplements is to support the HPA-axis' natural fluctuation and homeostasis function to maximize recovery from anxiety, burnout, and PTSD.

Hemp Oil (CBD) Full Spectrum with <0.3% THC is the hottest nutritional supplement in the US, reaching nearly $1B in 2018 or 3% of all nutritional sales in just a few years on the market. The reason behind this incredible success is twofold. Researchers and patients have found benefits for both physical and emotional issues. It has also been found to be extremely safe with minimal side effects, risk factors, addictive tendencies, or attenuation.

A recent study showed that 91% of PTSD sufferers using CBD felt dramatic relief. Additional studies have shown that CBD reduced cortisol in stressed subjects, the key component of the HPA-axis, that correlated with them feeling relief from stress. Another large study recently showed that 80% of participants said their anxiety was relieved by over 75% with the use of CBD with no side effects.

Full Spectrum Hemp/CBD oil's mechanism of action is through the Endocannabinoid System, which directly interacts with 65 biochemical pathways in the brain and body. There is an extremely high affinity for receptors in the Hippocampus and Hypothalamus (HPA-axis), which explains why it is effective for treating anxiety, fear, stress and PTSD. Research has concluded that CBD can reduce past and present fears thus reducing stress and anxiety. The results suggest that CBD can reduce acute Fight-or-Flight responses to stress, and it limits the consequences of emotional trauma to the mind and body. There are numerous additional pathways by which CBD can mitigate stress including; improving sleep, reducing pain and promoting an overall sense of wellbeing.

The dosage for full spectrum Hemp/CBD oil is very broad. It is recommended that a person start with 10 mg of CBD a day in a liquid oral form, taken under the tongue (double that amount if taken in capsule form). It takes about a week for CBD to build up to full strength, so do not rush the process. You can double the dosage if you still have symptoms after a week. You continue to double the dosage until your symptoms resolve or no additional benefit is felt. While there is no risk in taking too much, there is also no benefit, and overdosing may limit the benefits. While many patients feel relief with 10 mg/day dosages, studies have used 300+ mg/day safely and effectively.

Phosphatidylserine (PS) is a nutritional supplement that is usually derived from soy. It is an important part of cells' membrane and it is part of how cells communicate with each other. While it can be found throughout the body, it is found much more densely in the brain and nerve system. Research has shown that anxiety with PTSD is linked to a shrinking hippocampus, which is part of the larger HPA-axis system. A smaller hippocampus is known to trigger flashbacks and fear in PTSD sufferers. This issue is exacerbated by sufferers self-medicating with alcohol.

Supplementation with PS can help restore normal Hippocampus-HPA axis function and mediate the symptoms of fear and flashbacks. It has the added benefit of helping to restore normal memory function. The mechanism of action is thought to be by the normalization of the release and response of cortisol, the main hormone of the HPA-axis. A typical dosage of PS is 300 mg/day, preferably 100 mg – 3x day.

Omega 3 oils (think fish oil, but there are others) play an important part in repairing the damage that long-term stress has on the brain. This should be of no surprise since the brain is more than 60% fat. Researchers have determined that Omega 3s help heal the brain and reduce symptoms through four main ways; they reduce inflammation, they stimulate healing through Brain-Derived Neurotrophic Factor (BDNF), they reduce and regulate cortisol (the key hormone in the HPA-axis), and improve cardiovascular activity to increase blood flow.

It is also known that alpha-linoleic acid, another Omega 3, is directly linked to reducing fear in PTSD sufferers and the general public. DHA, another Omega 3, can increase the accumulation of phosphatidylserine which helps restore balance to the HPA-axis and mitigates anxiety. EPA and DHA have a synergistic effect with Hemp oil improving its effectiveness by 10+%. There is strong evidence that Omega 3s can directly influence other biochemical pathways in the body providing multiple avenues to reduce anxiety, fear, stress, and PTSD while resetting the HPA-axis. The recommended dosage for Omega-3 is 2000+ mg/day, lower dosages were not found to be effective.

ADAPTOGENS are a loose family of nutritional supplements that are thought to help the body "adapt to stress." Their mechanisms of action all differ but their goal is the same, to restore the body to homeostasis this is achieved by stabilizing the HPA-axis.

Magnolia Bark has two main components, honokiol, and magnolol, which have been a part of traditional Chinese medicine for centuries. Research has shown that Magnolia Bark can pass through the brain-blood barrier and is neuroprotective. Its mechanism of action is through the down-regulating of Glutamate receptors, which overstimulate the mind and body. It also works through the Endocannabinoid system in a similar manner to CBD. Animal studies have shown that Magnolia Bark has a direct regulating effect on the HPA-axis which reduces the negative effects of stress and helps with the associated depression. A typical dosage would be 250 mg/day an hour before bed. An additional 250 mg can be used for break through anxiety.

Roseroot (Rhodiola rosea) has been shown in research to reduce cortisol and down-regulate the HPA-axis. Roseroot (Rhodiola rosea) has been shown in research to reduce cortisol and down-regulate the HPA-axis. It has the benefit of working within 30 minutes and lasting for up to six hours making it one of the most effective adaptogens. Rhodiola dosage at 600 mg/day has been shown to reduce burnout and stressed induced fatigue.

Ashwagandha is unique as an adaptogen because its mechanism of action involves modulating the GABA receptors to promote a sense of calm and reduce triggering the HPA-axis. Research has shown that a dosage of 300 mg twice a day is helpful for stress reduction and weight loss.

The examples above are only a sample of the adaptogens available. Adaptogens have been linked to numerous health benefits: improved cognitive function, sleep, energy, moods, physical endurance, sexual desire and function to name just a few. The underlying reason for their wide-ranging health benefits comes from their combined ability to reduce the function or stimulation of the HPA axis, which relieves overstimulation on both the endocrine and nervous system.

Nutritional supplements offer several advantages over other methods to help PTSD sufferers including; they are highly effective, safe, affordable and have minimal side effects. Nutritional supplements also work with the mind and body, unlike drugs that try to control the mind and body. Many sufferers start to feel relief right away with nutritional supplements which encourages continued use and prevent frustration from waiting for a change.

Nutritionally supporting the HPA-axis so that a Veteran will have an appropriate response to stress is a key step in healing PTSD. The HPA-axis can be neither to active or sluggish when responding to stress or both physical and emotional symptoms will occur. The HPA-axis response needs to be fluid and fluctuate throughout the day and night and nutritional supplements allow for this, but medications do not. The next key step to healing PTSD is to quickly and efficiently remove trapped emotional traumas so that the HPA-axis is not constantly being stimulated or stressed.

"I have been on the program for three weeks. There has been an 80% difference in my mental state of being. I am much happier and my depression is almost non-existent. This is an awesome program." – Patrick

Emotional Desensitization to Release Trapped Traumas and Emotional Triggers:

A simple way to describe how a trauma leads to PTSD is to compare it to a record player playing the same song over and over again. The song is the trauma and the mind is the record player, the song becomes the music of your life as the trauma is always in the back of your mind. Nutritional supplements are excellent for rebuilding the mind-body and reducing the volume of the music, but emotional desensitization techniques stops the music. I like to describe emotional desensitization as taking the record off the record player and putting it on the shelf. We are not denying the trauma happened, but it doesn't have to be the background music of your life. There may be occasions when the record (trauma) comes off the shelf and plays again, but if it goes back on the shelf it has become a bad memory not a trauma.

NET is the main technique used to achieve emotional desensitization by physicians while The Emotion Code is used frequently by the general public. NET is an excellent way to help the mind acknowledge, accept, process and move on from past traumas and stressors. It is not cognitive therapy or talk therapy but instead a technique that quickly allows for a trauma or stressor to be recognized and processed through a series of questions and tapping of the acupuncture meridian system (no needles). A recent study on NET revealed that normal brain function is restored for PTSD sufferers in as few as six sessions. NET can often relieve years of emotional trauma starting with the first session while a full program may take 6-12 sessions.

NET seems simple, so how can it be so effective? Most people exposed to a trauma will naturally processes the event and moves on with just a bad memory. A percentage of the population will not be able to process a trauma and the mind will continue to play the event over and over again trying to make sense and find a way to process it. NET simply and effectively identifies the trauma and then gives the mind a pathway to process it. NET works because it is simply assisting the brain to do what it wants to do. Note: There is no way to predict who or what trauma will cause PTSD. The factors involved in developing PTSD include: genetics, personality traits, history, present state of mind, nutritional status and numerous other intangible factors. An example is an introvert may get past a friend being hurt in a battle, but an extrovert may not. An extrovert may tolerate general combat as long has he/she is with their squad, but an introvert may find it traumatic being in constant close quarters.

"I am a service-disabled Veteran diagnosed with severe PTSD. I have a Service Dog who provides care and security for me as well, but has not been 100% successful. The addition of The Resiliency Program using supplements and holistic treatment has enhanced my ability and desire to actually live life to the fullest. I am feeling better about myself and am no longer in a fog. Medicines and psychological care from the VA were substandard and made me feel worst. Thank you Dr. Z..." - Jason L.

When a person has PTSD there are two factors involved in every case; an abnormal fight-or-flight pathway and trapped emotional trauma. The Resiliency Program success comes from the fact that it works with the mind and body to restore normal functions and homeostasis to the fight-or-flight pathway and gives the mind a way to process the trauma. There may be additional factors involved in each case, but The Resiliency Program is an excellent first few steps toward restoring health, wellness and quality of life!

Biography:

I have been in practice in Freehold, NJ for 30 years. I am a board-certified chiropractor and nutritionist. I have authored a bestselling book on Amazon titled, Misdiagnosed: The Adrenal Fatigue Link. I have lectured to physicians across the country, at the VA's Warrior Related Illness and Injury Study Center, the Pentagon and to the command at Quantico. I have also been a member of the Joint Civilian Orientation Committee for the Department of Defense. The Resiliency Program, which I developed and direct, has helped 100s of Veterans to achieve a happier, healthier, and more fulfilling life.

Should you require more information on this subject, I can be reached at szodkoy@hotmail.com.

CHAPTER 38 - THERAPEUTIC RIDING PROGRAM

Olivia Taylor, Program Director
Northern Virginia Therapeutic Riding Program, Inc.

At Northern Virginia Therapeutic Riding Program (NVTRP) in Clifton, Virginia, we serve Veterans and have seen firsthand the changes and impacts riding and working with horses can have them. While information provided in this chapter is specific to NVTRP and our programming (therapeutic riding is only one type of service in the multi-faceted Equine-assisted activities and therapies (EAAT) industry), we truly believe in the power of horses to enrich and change the lives of Veterans.

EEAT is a growing area for Veteran recovery. Horses have proven time and again how powerful they can be for helping heal all kinds of mental, physical, and emotional trauma. Horses — prey animals with a fight or flight instinct — have a lot in common with Veterans, who have also learned to be on high alert at all times. Because of this, many Veterans find they can easily bond with the horse on an empathetic level.

Working with horses presents unique challenges for Veterans. When interacting with a horse, a Veteran has to stay emotionally present and in the moment, and constantly aware of an equine partner's feelings and needs. Horsemanship is often a stepping stone for working on other issues in a Veteran's life. Veterans can carry lessons learned while working with their horse into other areas of their lives — whether it's improving personal relationships, succeeding in a civilian job, or simply learning to relax and take time to enjoy themselves.

In therapeutic riding, individuals learn to work with and ride horses, taught by an instructor trained to work with individuals of all backgrounds and abilities. Through these lessons, people experience all sorts of other wonderful benefits — spending time outdoors; socializing with staff, volunteers, and classmates; gaining confidence from riding a 1,000 pound animal; and building physical strength and balance, as well as the emotional intelligence needed to connect with their equine partners.

At our program, we offer group therapeutic riding lessons for Veterans recovering from physical, mental, and emotional trauma. At each lesson, before they ride, Veterans work with their horse on the ground in activities such as grooming, tacking, leading, or lunging, so they have an opportunity to connect with their horse before they get in the saddle.

Sessions are usually a mix of unmounted horsemanship and riding. Participants will first meet with their instructor and other classmates and learn about their assigned horse for that week's session. Each participant gets their own horse for the class. We try to keep a participant on the same horse for at least a few consecutive lessons, so the Veteran has a chance to get to know a horse's personality and movement. Once the Veteran has groomed and tacked their equine partner in the barn area, they will move to the riding ring where most classes take place. Some classes may move to an open field for more of a challenge once the class has appropriate control and confidence for the change. Many times, before mounting, the participant will work on ground control. This might include guiding their horse through obstacles or working on setting personal space boundaries with their horse. Once mounted, participants will learn how to control their horse as well as their body position on the horse to move through harder and harder exercises. Over time, the Veteran can learn to walk, trot and canter, move through obstacles while riding, practice drill team patterns and implement equine training techniques.

Veterans don't have to have any horse experience — instructors will teach participants from the ground up, literally. For Veterans with prior horse experience, lessons provide an opportunity to enhance their skills and learning NVTRP's wonderful herd of horses. By coming to weekly lessons, Veterans can progress through skills and work towards their personal riding and horsemanship goals. One of our Veteran riders who has been in our program for three years is now working towards his goal of becoming an instructor.

And riding isn't just about time spent in the saddle. To truly become skilled horsemen and women, Veterans have to master skills such as emotional regulation, calm and clear communication, strength and balance, confident leadership, and an emotional openness to allow a bond to form with their horse. Riding can give Veterans a new hobby or even bring back nostalgic memories from being around animals as a child. It gets Veterans outdoors, physically active, and into a community of not only accepting, caring staff and volunteers, but also fellow Veterans.

We have a herd of 14 horses, all unique in their size, movement, and personality. The horses are donated, bought, or leased by the program, and come from a wide variety of different backgrounds and experiences. Each horse brings something different to the table. Often, Veterans will bond with a horse through learning about a horse's background or finding a personality trait in the horse that's similar to themselves. Veterans often find a favorite, but sometimes have the best lessons when they work with a horse who challenges them. Horses are non-judgmental companions. This quality allows Veterans to be open and vulnerable, and to try things they might not otherwise. To work successfully with a horse, Veterans practice communication skills such as body language, allowing for processing time, and giving clear cues. Skills developed in interactions with horses can transfer over to person-to-person interactions but are often emotionally easier for a Veteran to learn and practice with a horse as their partner. Growth happens when a Veteran is able to be self-aware and problem-solve through challenging situations.

NVTRP's Veteran program is offered at no-cost to participants. We receive grants from generous organizations such as Boeing, Northrop Grumman, Disabled American Veterans, Disabled Veterans National Foundation to cover the costs, as well as grants through the Professional Association of Therapeutic Horsemanship (PATH).

Along with providing weekly sessions, NVTRP aims to provide services that bring the larger communities of Active Duty and Veterans together. As our military program has grown, we've started hosting annual one-day events for Veterans. One such event is Hoofprints for HERoes, an event for women and children that was originally created and fundraised for by a volunteer who is a woman Veteran and saw a need. This event creates a unique opportunity for women military service personnel to share an activity with their children and also find a support group of others with similar experiences.

NVTRP also partners with a licensed counselor who offers equine-assisted psychotherapy and will do group psychotherapy sessions during some of NVTRP's military events.

NVTRP is proud to be able to offer these services to Veterans. Looking at the impacts of these services, our participants say it best. When asked how working together with their horse made them feel, Veterans said the following:

"Made me feel wanted, worth something."
"Made me feel very grounded and connected."
"Happy, an emotion I haven't felt in a while."

NVTRP is committed to creating a space for recovering military service personnel that provides them peace, a supportive community, and a non-judgmental connection with our amazing horses. There are many wonderful organizations that provide equine-assisted activities and therapies across the country, and we encourage Veterans to get involved and allow the power of the horse to help them through their individual struggles.

Visit https://www.nvtrp.org for more information.

CHAPTER 39 - TIBETAN MEDICINE AND PTSD

Mary Friedman Ryan, MSC, Ph.D., DIP, CHM

As a doctor of Chinese medicine, I have practiced among many different populations of people, from the very rich to the dispossessed. One of my favorite groups of people to work with are the Veterans of Foreign Wars that grace my clinic every few months or so. They are invariably a tremendously courageous group of people, and I admire them all.

All practitioners of Chinese medicine have fought the battle of finding a rental office space that is affordable so as to make fees for service as low as possible. At long last, I've found my home in one of the poorest counties in Massachusetts, Franklin County. The rents are low, and the population warm, loving, friendly, enthusiastic, and, well, poor. Among them are many Veterans. They struggle with their memories of life overseas: where rules are different, and what happens there, stays there, and can't be understood by family at home. What is witnessed is so overwhelming, emotionally, that there are no words. Images go unprocessed deep into their bodily systems, and come out in Post-Traumatic Stress Disorder (PTSD), or rLung, as we call it in Tibetan medicine. In Tibetan medicine, we know that the Mind affects the Body. Indeed, there can be symptoms of mysterious pain, nightmares, insomnia, heart problems, digestive issues, skin rashes, outbursts of anger, despair.

For the struggling Veterans that come into my practice, we always take our time. Healing happens on the physical level, with Tibetan and Chinese herbal medicine to help with sleep and organ disharmonies, and on the subtle, energetic level through using meditation, Tibetan healing exercises, and more subtle herbal formulas that address nourishing the nervous system, and helping with sleep. Routine is considered a crucial part of healing. We go over foods that suit their constitution, routines of breath work, intention setting for the day, small goals leading to larger goals. As time moves on, it's not the practitioner that does the work: it's the patient. Among my PTSD Veteran patients, I am enamored by their ability to really commit to treatment, and want to change. Change comes quickly with Tibetan medicine, with mental health issues such as PTSD. The subtle treatment of the rLung" or Wind element in Tibetan medicine is very effective. As Dr. Dhadon Jamling, a Tibetan doctor I trained with, said to me, "you cannot see the rLung (the Wind) in the body, but you can see it's effects, just as we see how the Wind outside causes trees to move, even though we don't see it."

When Tashi Delek Lobsang, a thirty-one-year-old monk, came to the clinic during our rLung study, I recognized him immediately. He was the warmly-smiling man I passed daily in the narrow, muddy streets of Dharamsala. He always remembers everyone's name and greets them as they pass by. He is tall, angular in build, and strong. He is fit, and his body shows the health and vigor of a monk who wakes up early. His days are filled with the simple, physical labors of maintaining a fully operational monastery. He is generous, very reliable, and a true scholar of Tibetan Buddhism. Many people respect him for his impressive debating skills. Lobsang tells us that he cannot fall asleep easily and startles awake often during the night. He has ominous feelings of dread and fear, especially around dawn and dusk, which is the circadian rhythm of rLung. He says he feels anxious when embarking upon simple tasks. These tasks could include meeting a new person, buying food at the market, or even tutoring his students at the monastery.

Transitions are difficult for him starting a conversation, walking into a room, going into the sleep world, etc. This is typical of rLung Imbalance. The anxiety makes transitions difficult. His anxiety manifests with severe heart palpitations, breathlessness, and thoughts of bad things happening that he knows to be unrealistic or untrue. He cannot control his thoughts at these acute times, in spite of his intense meditation training, and this frustrates him even more. He talks to us about his feelings of dread for the future, and although he knows they have no ground, they possess him, and limit his lifestyle as a monk. He doesn't know what to do. We cannot fully understand Lobsang's case without also knowing his history. Upon interviewing him, we learn that he escaped Chinese-occupied Tibet one year prior and made the grueling months-long journey to Dharamsala. He walked almost the entire way, which would be almost 1,000 miles. Lobsang tells us of his journey:

"I was with three other people, and we had very little money. We slept, hidden, during the day, and traversed hilly dangerous territory at night, constantly worried about being caught . . . I worried so much about my friends and that if we were caught that we would get the other people who helped us on the way in trouble, too. At the border we all separated. It was the safest way but then we were unable to find one of our friends again, and we have not heard from him since."

When Lobsang arrived in Dharamsala, he was welcomed into one of the local monasteries with a letter from a previous teacher that he had carried with him. While this was comforting, he still struggled to re-establish himself in a new city, as a refugee monk. Lobsang had to work very hard to prove himself and to keep up with his studies. He also had to learn English, do many new chores unfamiliar to him, and overcome the great loneliness that he felt. Lobsang succeeded, yet it seemed to take a great toll on his health. Constant overwork, worry, and denying himself simple pleasures for months on end ultimately led to the worsening of his symptoms.

Lobsang's physical symptoms are common for rLung Imbalance. He complains of physical pain traveling throughout his body, like small lightning shocks with an odd sensation of numbness in his skin. When he awakens during the night from pain, he is unable to go back to sleep. He also tells us of severe constriction at the nape of his neck and a feeling of fullness in his chest, as though he cannot breathe. It helps him to take in large gulps of air, and to arch his back, stretch, and release the feeling of tightness around his chest. When he experiences the heart palpitations, the constriction in his voice and in his chest, as well as the pain in his neck, all intensify. Sometimes the worsening mental anxiety and the painful bodily sensations hurl him into a full-blown panic attack. The "time" when rLung symptoms are usually at their worst is at dawn and dusk, when Lobsang feels the most anxiety. He also complains of epigastric pain, gurgling in his stomach, and acid indigestion. This happens when he forgets to eat.

During his evaluation by Dr. Jamling, I watch as she takes his pulse on his wrist and confirms that it is empty, which means it disappears with pressure. She explains that an empty pulse feels like a small bubble floating on the water.

She points out that his tongue is reddish pink and peeled, with no coating on it. There is very little to almost no moisture on his tongue. His urine reveals rLung issues as well; it is clear, watery, and tinged with a bit of a blue. His skin and hair are rough to the touch, dry, brittle, and in desperate need of some moisturizer. In Tibetan Medicine, the lungs and the skin are believed to be one single organ that suffers when there is a lack of proper circulation of rLung in the chest. When rLung is out of balance, it can cause dryness in the body.

Dr. Jamling announces her diagnosis of rLung disturbance. She says the rLung is like the wind and can get stirred up. Lobsang's rLung has moved out of its resting places, first invading the stomach channels, and now working its way up and affecting the area around the heart. Lobsang confirms her diagnosis, saying that at first, it was mainly stomach problems that debilitated him, along with the obsessive worrying over small details that seemed to increase over time, making transitions difficult and filling him with fear and dread.

In order to treat Lobsang's rLung Imbalance, Dr. Jamling explains to me that we must pacify rLung by focusing on the areas in which it has invaded: the stomach and the heart. Interestingly enough, Dr. Jamling does not prescribe the usual rLung herbal pill medication. She believes that we can heal Lobsang just through the use of food, moxibustion, massage, and some practical advice. His strong demeanor, straightforward honesty, and the strength in his eyes and voice say to Dr. Jamling that this is a patient whom the rLung has not "completely possessed."

Here is the complete "prescription" for treating Lobsang with explanations where needed: Dr. Jamling recommends that Lobsang eat nutritious foods such as meat, especially beef and lamb. Fish is also particularly good because of its oils (the oils will help Lobsang's dryness because they moisturize the interior of the body), and it can be fried. She also recommends Lobsang drink nettle tea along with eating some nettles cooked lightly in pepper, which anchors the rLung and helps settle the energy into its resting places. Rice, first cooked and then fried in butter, is also a staple food to pacify rLung; other ingredients can be added to it, such as garlic, onion, and ginger, all of which pacify rLung. Lobsang's case involves the heart channels, so Dr. Jamling emphasizes the use of angelica root in stews, salads, and rice. Sunflower seeds and peanuts are easy snacks if he feels a panic attack building. A simple tea recipe of asafetida, nutmeg, cardamom, and ginger would also calm his mind. It can be made into a tea that he drinks throughout the day. Mint tea is also allowed, as well as chamomile tea.

  She explains to us that there are certain foods he should avoid, including bitter foods, such as eggplant, mustard greens, arugula, and spinach. Black tea and coffee are forbidden. Chocolate is to be avoided. He should not eat any cheese, but especially not goat cheese, which is considered "Rough and Light." Instead, Lobsang needs to eat nutritious foods, such as certain meats, stews, and food that are easy to digest. Rough food is food that is hard to digest. Light food can be thought of as any stimulant that will affect and speed up the mind. This type of food is usually not very nutritious. The Tibetan concept of Rough and Light foods may be difficult to understand. Moxibustion — Every time Lobsang visits the clinic, Dr. Jamling and I perform moxibustion on him, burning the herb Artemisia vulgaris on the front and back points of the body.

Aromatherapy — Dr. Jamling gives Lobsang a special rLung incense stick for him to burn at dawn and in the evening — the times of heightened rLung energy and anxiety. She shows him how to breathe it in. The theory behind incense aromatherapy is that the breath is intimately linked with the mind. By deeply breathing in the incense, the mind calms down. The special ingredients in the incense bring soothing herbs in minute quantities into the energetic channels where rLung resides. Some of the ingredients of this incense recipe include: aloeswood, myrobalan, asofoetida, Aquilaria, and roseroot. The herbal pills contain the same herbal ingredients as in the incense, but in differing quantities and combinations. Dr. Jamling actually makes this special incense in her monastery in Dharamsala. It is made from a "secret" recipe from The Four Tantras, the main Tibetan medical text. For generations it has been used to ease the symptoms of rLung Imbalance.

Bodywork — For Lobsang, both his stomach and his heart are affected by the rLung Imbalance. Dr. Jamling recommended massaging the rLung points on both the front and back of the body to help with this kind of imbalance. The warmed massage oil is a mixture of sesame oil, fennel seeds or star anise, caraway seeds, and nutmeg. Massage is an important part of the treatment, and Lobsang takes it upon himself to find someone to do the massage every day in the first weeks of treatment.

A Tibetan Healing Exercise to Help with rLung – Dr. Jamling recommended that Lobsang roll his head around completely three times in one direction, and three times in another, very slowly, every morning and evening after using the incense. This relaxed the shoulders and also facilitates the smooth flow of the life channel energy between the head and the heart. It also grounds him.

Less Meditation, More Gentleness – Dr. Jamling instructs Lobsang as he listens intently, "There must be a gentleness toward your mind. It should not be strictly controlled, just watched. Meditation attempts to control the mind, and too much meditation can intensify the rLung Imbalance." He nods as she continues, "The medical texts recommend that monks with rLung Imbalance avoid thinking too much or sitting and meditating excessively." Dr. Jamling also tells him that she will talk to his abbot (the monastery leader) about slowing down his meditation practice until the rLung disturbance is resolved.

Over the next six weeks of treatment, I witnessed Lobsang blossom into a completely relaxed person, free from anxiety – a debilitating condition that affected every aspect of his life. We treated Lobsang once per week with moxibustion, and he received massage weekly from an assistant at the monastery. He followed our recommendations for dietary restrictions and refrained from meditating intensely. He appears happier and more encouraged as the weeks go on, and he seems almost relieved to be freed from the practice of intense meditation. Lobsang appears more grounded, less anxious, and he has put on some weight. At the sixth clinical visit, his pulse has returned to normal, and he tells us that he has not had any anxiety or panic attacks in two and a half weeks. He still experiences some stomach gurgling and anxiety when hungry, but when he eats his warm soup, this disappears. Lobsang continued to check in with us over the next couple of months, and only comes to the clinic occasionally, as needed. Lobsang has learned to manage his anxiety. He has stopped taking the special incense in the mornings, phasing it out almost completely until he no longer needs it except if he feels the uneasiness coming back. While he has a tendency for rLung disturbance and it could potentially return, Lobsang now knows how to manage his lifestyle to keep himself in balance. Success in Lobsang's case gives me great hope that these simple changes can give him, and others anywhere in the world, the quality of life they so desire. Cheers to Tashi Delek Lobsang!

Dr. Jamling said to me, many years ago when visiting the United States, "There is so much rLung in your country, we need to write a Healing Anxiety Book in English about rLung!" And she was right. Sixty percent of the patients in my practice in the United States suffer from anxiety. Anxiety, stress, mental restlessness, even severe mental illness (which Tibetans call srog-rLung, pronounced sok-loong) affects millions of Americans. Anxiety disorders are the most common mental illnesses in the United States, affecting 40 million adults age 18 and older (or 18% of the United States population, as reported by the National Institute of Health). Tibetan medical treatments for rLung could help solve this problem and bring down this statistic. Tibetan medicine has a deep understanding of the mind-body connection and for centuries has documented successful treatments for rLung Imbalance. The primary reason for Tibetan Medicine's success with anxiety lies in its ability to understand the chi mechanism in the body—the vital force that cannot be seen. Tibetan medical doctors also can recognize three main constitutional types of people, and thus treatment is more holistic and tailor-made to each individual. Tibetan Medicine is successful with anxiety because it not only uses oral medicine (an herbal pill formula), but also applies diet, bodywork, and mental health practices (for example, meditation) to help develop healthy lifestyles leading to mental clarity and inner peace. In the future, I would like to see Tibetan medical treatments becoming the new standard for all mind-body illnesses.

Anxiety can stem from an imbalance of a particular constitutional body type or from a behavioral activity that is responsible for the disease, such as improper diet or continued overwork. A combination of any of these can cause a body to become imbalanced and start to break down, energetically speaking. In the United States and in other parts of the world, this way of living seems almost the norm. Needless to say, rLung Imbalance is running rampant and existing under the guise of being labeled simply "anxiety," leaving people to their own devices to figure out what to do for treatments, or not do anything at all.

When I was first being introduced to Tibetan Medicine through working with Dr. Jamling, she said to me: In Tibetan Medicine, two people can come into the clinic with, let's say, the same red rash on the arm. On the surface of the body, it looks like the same disease, but they may actually have very different underlying imbalances. Upon hearing this, I realized that finding the underlying imbalances is crucial to solving an rLung imbalance successfully. Each underlying pattern of imbalance involves differing amounts of the mind and body's energies. For example in biomedicine, a person may have what is just called "anxiety." In Tibetan Medicine, a person may have anxiety with an underlying imbalance of an organ system, or anxiety with an imbalance of one of the

Three Humors: Wind (rLung), Bilye (Tipa), or Phlegm (Bad-Gan).

The primary goal of Tibetan Medicine is to help people settle their minds and root themselves in a grounded lifestyle. Their healing advice is rooted in simplicity. In contrast to the actual sophistication of Tibetan medical knowledge, the remedies for mental imbalance, such as anxiety and sadness, or even depression, are simple, earthy, and enjoyable. While herbal medicine can be helpful, you must consult a Tibetan Medicine practitioner for a prescription. However, even without herbal pills, these simple techniques and recipes, such as dietary changes, meditation, acupressure, massage, and the rLung incense can be applied by anyone. This simple approach can be profoundly helpful in relieving, soothing, and calming most anxious and stressful thoughts. They are also inexpensive and ecological. The meditation techniques can easily become a lifelong learning tool for understanding oneself more deeply.

As a practitioner of Asian medicine in the United States, I work with many people who want to transition off anxiety medication, and I witness them emerging from their anxiety whole and complete, with the ability to feel more deeply than they did before. When I first meet them, they almost always appear to be addicted to their anxiety medication and experience various side effects, such as being overweight or suffering from insomnia. Many are still anxious despite taking the medication. As one woman said to me, "It took me two years to come off my anxiety medication. I still have deep-seated fears sometimes, but I also now have my life back. I have lost weight, and there is less of a wall of medication between me and the world...my social anxiety still rears its ugly head in certain situations...but I can handle it because I've learned the tools to deal with anxiety thanks to your guidance." When people follow the simple path of more wholesome habits, especially the calming of the mind through meditation, exercise, and diet, life is observed more clearly. People start to grow and evolve at a much faster pace than if they were continuing their lives with a muddy and agitated mind.

The agitated mind takes up a lot of energy. By deepening our spiritual life, or whatever you want to call the path of Tibetan Medicine, we find lasting joy and happiness. The holistic approach of Tibetan Medicine for relieving anxiety and rLung Imbalance results in a stronger person, both mentally and physically. My clients who come off their medication feel like they've accomplished much and have a deeper sense of themselves. They have successfully developed new healthy personal habits thanks to Tibetan Medicine and their own discipline and hard work. They are meditating, exercising more, using the Tibetan incense, and have new dietary habits that are more nourishing for their constitution. By eliminating or reducing their anxiety medication, they feel more aware of themselves and others. It is as if they feel more connected and involved in their lives, like the medication had buffered and separated them from the world around them. They feel more in contact with reality, exactly as things are. Many clients remark on how intensely joyous and wonderful life is, but also how intensely the struggle of life requires a new kind of courage for them. When working with anxiety medication, I always work closely with a person's doctor. Sometimes a person can only lessen the medication by milligrams. Even so, they still come away more aware and with healthy lifestyle tools that bring them closer to themselves, their inner self, their constitutional type, and ultimately, more confident and stronger when facing their fears.

While the United States has mostly focused on making technological advances, such as electricity, the telephone, nuclear weapons, computers, and cell phones in the last hundred years, Tibetan Buddhist scholars have concentrated on making inner developmental advances for the last thousand years. Tibetan Buddhist monks have mapped out an inner psychology or roadmap of the mind and the way in which it is intertwined with the body. This mind/body connection also shows us how to prevent mental instability as well as how to heal ourselves when we do become mentally imbalanced. This has been the foundation for great advances in our understanding of both consciousness and psychology—knowledge we are only now beginning to appreciate in the West. Tibetan Medicine provides a more holistic approach to healing the cause of the symptoms, not just the symptoms themselves. What is unique about Tibetan Medicine is that its roots are in Buddhism. Buddhist monks found that by directing the flow of their rLung, or their vital force, they were able to feel calmer. Their minds were more at peace. It has been over two thousand years since Buddha walked the earth. The religious documents of those times describe his concrete practices for a calmer mind, which later grew into larger tractates that became recipes for treating mental health. Buddhist monks often acted as the doctors in their communities, and thus evolved one of the greatest medical systems in the world. We are only now just beginning to tap the knowledge Tibetan Medicine has of the treatment of psychosomatic illnesses.

The Buddhist medical texts state that all disease originates in the mind. A person's basic cravings, anger, and slothfulness of the mind can have a negative effect on their body. Since the root of all disease, and of all suffering, is the mind, Tibetan doctors always ask themselves first, what is this patient's mood? How is the suffering expressed? Is it anger? Is it sluggishness? Is it constant worrying and craving for something different in life?" This suffering of the mind will affect each organ of the body differently, depending on its quality. Dr. Jamling expressed an important distinction about suffering: In the West . . . suffering is seen as a bad thing . . . But this is not always so. Imbalance in the body/mind is not necessarily a negative thing. A Tibetan doctor may say to a patient that the actual mental affective state itself is fortunate, as it is a milestone of awareness that can help the patient more firmly put their foot on the path of enlightenment, the path to understanding the nature of their own mind. In Tibetan Medicine, suffering is seen as an opportunity to discover more about oneself, to grow and expand one's consciousness. While attending a Buddhist gathering in a small temple courtyard in Northern India in 1997, a small and frail-looking Lama returning from the United States told an interesting story that has since made its way around Buddhist circles, with varying details:

A medical doctor, a surgeon of known repute, was in a terrible car accident. His car was hit head-on by a drunk driver, and he swerved to the other side of the highway, tipping his car over twice, thus causing a monumental 16-car accident. The man's car landed in the ditch at the side of the highway. It took several hours to extricate him from the car. He was then rushed to the emergency room, suffering from a severe head wound that caused blindness in one eye. Both arms and legs were broken, and he was rushed into surgery to place permanent pins in both arms and to extract metal from his right leg. Multiple bruises and injuries to internal organs meant that he had to stay in the hospital for over three weeks, until all his vital signs had stabilized. He was not married, but friends gathered every day and evening to attend to his needs. On the tenth day, his Buddhist teacher visited him and bent over him as he lay in traction on the bed. The venerable teacher shook his head vigorously back and forth, back and forth, and repeated to himself, "Lucky, lucky man!"

You may ask how anyone could look at that broken man in a hospital bed and say to him that he is a lucky man. But think about the reasoning of the Tibetan mind. The Lama recounted that the Buddha described three kinds of suffering: 1) the suffering of pain, 2) the suffering of change, and 3) the suffering of conditionality, or conditioned, limited existence on earth. The lucky man from the story is indeed "lucky" because in one moment in time, the three kinds of suffering were made evident to him. This type of profound pain leads to what the Lama called, "The Clearing Field." This is where suddenly, all that seems important in one's life—reputation, possessions, good looks, youth—disappears, and the deeper meaning of life emerges, instantaneously, joyfully, and completely. It is this precious knowledge—greater than any material possession that was gained—that will never leave its master. It is an awareness that the lama says brings a certain "joy" unknown to the common man—hence the "lucky, lucky man" in the story.

Anxiety can make us suffer. It can also deepen our awareness and longing for serenity and peace. The tools in this book illuminate our awareness of ourselves. And there is nothing like the joy of regulating our rLung energy — it's like harnessing the wind!

**Visit https://www.bluedragonapothecary.com/specialized-care for more information or contact me at mary@bluedragonapothecary.com.

CHAPTER 40 - TRANSCENDENTAL MEDITATION

Bob Roth

I like things to be as simple and logical as possible. This is especially true when it comes to Transcendental Meditation (TM) — both in understanding and practice. I have been teaching TM for over 45 years now. For well over 5,000 years the TM technique was passed down from teacher to student, one to one: never in groups, never from a book. It has roots in the ancient noble warrior classes, where acting out of fear or anger brought disaster and defeat. Today it is for all of us who seek greater balance in life as well as more creativity, better health, less stress — and happiness.

The TM technique has been honed to 20 minutes, twice a day: once in the morning, ideally before breakfast; and again in the late afternoon or early evening, ideally before dinner.

You will learn this meditation from a professionally trained teacher in a one-on-one session and he or she will provide you with your own mantra — a word or sound that has no meaning associated with it — and will teach you how to think it properly, which means easily, effortlessly, and silently. You will learn that you don't need to push away thoughts, watch your breath, monitor bodily sensations, or visualize anything. You won't have to sit in any particular position either. The morning session wakes up your brain and gives you energy and resilience and the afternoon session gives you a reset...basically a way to start the next part of your day fresh.

The U.S. National Institutes of Health has provided tens of millions of dollars to study TM's effects on stress and heart health, while the U.S. Department of Defense has awarded several million dollars to study its impact on Post-Traumatic Stress Disorder (PTSD) among Veterans returning from combat in Iraq and Afghanistan. The change has taken time, but the TM technique is now recognized as a powerful treatment and preventative measure for so many of the stress-based disorders of our time — as well as an immensely practical tool to markedly improve health and performance. In the same way that we now recognize the importance of exercise and eating healthy, the world has come a long way with regard to understanding the critical importance of meditation in general and TM in particular.

I have taught Veterans with PTSD who have not slept more than one or two hours a night for several months because of terrible nightmares and sweats, but after their first or second day of meditating, they went home and slept through the night. Weeks later, they reported that sleeping through the night has become a new normal.

You can come to TM as a complete skeptic — like Dr. Richard Schneider, a retired Rear Admiral and President of Norwich University - but still be open to change. The more President Schneider learned about the tangible benefits of meditation, the more interested he was. So he invited me and my colleague Colonel Brian Rees, a medical doctor who served five tours in Iraq and Afghanistan, to meet with him and his whole administrative team, and talk about starting a pilot program teaching TM. "I support the idea of the program," he told me at the time. "But I have to learn myself before I suggest it to any student. I have to lead from the front."

He announced the TM pilot program in a letter to the inbound class and their parents. "We got overrun with parents who wanted their kids to try it," he said. "We did a control group of a platoon of about 30 kids who got the training, and 30 of those who didn't. Within three weeks, the kids who didn't get the training were complaining like they were disadvantaged," said President Schneider. "Because the meditating kids weren't getting yelled at, they were staying awake in class, they were performing better. So, they wanted it. And I told them, 'You'll get it but you're going to have to wait.'"

I find that many people are able to see the value of meditation in their own lives when they see what it does for Veterans. "If the technique can work for these men and women who live with the most toxic levels of stress and anxiety," the thinking goes, "then maybe it could work for me."

Meet Melanie Pote.

She was 18 months into her service in the U.S. Army when things went wrong. Around seven in the morning on March 20, 2002, she was finishing her night watch of ammunition at Fort Drum in upstate New York. It was training week, and Melanie and other members of the 110th Military Intelligence Battalion were getting ready for a day of rifle practice on a nearby range. But first they had to line up for breakfast at the mess tent. "Because I guarded the ammo at night, I was usually first in line, right at seven o'clock," Melanie told me. "But for some reason, I kept stalling. The guy who relieved me said, 'come on, it's been 15 minutes. Get going.' So, I did."

At 7:20, Melanie was fifth in line when two artillery shells fell far short of their drill target and sent shrapnel ripping through the mess tent. The cannon shells, each with the power to rip apart a tank, were fired after members of another battalion "acting in a negligent manner," according to Fort Drum's then acting commander.

"We saw the shells coming." Melanie recalled, "And then there was the explosion. The first person in line was killed instantly. That's where I usually was. And another Sergeant whom I knew very well was killed. He didn't die right away. He died later. But I watched him struggle as we tried to take care of him."

Melanie was thrown through the air. "I didn't even realize I was hurt," she said. "I was trying to help everyone else. Then I saw I had two pieces of shrapnel in my left leg." Her wounds healed, but the trauma remained. "You just don't plan for that on your own base," she said. "You plan for it over there, in Iraq." Melanie went home, and things only got worse. "From my experience with military PTSD, there's a lot of triggers. There are so many noises that happen — a car backfiring or fireworks — that will bring up a previous event."

Worse, even the anticipation of being triggered caused Melanie to live in a clenched state of panic. "I had tightness in my chest and pain there all the time," she said. After a decade of feeling untethered, Melanie, now a tattoo artist working out of Lawrenceville, Georgia, sought the expertise of a therapist who helped her work through her survivor's guilt. Still, she lived with that inescapable fear. "For a long, long time," she said, "I was very lost."

Melanie looked into TM in 2016 and decided to learn. "Within two weeks of practice, I was driving my car down the road, and I realized, 'wait, I don't have any tightness in my chest. I don't have that constant feeling of dread that I am going to die.'" She pulled over and called her meditation teacher. "I was laughing because it seemed so crazy. I'd lived with this anxiety for so long, and meditation was the missing piece to heal it." There are moments, of course, where Melanie's trauma returns, but the effects are not as severe, and it dissipates more quickly.

While Veterans make up only 9% of the population, they account for double - 18%. - the number of U.S. suicides. The first study of TM as a treatment for PTSD involved combat Veterans of the Vietnam War. The trial showed a 52% reduction in anxiety symptoms, a 46% drop in depression, and a 40% reduction in symptoms of PTSD after three months' practice of the technique. Veterans who couldn't sleep finally found relief, and many who'd turned to alcohol abuse were able to ease off their drinking.

Thousands of Veterans have learned TM. Research on Veterans who meditate has shown that the technique reduces the psychosocial symptoms of stress, anxiety and depression, and also balances serotonin and norepinephrine, and regulates the sympathetic nervous system. Recently, a study of Veterans from the wars in Iraq and Afghanistan showed a 48% reduction in symptoms of PTSD, and an 87% improvement in depression. The results were evident after just two months of practicing TM.

In 2010, the David Lynch Foundation began offering TM to Veterans, Active Duty military personnel and Cadets - and their families — through our Operation Warrior Wellness (OWW) initiative. That's how Paul Downs learned to meditate. In his eleven years serving as an infantryman in the U.S. Marine Corps, Paul was deployed in hotspots and combat zones throughout the world. In the Middle East alone he served in Iraq, Oman, Qatar and Kuwait. When Paul left the Marines, one of the things he looked forward to most was being close to his young children. But what he didn't realize was just how much his identity as a Marine meant to him. When Paul left the Corps, he said, he lost pretty much everything: his tribe, his sense of self, and all that he knew to be true. Because of that, he lost his sense of forward momentum, purpose and connection.

Paul suffered from PTSD. To outside observers, he told me that he might have seemed like "just another angry, disgruntled Veteran." He sought help from the VA, looking for guidance, direction and connection but nothing seemed to help and he quit trying. "I was drowning in fear and sadness," he reflected. "After months of putting away the uniform, I developed a pretty detailed plan for suicide. But while sitting in my truck, ready to proceed, a thought hit me: to die by my own hand was not my birthright. It is not the way of the warrior. Warriors have a deep appreciation for life and are not victims of circumstance."

Paul reached out to the Boulder Crest Retreat in Virginia, a highly respected in-residence center for Veterans seeking to heal the hidden wounds of trauma. There he learned TM. According to Paul, "TM is different. You can take it anywhere and do it anytime: at home, on an airplane, sitting in traffic, anywhere. Veterans need this meditation. We need to learn how to regulate so we can be calm, cool and collected at home, just like we were trained to neon the battlefield. TM has worked for thousands of my brothers and sisters. It's given me the opportunity not just to survive on earth but to thrive here — and to live a life that is truly full of purpose, meaning, connection and service."

Boulder Crest Retreat, which is in Bluemont, Virginia, is the nation's first privately funded wellness center dedicated exclusively to combat Veterans and their families. It provides a free, safe and sacred place for nearly 700 Veterans and their families each year to rest, reconnect, and recharge. It also serves as a model location for implementing the Operation Warrior Wellness (OWW) "Resilient Warrior" program.

Since its launch in 2010, the OWW initiative has partnered with leading Veterans service organizations, Army and Marine bases, and VA medical centers across the country — as well as with military colleges in order to create a new generation of more resilient officers. The TM-based Resilient Warrior Program has been extensively researched by over 400 peer-reviewed studies, including over $26 Million in grants from the National Institutes of Health to study the program's effectiveness for reducing stress and heart disease. Key TM findings for Veterans include: 40-55% reduction in symptoms of PTSD; 42% decrease in insomnia; 30% improvement in satisfaction with quality of life; 25% reduction in plasma cortisol levels; decreased high blood pressure — on par with first-line anti hypertensives; and 47% reduced risk of cardiovascular-related mortality.

More than 500,000 U.S. troops deployed since 2001 suffer from PTSD – a small fraction of our Veterans who served in our armed forces. And yet, less than 12% will actually receive adequate care due to a lack of effective treatments, fear of stigma or insufficient resources. Half of those with PTSD won't receive any care at all. Left untreated, PTSD cripples functioning and places Veterans at great risk for violent and self-destructive behavior, including alcoholism or drug abuse; severe depression, anxiety or emotional numbness; family and employment problems; suicide – today more than 6,500 Veterans die by suicide every year.

It is imperative that we help Veterans and the brave men and women still in active-duty deal with the stress that stays with them long after they have returned home. TM is an incredibly simple, accessible, evidence-based tool that can help those overcome the stress and anxiety from the theater of war, thus allowing them to lead healthier, more resilient lives. The same is true for those under Reserve status who have deployed. When these men and women come back home, they deal with the same kind of difficulties as do active-duty personnel. Often they are expected to return to their regular jobs and to deal with their inner difficulties and traumas on their own.

My Dad hoped I'd be a doctor, but it wasn't for me. When I was 10 years old he tried to get me interested in medicine by bringing me along to Fort Miley. Saturday mornings, he'd find me throwing my baseball against the concrete wall in front of the garage, scooping up grounders with the worn Willie Mays glove I slept with every night. "Okay Bobby," he'd say, "we're going to go to the hospital, and I'm going to read one x-ray. Then we'll go to Candlestick Park."

Candlestick Park was where my beloved San Francisco Giants played. The idea of going to a Giants game was for me. So I would go to the VA Hospital at Fort Miley in San Francisco and sit in the hospital waiting room. Invariably, one x-Ray would become two, then ten, and then too any for me to count, because there were always emergencies. I used to sit there for hours. And I watched these war-torn, sad-faced Veterans rolling up and down the sterile corridors in wheelchairs and bandages. Broken men. Seeing their physical and emotional pain left a deep impression on my heart. Maybe that's why I am drawn so much to work with Veterans today.

Every day I read in newspapers that mental health is increasingly at the forefront of the national debate – and for good reason. Does anyone really know what to do? Do we medicate every child who may be a bully or who is bullied? Do we continue to hand out cocktails of drugs to Veterans with PTSD? While some of the medications are helpful for some, too many Veterans are non-compliant; many don't like the numbness and disorientation. They often feel medicated up, and so they refuse to take the drugs. Maybe they just want something better.

Just visit https://www.tm.org for more information or to locate your closest TM center.

CHAPTER 42 - VETMOTORSPORTS

Peter Cline (VETMotorsports)

I was raised in Upper Arlington and Cleveland, Ohio and graduated from Ohio State with an English degree. Through the years I worked at various jobs including bartending, waiting tables, motorcycle shop parts counter and am currently employed in state government. Side jobs included twenty years of playing music, touring, recording and a record contract. Not far behind I got married and became a parent while also continuing to work in my government job and maintaining my semi-professional motorcycle racing career. I currently volunteer my spare time as Executive Director with VETMotorsports and serve post 9/11 Veterans nationwide. My journey has not been straight and predictable. It seems that I'm always looking for new experiences and thrive on connecting with people. These relationships have helped me achieve something greater than the sum of its individual parts.

I entered the world of motorsports as a competitor, but severe injuries that I suffered during a qualifying race became the catalyst for a different kind of opportunity. Rather than continuing to race, I instead founded VETMotorsports, a nonprofit group that organizes and funds motorsports experiences for injured post-9/11 Veterans who are having trouble adjusting to civilian life. I got the idea based on therapies I saw being done in the United Kingdom as well as a chance viewing of a BBC broadcast that prompted me to create this life-changing organization for injured Veterans. The BBC program showed how injured troops used motorsports to recover, and I believed that the same approach could work in the United States. As a former professional motorcycle racer, I facilitated race experiences across the States during the racing season and focused on fundraising and outreach to partners during the off-season. I wanted the experience to be very hands on and immersive and not a parade of Veterans just getting thanked for their service. Veterans could ride or work in the pit, and could benefit from the cultural similarities of motorsports to military culture.

I knew that the first event we held would really affect the motorsports team. But how the event positively affected the veteran participants was overwhelming. From that point, I knew we had a concept that had the potential to really transform the lives of those attending and participating in our events.

Inspired to empower disabled Veterans through motorsports, our team took the leadership role to show value to those suffering injuries in combat. In doing so VETMotorsports became the first American motorsports team to fully integrate disabled Veterans into an active race team environment. By working with injured combat Veterans local warriors are included into motorsports events. VETMotorsports allowed our Veteran crew members to focus on abilities instead of disabilities, to show value to Veterans and to heal and empower through motorsports. The program allowed me to take 12 plus years of relationships and create this thing where the sum of the parts make a huge difference to those Veterans participating.

The program is about creating a culture where injured war-fighters are welcome, where we can provide them an outlet that shows them their self-worth and hopefully create an opportunity for them to succeed outside the program. We provide Veterans struggling to re-assimilate to civilian life the opportunity to work with professional motorcycle and auto racing teams. The program has become an award-winning, non-clinical outreach program that honors and empowers post-9/11 Veterans with service-related injuries through active participation in motorsports. It provides inspiration and motivation for participating Veterans by making them part of a new team and giving them a new mission.

We find the Veterans that are interested in participating as a nonclinical therapy and we connect them to the resources. It's always a hands-on activity — mental stimulation, physical stimulation, creating teamwork. We'll fund it, we'll pay for their experience and lodging, food, and gas. What it does is gets them back into the environment of high adrenaline so they can understand that adrenaline rush is normal and also gets them to work in the civilian populations which they have a hard time integrating into.

We continue to do everything we can to try and reduce the Veteran suicide rate. Having the Sports Car Club of America (SCCA) and the SCCA Foundation work hand-in-hand with us for a second year, to honor and empower these brave service men and women, is incredibly validating and gratifying. We can't thank everyone at the SCCA enough for taking up this important cause. They understand and embrace what we're doing, and they're going to make a tremendous difference in these Veterans' lives.

Since the program was founded, VETMotorsports has helped more than 190 Veterans with service connected injuries and caregivers participate in more than 75 motorcycle and auto racing events across the United States.

J. Alberto Fait: I heard about an event here in California and I went to it and participated. I met Zachariah Collett, who happened to serve in the same brigade that I did. We had never met before but we had a lot in common, so that made the experience super pleasant. It was more the community itself that made the difference. VetMotorsports did a great job but the racing community as a whole welcomed us. That is what made a real difference. I emailed Peter Cline and told him that I loved the mission of the organization and that I was interested in trying to help make more VetMotorsports events possible in California, and specifically in the Bay area. It took about three to four months of phone tag until we finally had a sit-down conversation, and when we did, Peter invited me to go to Texas to help run an event there. After that we were up and running in California. We successfully ran three events in 2018 and have more planned for 2019.

Once the first event got started we were very much welcomed. There were no stupid questions. We could talk to the other drivers. Everyone was appreciative about what we, as an organization, had done in the past so there was an open door. Some of the drivers even volunteered to give us a ride in their cars and talked about their cars with the Veteran participants. I grew up drag racing...not legally...and in that community people don't want to talk about their cars, they just wanted to race. Here, everybody was welcoming, they were giving out driving tips freely and they were offering suggestions. It was a very different environment. Zach definitely made the event great. He was constantly taking care of us, making sure we were okay, making sure we were having fun and making sure we stayed hydrated.

My wife also noticed quite a bit of a change in me, realizing that I figured out a way to meld my two worlds. I love cars, I love racing and I love driving but at the same time I am a Social Worker and work at the VA...so I also love helping Veterans. With my involvement in VetMotorsports, I get to do both. She also noticed that I was more outgoing and that I try to talk to people more than I used to. We utilized the connections I already had within the Veteran Service offices at the VA and some of the people who participated with me the first time. I let them know that we were doing another event and we're looking for any Veterans that would be interested in participating. So very quickly, I'd say in less than two weeks, I had all four slots filled. Thus far we also try to give a slot to a Caregiver if they come to the event along with their Veteran and have a desire to participate.

The thing that stands out the most in my mind about these events is the camaraderie. I think back to the days of being in uniform and it is very similar to that. The event I first participated in, everyone was Operation Iraqi Freedom/Operation Enduring Freedom, so a lot of the other participants were relatively young...actually I was the oldest one there. I went into the military at age 26. So just trading stories about our deployments and the camaraderie that got rebuilt, interestedly enough because I am in the mental health profession; the rapport built so quickly just on the commonality that we had all served was tremendous. Even now, in the last event that I did, I had a Vietnam era Veteran who was isolating, and he got connected with another Veteran from the same era who was more outgoing and who was more connected to resources and getting out to do things. They ended up exchanging numbers, and I remember thinking, as the event was wrapping up, that this is why we are doing this...because this Veteran who was isolating can now break out and go do things that he couldn't before.

I meet with everybody, as a group, before the events actually begin...providing a sort of safety and rules briefing as well as providing a reminder to all concerned to stay hydrated, things like that. From there I tend to run between the club and the drivers and I will typically have a driver on the track and then another set of drivers who are working the track. This means that they are resetting the cones if they get hit, things like that. So I am constantly running and coordinating activities, and because of this, we have actually gotten our Veterans 'rides' in some very interesting, unique, and expensive cars. By rides, I mean that the Veterans get to go out on the track with another driver to experience the ride in a different car and even help familiarize them with the track. In doing so we were also able to identify other Veterans who are doing these events as well, as individual participants. So all of a sudden it seems like we are back in uniform, we are talking smack to each other, and it's a really fun time. I had a married couple at the last event that I did, and the wife actually had a better time than her husband.

Basically, there's a clinical term called prolonged exposure, which is basically being exposed to something that brings anxiety (with PTSD, at the end of the day, at the root of it is anxiety) and part of the therapeutic treatment for that is to expose you to someone that brings you that anxiety. So, a crowd, loud noises, an unknown location; all these things can be very triggering. So in preparation for the first event I actually coordinated with the PTSD Clinical Team at the VA and I received 'clinical' advice from them. That said, it is the Prolonged Exposure part that seems to be the most helpful to the Veteran participants...that and the camaraderie. From there you are going through the experience with everybody else and, by doing that, you kind of block out the things that cause you anxiety. The triggers to your anxiety just kind of fall by the wayside. What happens afterwards, that's where I'd love to do follow-ups. At the last event there was a Veteran who did the first event along with me and he was talking about how he was a little bit more daring about going out and trying different things after the first event. That's really the value of the organization, to really try to break the Veterans out of isolating, or drinking excessively...whatever their isolating behavior might be. It's breaking them out and showing them that this is an alternative way to have fun. It's an alternative way to get adrenaline. When we were in combat many of us were heavily caffeinated with energy drinks and coffee. Many of us smoked and had nicotine in our systems. All these things changed the chemistry in the brain, and when we do this constantly, like going outside the wire, when you come back some of those centers in the brain get depleted. So how do you refill that...how do you get that dopamine back? I think many Veterans struggle with that. This definitely helps the Veterans out with this issue because the dopamine is hitting, and they are feeling prideful and getting joy from their participation. I've been able to connect with people like Mary Pozzi, the National Champion for the SCCA, and she's coaching most of my drivers. She is an amazing gal. She doesn't even run in the women's division, she runs in the men's division. She even got me teary eyed when she was thanking me for the opportunity to help the Veterans improve their driving skills. It was quite emotional for me.

As far as an outcome measurement tool, I do look at effect because I am always contemplating things from a clinical standpoint. I also try to determine whether someone is isolating or is just shy. I tend to be loud and boisterous and tend to take control of situations, so for me it's a little bit different. At one point I do recall that Peter did mention Ohio State maybe doing some research with VetMotorsports, as far as, or in relation to, clinical outcomes.

For the first event, I had a participant bring his RV, and the RV was parked 300-400 meters away from where the cars actually drove. So that RV served as a 'barrier' for the Veterans in relation to excess noise, if they needed to get away from the noise. Also, the cars aren't really that loud because they are all street legal vehicles, so they aren't like real race cars. There is part of my job in what I call Hosting, and what Peter calls serving as a Director. But the best part of Hosting, for me, is making sure that people are comfortable, including the Veterans and their Caregivers.

These events take place on Airfields mostly. The distance is usually about 1/2 mile to 3/4 mile. It's more about agility than it is speed...and the average speed is usually only 50 miles per hour. Of course, the more tricked and modified cars are going to hit higher speeds but the cars that we take out are typically not very high horsepower.

Mary Pozzi: I have been involved with VetMotorsports events twice now (as of September of 2018). Both of my experiences have been very positive. My first experience was in 2017 at the Sports Car Club of America (SCCA) CAM event, in San Diego for an Autocross event at Qualcomm Stadium. The second event I did was held in 2018 in Crows Landing, CA at the Naval Air Station base.

At the first event there were three former enlisted military members who had all served in the Middle East, and they were with a representative from VetMotorsports who was looking for a volunteer to help familiarize them with Autocross. They had rented a Camaro from one of the rental car companies and all three of them got a chance to compete. I got to serve as their mentor after having done the sport for over 40 years myself. I took them under my wing and explained everything I knew about Autocross, how to drive smoothly, and engaging in tactical driving (using finesse instead of just flooring it). They had mini-competitions between themselves, and I got to ride with each of them, and then they also got to take Autocross runs on their own. They all had a wonderful experience.

The same things occurred during the second event I assisted with. We were able to get the Veterans involved in motor sports activities, and we had five participants at the ready this time around. This time around I approached VetMotorsports instead of them approaching me. I just volunteered and they were glad to have me. It ended up working out really well. We had five individuals, including one female, and I did the same things that I did for the Veterans during the San Diego event. This time they had a little four-cylinder Mazda or Ford...something like that. They all got to drive it, they all had a good time, and they all learned a lot about driving. A few of them even decided to take their own personal cars out and then come back at a later date. This is because we hold events, or rather competitions, throughout the year. So, I shared my email and my Facebook page with several of them and told them to let me know when they were going to 'go out' and that I'd come out and ride with them and help them get really good at the sport.

The way I look to instruct is I try to teach folks by working on the positives. Everybody makes mistakes at this, and if this sport was really easy we'd have more people doing it. I always tell folks to go into a corner slow and come out fast, and if you go in fast you're usually going to come out backwards. They tested that out a little bit and they found out I was right. But, as I said, I try to work on the positives. If they make a mistake we deal with it, laugh about it, and then try and correct whatever it was that needs correcting. Autocross is a really safe sport. It is one car on the course at a time, it's kind of like downhill Slalom skiing. They start at the top and then they follow the course and whomever gets down to the bottom the fastest wins. In Autocross it's the same except that it is usually done at an airport or in a parking lot and we set up traffic cones. The cars are put into solo and ladies classes, and there is even a Novice Program for people who are just starting out.

We try to make it fun. We tell people that they come for the cars and they stay for the people because the competition ends when you pass the checkered flag and stop the clock. Everybody shares a beverage afterwards, talks about the day, and shares laughs. We also learn and we talk and we share the commonality of the car...that's what makes it such a neat sport. I tell folks it's very safe to do because the risk to your car is very minimal. I am not saying that something can't happen, but it's very rare that it does. If you are going to participate in your street car, then it will serve to make you a safer driver on the street because the speeds you are Auto crossing as the same speeds that you drive on regular streets. It's more on precision driving than it is on top speed.

It was such a positive experience for me because I got to take newcomers to the Autocross sport and got to see how they progressed in the sport, and how they gained confidence behind the wheel (and in themselves) and seeing them learn about what the cars could and couldn't do. They got to explore their limitations and discover capabilities they didn't know they had. It was really pretty cool. They all had big grins on their faces afterwards. It's funny...they were all within half a second of each other time wise, and they started out all over the place. It didn't matter if they were stone slow or they were fast, everybody cheered them on when they came in, we had an announcer who talked about VetMotorsports and said how happy they were that the organization and the Veterans were there. It was very positive from all facets. VetMotorsports was just looking for people to help them out and I said sure, that I'd be more than happy to. I wasn't competing until the afternoon so I had all morning to dedicate to coaching the Veterans. It just so happened that both times I ended up coaching the Veterans, I was already at the location preparing to compete myself. I am a 12-Time National Autocross Champion, and I also do a lot of coaching and instructing with companies that actually have paid students that come to do this.

To me this time in my life is about giving back. I feel like it is a time to develop the next generation to become involved in our sport. I am really proud to have been involved with VetMotorsports, and I hope our relationship continues into the future. If I can make a little bit of a difference for each Veteran and help return them back to where they came from, and also let them know that what they did is appreciated, then I'm all for it. VetMotorsports made that happen for me and for 'my' Veterans.

For more information on our program please be sure to visit: http://www.vetmotorsports.org.

CHAPTER 42 - SUICIDES: COMPLEX SOLUTIONS ARE NEEDED FOR A COMPLEX PROBLEM

Rory Riley Topping, Esq.

The first time I met Tommy Rieman he seemed like a totally normal guy. At the time, I was serving on the Board of Directors for Veterans Bridge Home, a Charlotte-based non-profit that seeks to help Veterans transition from the military to civilian life, where he was on the staff. Although I knew he was a Veteran, I assumed that he, like a vast majority of the Veterans we saw there, probably encountered some difficulty during the transition but that any such difficulties were mild to moderate in nature and short-lived based on the services organizations like ours provided. As someone who had spent a career studying Veterans policy issues at VA, in the halls of Congress, and as an advocate representing Veterans in federal court, I had a general awareness that suicide among Veterans was a rising issue. But, like many DC-insiders, I got easily caught up in big picture ideas and policy-based abstractions when it came to confronting it.

So, when I was asked to write this chapter on the current status of the Veterans' suicide epidemic, and how we, as a society, can improve our prevention efforts, I immediately worried that I'd be perceived in that manner — as an unsympathetic DC-insider who couldn't relate to the real struggles faced by real Veterans contemplating suicide. After all, I'm not a Veteran myself, nor (thankfully) am I suicidal.

Although my husband is a Veteran, he never saw combat, and he was fortunate enough to transition directly from the Army into graduate school at Harvard. Despite losing my husband's sister at a young age as a direct result of her service-connected injuries, the life my husband and I lead as it relates to his service is less complicated than it is for many other families.

My thought process on how to approach this chapter changed when I got to know Rieman and not only learned his personal story, but when he also gave me permission to tell it here. Rieman's story is a powerful one. Like many Veterans returning from the conflicts in Iraq and Afghanistan, Rieman's story is one that is marked by Post-Traumatic Stress Disorder (PTSD), substance abuse, and suicide. But, unlike many Veterans, Rieman's story is also one of success, perseverance, and a bit of luck. His suicide attempt failed and, in many ways, it was a blessing in disguise.

Despite many dark days, Rieman's story is the story of why suicide prevention is so important. As I mentioned initially, when I first met him, I had no idea that someone who was such an integral part of our organization had such a personal tie to our mission. It was a classic example of "I'm not only a Director, but I'm also a client." That's when it clicked for me. Despite my time in various high-powered organizations, I would never understand the Veterans suicide epidemic until I spent more time with Veterans like Rieman who had the ability to articulate what the 20 Veterans a day who die by suicide will never be able to. I couldn't relate personally, but what I could do was use this opportunity and my ability as a writer to tell these important stories with the hopes that maybe, just maybe, some of my fellow DC-insiders are listening.

The story of the Veterans suicide epidemic is actually a story about how real people struggle to deal with real feelings in the face of a culture and society that encourages them to simply suppress these feelings. Feelings such as hopelessness, helplessness, isolation, and overwhelming pain. Feelings that are negatively stigmatized or viewed as weakness.

Preventing Veterans' suicide is the story of how to ask for help to overcome these feelings. It is not a story about government programs, nor how good or bad the Department of Veterans Affairs is or isn't.

And, Rieman's story is one that shows that, with the proper community support and interventions, these uncomfortable feelings and thoughts of suicide can indeed be overcome. Rieman's story is a story of hope for other Veterans who may be struggling, to let them know that they are not alone, and that they, too, can defeat the enemy within. It's also a story that enables those of us non-Veterans know the types of things we can do to help.

Rieman's personal story, as it relates to his suicide attempt, begins with his deployment to Iraq in 2003. Rieman was shot in the arm and the chest while using his body as a shield to protect his gunner. He kept fighting through his injuries and lead his team of eight to safety. Afterwards, Rieman was hailed as a hero, receiving a Purple Heart and Silver Star. He was also being recognized by President George W. Bush at the State of the Union address, where the President described him as "earn[ing] the respect and gratitude of our whole country." His face was featured on the cover of an XBOX game and his likeness made into an action figure. To put it simply, his fifteen-year career in the Army seemed like heroism personified.

However, like many Veterans, Rieman was struggling on the inside despite all the fanfare on the outside. "I left the military because I was mentally and emotionally broken, so I just walked away," Rieman said of his decision to leave the Army in 2014, "but what broke me more so than war was the transition. My identity was wrapped up in the military. I had no understanding of my purpose or lack thereof, so I turned to substance abuse, and I attempted suicide."

Rieman first contemplated suicide when he re-deployed to Iraq in 2010. He spent an evening with his gun in his mouth, switching the safety on and off, and contemplating whether or not to pull the trigger. His roommate at the time intervened and, after a brief stint at the Army's combat stress center, was returned to his tour of duty. In the interim, Rieman's PTSD symptoms increased, and he began to self-medicate with prescription pills and alcohol. As a result, his marriage crumbled. "I wrote a goodbye letter to my kids, letting them know that I loved them more than anything and leaving was not what I wanted to do, but I felt like it was all I could do to make their lives better because they would be better off without me," he recalls. And then he got into his truck, hit the gas, and closed his eyes as his steered towards a tree.

As fate would have it, Rieman survived the collision. Rather than being punished for his actions or sentenced to jail for DUI, Rieman instead received compassion from the community where he resided in North Carolina. He was assigned to a Veterans Treatment Court and, with the help of mentor who was a fellow Veteran, he fulfilled the program's requirements. According to Rieman, the respect and compassion he received from his community is what truly helped him get his life back on track. He now devotes his career to helping other Veterans do the same.

As evidenced by the many caveats and treatment techniques discussed in the preceding chapters of this book, PTSD has a real impact on real people like Rieman. When real people are hurting and don't receive the treatment that they need, they may turn to thoughts of suicide, as evidenced by Rieman's cautionary tale.
Importantly, not all Veterans are as fortunate as Rieman. One of the less fortunate Veterans who was also struggling with substance abuse after service was U.S. Army Sergeant John Toombs. When Toombs was turned away from a VA emergency room, he ended up taking his life on the property shortly thereafter. In a recorded message, Tombs stated: "When I asked for help, they opened up a Pandora's box inside of me and just kicked me out the door. That's how they treat Veterans 'round here."

According to Toombs' father, David Toombs, "As far as my son, he told me the main trigger for him, was that hopeless, helpless feeling, that would draw you so far down." For many Veterans suffering with PTSD, overcoming those feelings of hopelessness and helplessness can feel like a Sisyphean curse — every time they seem to make progress, they end up sliding backwards. As Rieman confirms, this feeling that the cycle can never be broken is often what leads to suicide. Of course, as Rieman knows personally, the cycle can be broken, but doing so requires hard work on the part of the individual. However, it also requires a broader societal shift to re-shaping our cultural approach to the military, mental health generally, and the inter-relationship between the two.

The remainder of this chapter consists of several ideas (and their historical origins) that Rieman and I discussed to assist Veterans and non-Veterans alike in charting a path forward toward ending the Veterans suicide epidemic.

Currently, stakeholders in the Veterans' community, talk a lot about the Veterans' suicide epidemic, and how to prevent Veterans suicides. I believe 'suicide prevention' to be somewhat of a misnomer. Yes, we certainly want to avoid any Veteran reaching a point where they feel that suicide is their only option. But, oftentimes, there are many intervening steps that can be taken before a Veteran arrives at this point. Indeed, as noted by David Toombs, the main culprit is often feelings of hopelessness and helplessness, so I feel that keeping the focus on embracing a positive behavior, i.e., "Promoting hope," is more productive than just focusing on preventing a negative, i.e., "Preventing suicide." In other words, rather than just being focused solely on suicide prevention, we should be focused on mental health and wellness more broadly. If the focus is on optimal mental health at all times, we can ultimately make more progress than we can by focusing on suicide prevention alone. As the VA itself acknowledges, "[t]o prevent Veteran suicide, we must help reduce Veterans' risk for suicide before they reach a crisis point and support those Veterans who are in crisis."

One simple solution, that is rarely discussed by stakeholders in the various conversations about suicide prevention, stems from the old adage that when life becomes difficult, simply slow down, pause, and take a breath. According to Rieman, this is particularly helpful for Veterans who struggle with the stress of transition, as well as combat. "There is a saying that time heals all, and I truly believe that," Rieman states, reflecting back on his experience, "there are lots of different programs in place [to assist Veterans in transition], but I wasn't ready to take them seriously." He continued, "If we want to improve overall health and well-being, we need to slow down the transition process and allow Veterans the time they need to process all of the changes they are going through."

Rieman's sentiment about the power of pause is also echoed by Dr. Chrisanne Gordon, a physician who specializes in Traumatic Brain Injury (TBI) and founder of the Resurrecting Lives Foundation, a non-profit that specifically focuses on assisting transitioning Veterans with TBI. "We are all part of the race that is modern existence. We text, we Instagram, we communicate in short bursts of conversation to save time – and we believe in instant gratification," states Gordon. And, she continued, "In our military, a second can literally be the determination of life or death, and decisions must be made in fractions of a second." Rieman reiterated, "The things that keep you alive in war kill you as a civilian. You're told that you're invincible and you can defeat any enemy." Thus, for many Veterans, de-conditioning them from this way of thinking is a process that takes time, particularly when they are working on defeating the enemy within.

Because of the fast-paced nature of the world we live in, many Veterans may experience frustration at the lack of a quick-fix for their mental health. Encouraging Veterans, whether they are struggling with their mental health or not, to simply take time to pause and reflect on what they are going through is one of the many steps that can be taken before a veteran reaches the crux of suicidal behavior.

First, pausing promotes reflection on intentional choices rather than simply reacting to circumstances that may feel beyond ones' control. Second, scientifically speaking, pausing activates the parasympathetic nervous system, which helps us to feel calm by reducing tension and anxiety. And, finally, once our nervous system calms down, we have more capacity to avoid reacting out of habit or raw emotion and instead choosing a more thoughtful and reflective path forward. To paraphrase Nelson Mandela, our choices in life should reflect our hopes, not our fears.

Of course, the power of pause alone is not enough to reverse the suicide epidemic. Even if one does pause and acknowledge that they are struggling, what happens next? For example, when it comes to mental health, the culture of the military and asking for help are often at odds with one another. "I thought the definition of a man was to beat my chest and say, 'I got this,'" states Rieman, reflecting on his own challenges overcoming military culture, "but if you want to look at yourself and be happy, you have to ask for help."

Although significant progress has been made since the Vietnam era in acknowledging and treating PTSD, American society as a whole continues to struggle with the stigma around mental health. As elaborated on in a 2011 Government Accountability Office Report about VA Mental Health services, Veterans often experience "[p]erceptions that as a result of accessing mental health care they will be viewed negatively by others such as peers or employers. For example, Veterans may feel that by accessing mental health care they will be perceived as weak or having lost control." Feelings of fear of being perceived as weak are enhanced by a culture that rewards bravery and heroism.

So, how do we take a population that is hardwired toward not asking for help, to do in fact just that? There is no simple answer to this question. Of course, if there was, there would presumably be no need for this conversation. Since that, unfortunately, is not the case, here is an overview on some additional things we can do that will collectively make a difference.

First, it's important to understand that Veterans' suicides are not a new topic, but one that we, as a society, did not begin to understand until very recently. Although issues pertaining to Veterans' suicides have received increased media attention over the last several years and were even labeled an epidemic this past year, Veterans have struggled with suicide, suicidal thoughts, and mental health ailments for generations. During the Civil War, for example, many Veterans died by suicide based on what they experienced during the war, but also from the economic hardships they experienced afterward. And, some killed themselves before going into battle, for what is speculated as fear of being unable to live up to honor and bravery expected of them during the fight. Despite the number of soldiers who suffered as a result of their Civil War service, the pressure of war and its impact on mental health were seldom studied until World War I, when it was observed that large numbers of Veterans exposed to combat returned with "shell shock." PTSD, as a diagnosis, did not emerge until after the Vietnam War, and clearly, Veterans of the Operation Iraqi Freedom/Operation Enduring Freedom (OIF/OEF) conflicts are still struggling with it.

Society did not pay much attention to suicide generally until 1998, when Congress declared suicide a national problem and declared suicide prevention as a national priority, acknowledging that "no single prevention program will be appropriate for all populations or communities." Veteran suicide did not gain recognition as a separate issue until approximately the mid-2000s, when opposition to the wars in Iraq in Afghanistan caused many to re-focus on the plight of Veterans returning from a combat zone, including an emphasis on the impact of disabilities such as PTSD, TBI, and severe physical wounds such as shrapnel injuries and amputations. This led to a number of federal health policy initiatives that, although well-intentioned, must be viewed as a starting point, rather than as all-encompassing solutions. Complex social problems such as Veterans' suicide can't be solved simply by legislating, which typically involves throwing more money and more people at the problem. Nonetheless, over the past decade, Congress has done primarily just that.

In 2007, Congress passed the Joshua Omvig Veteran Suicide Prevention Act, which was named after an Iraq War veteran who committed suicide in 2005. The legislation captured the sense of Congress that "suicide among Veterans suffering from [PTSD] is a serious problem" and that VA "should take into consideration the special needs of Veterans suffering from PTSD and the special needs of elderly Veterans who are at high risk for depression and experience high rates of suicide." The House report accompanying the legislation also noted that "[t]he stress of combat, along with the stigma that exists for soldiers and Veterans seeking mental health care, can intensify and trigger a complex set of behaviors that may lead to thoughts of suicide." The legislation's intended purpose was to strengthen suicide awareness, prevention, and education programs throughout the VA.

Despite this legislation, and a significant increase in VA's mental health staff and budget in the years that followed, Veterans continued to die by suicide at an alarming rate. In 2015, Congress revisited the issue, leading to the passage of the Clay Hunt Suicide Prevention for American Veterans Act, named for a Marine who served in Afghanistan who died by suicide in March 2011 at the age of 28. The purpose of the Clay Hunt SAV Act was to further expand suicide prevention programs and mental health services at the VA. Congress is again exploring legislative options in the wake of four Veterans who committed suicide at VA medical centers in April 2019.

"It's irresponsible for us to think that the government has it under control," states Rieman, with regard to legislative and clinical efforts undertaken by Congress and VA, "that's not a slap on them, it's just unrealistic." Rieman noted that one of the challenges with many government programs is their rigidity. "Lots of vets can't process what's happening internally, so we have to bend a little to help them get to where they need to be, rather than rule with a hammer," he states.

Indeed, the circumstances surrounding John Toombs' final moments is an example of how rigidity can work to hurt, rather than help some Veterans. Toombs was in the residential treatment program at the Murfreesboro VA that, although intended to be "an intensive therapeutic atmosphere," also "demand[ed] strict discipline." When, on the morning of November 22, 2016, Toombs failed to take his medication on time, he was abruptly kicked out of the program. His death by suicide took place only hours later.

"Real change happens in the community, and some communities are better at receiving Veterans back home than others." Rieman stated in response, clearly saddened by the account of what happened to Toombs, and tacitly acknowledging the community embrace that enabled him to pursue a much different path. "We need to better define what transition is – it's moving from one point to another. It's not just a one-time event that happens when you get out of the military. It extends far beyond that."

Rieman is correct that, ultimately, legislation is a starting point, as it authorizes necessary resources within the VA and other community organizations to address the suicide epidemic, but it should not be viewed as an ending point. Rather, if we truly want to change the way we discuss mental health – for both Veterans and non-Veterans alike — we must look far beyond legislation and into local communities to embrace a holistic approach to mental health and ultimately, suicide prevention.

One of the first things we can do is embrace public private partnerships within our communities. As the VA has acknowledged, it's clear that the Department can't solve this problem on its own, nor should we expect it to, when statistics show that only six of 20 Veterans who commit suicide received healthcare from the VA in the two years prior to their death. Because suicide is a complex issue that affects Veterans from all walks of life, there is no single agency or organization that can account for all causalities. Moreover, people within a Veterans' community are more likely to know the Veteran and are therefore in a better position to spot changes in behavior, i.e., isolation that results in withdrawal from regular community activities, which may be indicative of suicidal behavior. According to the National Action Alliance for Suicidal Prevention, suicidal behavior is multi-faceted, being influenced by a combination of individual, family, community, and societal factors. Accordingly, efforts to intervene prior to a suicide taking place are more likely successful when they involve a comprehensive effort between healthcare systems such as the VA, family and friends, as well as community programs.

According to Rieman, sometimes it is friends and family members that can make all the difference in the early stages of the struggle. "If you ask for help and you're told no [by VA or another healthcare provider], don't stop asking," Rieman stated emphatically, "keep going until you hear yes and you get what you need. The person who helps you doesn't necessarily have to a be licensed professional, they just have to be able to listen."

The second, and often under-utilized, thing we can do is to put proper funding and research into alternative therapy methods. As the various authors of the previous chapters outline, there are many, many ways to improve the health and well-being of someone suffering from PTSD and may be struggling with suicidal thoughts that do not involved pharmaceuticals.

Unfortunately, a series of pharmaceutical breakthroughs in the early-2000s led to an over-reliance on medication as a quick fix for mental health ailments. Many of those suffering wanted instant relief, which pharmaceuticals can provide. However, some of these pharmaceuticals also had unwanted side effects, and others were addicting. And, like mental health itself, some came with a stigma that caused those who could potentially benefit not to take them at all. Various alternative therapies not only have the ability to reduce dependence on pharmaceutical medications, but they may also motivate those reluctant to receive traditional therapy such as counseling to seek help and may also enhance the results of traditional treatment methods by making patients more engaged and more compliant.

Although both the VA and the DoD have begun to embrace alternative treatments, the government moves slowly, and that can be detrimental to a suicidal Veteran who needs immediate relief. "Not all people who have PTSD present with the same needs or the same symptoms, and no one prescriptive approach works for everyone," says Karen Soltes, LCSW, MAED, E-RYT, a founding member of the organization, Warriors at Ease, which works with yoga and meditation teachers to specifically work with service members and Veterans. Suicide prevention is similar; it does not present in the same manner in all Veterans and thus, there is not a single treatment that works across the board.

Next, more research is needed into the causes and effects of suicide directly. Although suicide is the 10th leading cause of death in the United States, according to the National Institutes of Health, it is expected that only $68 Million will be spent on suicide-related research for Veterans and non-Veterans alike. By contrast, breast cancer will receive approximately $708 Million in research funding, and prostate cancer will receive $243 Million. "There has been tremendous research on breast cancer and AIDS, which lowered mortality rates on diseases we once thought insurmountable," states Dr. Julie Cerel, a professor at the University of Kentucky and president of the American Association of Suicidology, "however, we have not had comparable research into suicide." In order to start implementing effective solutions, this has to change.

Finally, and perhaps most importantly, we have to remember not to lose sight of the human element. Each Veteran suffering from PTSD that dies by suicide is a real person who was suffering, and whose friends and families continue to suffer long after the act of choosing suicide takes place. This was an important conversation that ensued in the aftermath of a May 2019 House of Veterans' Affairs Committee hearing addressing Veterans' suicides. AMVETS, one of the nation's largest Veteran service organizations, did not hold back in venting its frustrations at the hearing's lack of personalization and emphasis on systems, instead. "The reality is laws, executive orders, investigations, awareness campaigns, meetings and hearings don't stop Veterans' suicide," said Sherman Gillums, Jr., the organization's Chief Advocacy Officer. He continued "[t]hey may undergird efforts that attempt to do. But the only thing that stops Veterans from killing themselves is 'hope'...[and] the fastest way to kill hope is to neutralize it with apathy, where process matters more than people."

Although, overall, the numerous conversations and forms of treatments regarding suicide prevention are a step in the right direction, it is also important to keep things in perspective. As with humans themselves, stakeholders in the Veterans community can benefit from the power of pause, and taking time to reflect on new treatments and alternative therapies as they emerge. "There are new ideas and new organizations popping up each week," Rieman cautions, "although I applaud them for stretching the limits, we need to be careful about giving people false hope that sets that person up for failure." Despite the challenges associated with so many new organizations and treatments — some of which will inevitably be more successful than others — most experts agree that progress is being made.

Nonetheless, as highlighted by Rieman, Gillums, and Toombs, we must make sure that, above all else, we maintain an environment that does not completely extinguish Veterans' hope. Hope that they will make it through the darkest days; hope that they will work through their pain and suffering; hope that life will once again be enjoyable. The philosopher Soren Kierkegaard once defined hope as "the passion for what is possible." And for many of our nation's Veterans, with the proper holistic emphasis on health and wellness, the possibilities are endless.

To reiterate my opening point, PTSD has a real impact on real people, and when real people are hurting, they may turn to suicide, believing it is their only way to stop their suffering. But, as evidenced by success stories like Rieman's, this does not always have to be the case. We, as a society, still have a great deal of work to do to not only help

Veterans, but to change how we view mental health as a nation. We are certainly on the right track, but we still have a long way to go.

"Every day I wake up and it's something new and it's a ride," states Rieman, "I'm clean and I'm sober, I've done a lot of work, because you can't think clearly when you're loaded. I'm aware now, and I know if I'm having a bad day what I need to do. I had to re-learn what emotions meant, and I went to a lot of therapy to do it. There was also a spiritual component to the process, which included gratitude training. There were so many things."

Currently, Rieman remains employed with Veterans Bridge Home, where he has taken on a more senior role in the organization. In addition to his ability to help other Veterans struggling with the transition from military to civilian life, he's realized the power of his own experience in helping move the conversation about Veterans' suicide and suicide prevention forward. And, he emphasizes that an important part of that process is that helping other Veterans helps him to continue to help himself. "I love being there for them," he states about his work with Veterans Bridge Home, "this is the most rewarding thing of anything I've done, and this is probably the proudest time of my life." And, in a world where staying alive in and of itself is a struggle, Rieman's ability to say something is the proudest time of his life is significant.

———

i George W. Bush, State of the Union Address (Jan. 23, 2007), available at https://www.c-span.org/video/?c888871/clip-state-union-address.
ii Interview with Tommy Rieman, conducted by author, May 23, 2019 (notes and recording on file with author).
iii Rieman interview.
iv Quil Lawrence, *A Vet's Suicide Pushes VA To Do Better*, NPR (Aug. 28, 2018), available at https://www.npr.org/2018/08/28/640918694/a-vets-suicide-pushes-the-va-to-do-better (last visited May 3, 2019); see also Sherman Gillums, Jr., *Stopping Veterans Suicide Starts on the Front Lines*, Not in DC, The Hill (Opinion), available at https://thehill.com/opinion/healthcare/441446-stopping-veteran-suicide-starts-on-the-front-lines-not-in-dc (last visited May 3, 2019).
v Alan Frio, *A Father Talks About the Pain of Veteran Suicide*, Nashville News 4 WSMV (Nov. 19, 2018), available at https://www.wsmv.com/news/a-father-talks-about-the-pain-of-veteran-suicide/article_db2debf8-ec4a-11e8-91f0-2b7b3cffb24b.html (last visited May 22, 2019).
vi Richard Sisk, *Lawmakers to Grill VA for Answers on Suicide 'Epidemic,'* Military.com (Apr. 29, 2019), available at https://www.military.com/daily-news/2019/04/29/lawmakers-grill-va-answers-suicide-epidemic.html (last visited May 3, 2019).

vii *VA National Suicide Data Report 2005-2016,* Office of Mental Health and Suicide Prevention, U.S. Department of Veterans Affairs (Sept. 2018), available at https://www.mentalhealth.va.gov/docs/data-sheets/OMHSP_National_Suicide_Data_Report_2005-2016_508.pdf (last visited May 3, 2019).

viii Rieman interview.

ix Chrisanne Gordon, MD, *A timely pause can save your life,* The Columbus Dispatch (June 12, 2018), available at https://www.dispatch.com/opinion/20180612/chrisanne-gordon-timely-pause-can-save-your-life (last visited May 28, 2019).

x Rieman interview.

xi Rieman interview.

xii It is important to note here that the suicide epidemic impacts all Veterans, not just those with PTSD. Although for purposes of this essay, the emphasis is specifically on Veterans with PTSD, there are many contributing factors to suicide. For example, in a JAMA Psychiatry study, it was noted that female soldiers were 2.6 times more likely than male soldiers to attempt suicide, and soldiers treated within the past month for a physical injury were three times more likely than those not treated for a physical injury to attempt suicide. See Lisa Rapaport, *Soldiers who attempt suicide often have no history of mental health issues,* Reuters Health News (Sept. 5, 2018), available at https://www.reuters.com/article/us-health-military-suicide/soldiers-who-attempt-suicide-often-have-no-history-of-mental-health-issues-idUSKCN1LL30V (last visited May 3, 2019).

xiii *VA Mental Health, Number of Veterans Receiving Care, Barriers Faced, and Efforts to Increase Access, Report to the Ranking Member, Committee on Veterans' Affairs, House of Representatives,* Government Accountability Office (Oct. 2011), available at https://www.gao.gov/assets/590/585743.pdf (last visited May 3, 2019).

xiv Brian Hicks, *The secret of suicide and the Civil War,* The Post and Courier (Apr. 8, 2012), available at https://www.postandcourier.com/archives/the-secret-of-suicide-and-the-civil-war/article_90bd364e-2311-5138-a5ef-48495ab2ac3e.html (last visited May 3, 2019).

xv H.Res. 212, *Recognizing suicide as a national problem, and for other purposes, 105th Congress (1997-1998),* available at https://www.congress.gov/bill/105th-congress/house-resolution/212 (last visited May 28, 2019).

xvi H.R. 327 – *Joshua Omvig Veterans Suicide Prevention Act,* 110th Congress (2007-2008), Pub. L. No. 110-110, available at https://www.congress.gov/bill/110th-congress/house-bill/327 (last visited May 3, 2019).

xvii *H. Rept. 110-55* (Bill Report – Joshua Omvig Veterans Suicide Prevention Act) 100th Congress (2007-2008), available at https://www.congress.gov/congressional-report/110th-congress/house-report/55/1?overview=closed (last visited May 3, 2019).

xviii Id.

xix *Clay Hunt Act Serves to Prevent Veteran Suicide*, The National Alliance of Mental Illness (2016), available at https://namimc.org/clay-hunt-act-serves-to-prevent-veteran-suicide/ (last visited May 3, 2019).

xx *S. Rept. 114-34, Clay Hunt Suicide Prevention for American Veterans Act*, 114th Cong. (2015-2016), available at https://www.congress.gov/congressional-report/114th-congress/senate-report/34/1?overview=closed (last visited May 3, 2019).

xxi Donovan Slack, *Veteran dies by suicide outside Cleveland VA hospital Monday, lawmakers demand action*, USA Today, (April 29, 2019), available at https://www.usatoday.com/story/news/politics/2019/04/29/veteran-suicide-va-facilities-prompt-bipartisan-call-action-veterans-affairs/3618756002/.

xxii Quil Lawrence, NPR.

xxiii Rieman interview.

xxiv Statement of Richard A. Stone, MD, Executive in Charge, Veterans Health Administration, Department of Veterans Affairs, Before the House Committee on Veterans' Affairs (April 29, 2019), available at https://docs.house.gov/meetings/VR/VR00/20190429/109382/HHRG-116-VR00-Wstate-StoneR-20190429.pdf (last visited May 3, 2019).

xxv *VA Releases Updated Veteran Suicide Data Report*, National Action Alliance for Suicide Prevention (Sept. 28, 2018), available at https://theactionalliance.org/news/va-releases-updated-veteran-suicide-data-report (last visited May 3, 2019).

xxvi Rieman interview.

xxvii Kate Jackson, *Treatments for Veterans with PTSD – Outside the Traditional Toolbox*, Social Work Today, Vol. 14, No. 2, pp. 18 (March/April 2014), available at https://www.socialworktoday.com/archive/031714p18.shtml (last visited May 3, 2019).

xxviii Jennifer Steinhauer, *VA Officials, and the Nation, Battle an Unrelenting Tide of Veterans Suicides*, The New York Times (April 14, 2019), available at https://www.nytimes.com/2019/04/14/us/politics/veterans-suicide.html (last visited May 3, 2019).

xxix Id.

xxx Sherman Gillums, Jr., *Stopping Veterans Suicide Starts on the Front Lines, Not in DC*, The Hill (Opinion), available at https://thehill.com/opinion/healthcare/441446-stopping-veteran-suicide-starts-on-the-front-lines-not-in-dc (last visited May 3, 2019).

xxxi Rieman interview.

xxxii Wisdom Quotes, *Hope*, available at http://wisdomquotes.com/hope-quotes/ (last visited May 28, 2019).

xxxiii Rieman interview.

Should contact be needed, I am reachable via http://riley-topping.com/index.php/attorneys/.

CHAPTER 43 - VIRTUAL REALITY EXPOSURE THERAPY

Dr. Albert "Skip" Rizzo, Director, Medical, Medical Virtual Reality - Institute for Creative Technologies Research Professor - Department of Psychiatry and School of Gerontology, University of Southern California (USC)

I am a Clinical Psychologist and Director of Medical Virtual Reality (VR) at USC. Over the last 23 years, my lab has conducted research on the design, development and evaluation of VR systems targeting the areas of clinical assessment, treatment, and rehabilitation across the domains of psychological, cognitive, and motor functioning in both healthy and clinical populations. This work has focused on Post-Traumatic Stress Disorder (PTSD), Traumatic Brain Injury (TBI), Autism, Alzheimer's, and other clinical conditions. In spite of the diversity of these clinical areas, the common thread that drives all of this work with digital technologies involves the study of how VR simulations can be usefully applies to human healthcare beyond what is possible with traditional 20th Century methods.

To view some videos on this work please go to: http://www.youtube.com/user/albertskiprizzo

Introduction

VR technology has undergone a transition in the last 20 years taking it from the realm of "expensive toy" into that of functional technology. These advances stand to offer new opportunities for clinical research, assessment, and intervention in the field of mental health and rehabilitation. Since the mid-1990s, VR-based testing, training, teaching, and treatment approaches have been developed by clinicians and researchers that would be difficult, if not impossible, to deliver using traditional methods. During this time, a large (but still maturing) scientific literature has evolved regarding the outcomes and effects from the use of what we now refer to as Clinical VR. Such VR simulation systems have targeted the assessment and treatment of cognitive, psychological, motor, and functional impairments across a wide range of clinical health conditions. Moreover, continuing advances in the underlying enabling technologies for creating and delivering VR applications have resulted in its widespread availability as a consumer product, sometimes at a very low cost.

The idea of using virtual reality to assess and treat the effects of medical conditions and pain is not new. VR first emerged in the late 1980s, and although the vision for its use clinically was sound, it did not take off then due to immature technology and prohibitive costs. With new more affordable VR equipment now on the market, VR is now ready for clinical settings. Systems that cost 10's of thousands of dollars back then can be purchased for a few hundred dollars and offer a more comfortable and high-fidelity VR experience.

Our Medical VR laboratory had its origins in the mid-1990's and derived from my early clinical work in the area of cognitive rehabilitation following brain injury, stroke, and other neurological conditions. In the early 1990s, I had become increasingly frustrated by the limited state of cognitive rehabilitation. I believe this was in part due to the absence of technology that could be used to automate training and provide a more compelling experience that would engage patients in the many repetitive and boring activities needed to improve brain "repair" and recover functional abilities. Thus, a big part of the problem was seen in getting a patient to do a sufficient amount of focused cognitive rehabilitative training. I would tell my clients that if they wanted to recover their brain function and everyday skills, they would have to put in the same amount of effort into rehab exercises as they would to learn to play the violin!

However, one day the lightbulb went off thanks to one of my younger patients and his Nintendo Game Boy. I was always struck by watching kids who played video games for hours on end and imagined, "What if you could get a patient engaged in similar well-produced sophisticated game-based content to do their rehab for that period of time?" Then one day, one of my patients came in with a new Gameboy and I watched him literally glued to playing the game, "Tetris" for more time that I was ever able to get him engaged with a traditional cognitive rehab task. If we could leverage the motivating nature of digital game technology, it might be possible to advance cognitive and physical rehabilitation following a brain injury. It would also be possible to systematically adjust the challenge level of the rehab activity in order to pace engagement with tasks presented at a level that was neither, too easy or too difficult for the patient and thus, keep them in what game developers call the "flow channel". If one could design rehab games that were that motivating, yet still specifically targeted the cognitive or physical process that needed rehabilitation within a functionally relevant virtual reality context, we might be able to not only increase the amount of training required to effect positive change, but we might also be able to draw in digital generation patients into treatment who might not otherwise seek treatment. We later saw this happen with young digital generation service members (SMs) with Post-Traumatic Stress Disorder (PTSD), who are at home with this technology, and are willing to participate in VR exposure therapy, after casting a blind eye to more traditional approaches that rely exclusively on talk therapy or effortful imaginal memory retrieval. It's not science fiction to them. It's engaging.

The use of VR technology offers unique capabilities for the treatment of a wide range of clinical conditions (Brain Injury, Stroke, PTSD, Autism, Phobias, Pain, ADHD, etc.). VR allows interactive, multi-sensory, immersive environments to be readily created that can be tailored to a patient's needs. At the same time VR provides the ability for clinicians to control, document, and measure stimuli delivery and resulting patient responses, offering clinical assessment, treatment and research options that are not readily available via traditional methods.

This chapter will provide an introductory definition of the technology and provide some discussion about our efforts to apply VR as a tool for conducting exposure therapy for PTSD.

What is Virtual Reality?

The concept and definition of Virtual Reality has been subject to debate by scientists and clinicians over the years. VR has been very generally defined as a way for humans to visualize, manipulate, and interact with computers and extremely complex data. From this baseline perspective, VR can be seen as an advanced form of human-computer interaction that allows a user to more naturally interact with computers beyond what is typically afforded with standard mouse and keyboard interface devices. Moreover, some VR formats enable users to become immersed within synthetic computer-generated virtual environments. However, VR is not defined or limited by any one technological approach or hardware set-up. The creation of an engaged VR user experience can be accomplished using combinations of a wide variety of interaction devices, sensory display systems, and content presented in the virtual environment. Thus, there are three common variations for how VR can be created and used.

Non-immersive VR is the most basic format and is similar to the experience of playing a modern computer or console video game. Content is delivered on a standard flat-screen computer monitor or TV with no occlusion of the outside world. Users interact with three-dimensional (3D) computer graphics variously using a gamepad, joystick, basic mouse and keyboard as well as specialized interface devices (e.g., treadmills, data gloves, and even handheld devices like the Nintendo Wii remote). Modern computer games that support user interaction and navigation within such 3D worlds, even though presented on a flat-screen display, can be technically referred to as VR environments.

Immersive VR can be produced by the integration of computers, head-mounted displays (HMDs), body-tracking sensors, specialized interface devices, and 3D graphics. These set-ups allow users to operate within a computer-generated simulated world that changes in a natural or intuitive way based on a user's motion and interaction. An HMD is used to occlude the user's view of the outside world, while simultaneously employing head and body-tracking technology to sense the user's position and movement and simultaneously send that information to a computing system that then uses that data to update the sensory stimuli presented to the user. The contingent tracking of user activity and near real time updating of the 3D content is said to create an immersive virtual experience. This serves to create the illusion of being immersed "in" a virtual space, within which users can interact. When immersed within computer-generated visual imagery and sounds of a simulated virtual scene, user interaction produces an experience that corresponds to what the individual would see and hear if the scene were real.

Another less common method for producing immersive VR experiences uses stereoscopic projection screens arrayed around a user in various configurations. Sometimes six-walled projection rooms known as cave automatic virtual environments (CAVEs) are used that allow for interaction in a less encumbered, wide field of view simulated environment for multiple concurrent users. However, such CAVE systems are more costly and complex, and are typically beyond the practical resources of most clinical service providers and/or basic researchers.

Regardless of the technical approach, the key aim of these immersive systems is to perceptually replace the outside world with the virtual world to psychologically engage users with simulated digital content designed to create a specific user experience. Immersive VR (most commonly delivered in an HMD) is typically the choice for applications where a controlled stimulus environment is desirable for constraining a user's perceptual experience within a specific synthetic world. This format has been often used in Clinical VR applications for PTSD and other anxiety disorder exposure therapy, analgesic distraction for patients undergoing acutely painful medical procedures, and in the cognitive assessment of users to measure performance under a range of systematically delivered challenges and distractions.

VR Exposure Therapy for PTSD

Think about the worst thing that ever happened to you and remember how you felt immediately afterwards. Now imagine that six months or a year later, you still felt that exact same way with the exact same intensity. That is PTSD and it has a significant impact on the mental health of Service Members (SMs) returning from the conflicts in Iraq and Afghanistan. This should be no surprise since war is perhaps the most challenging situation that a human being can experience. The physical, emotional, cognitive, and psychological demands of a combat environment place enormous stress on even the best-prepared military personnel. Today's SMs encounter many stressors in a complex, unpredictable, and fluid operational environment. Thus, exposure to stressful events characteristic of the recent combat theaters have placed significant numbers of SMs and Veterans at risk for developing PTSD and other mental health conditions. For example, as of June 2015, the Defense Medical Surveillance System reported that 138,197 active duty SMs have been diagnosed with PTSD. In a meta-analysis across studies since 2001, 13% of Operation Enduring Freedom (OEF)/Operation Iraqi Freedom (OIF) operational infantry units met criteria for

PTSD, and its incidence rises dramatically (25-30%) in units with the highest levels of direct combat. Moreover, since 2006, mental disorders account for more hospitalizations of U.S. SMs than any other major diagnostic category.

Theoretically, individuals suffering from PTSD often times experience fear or anxiety when confronted by events or locations that are reminiscent of those that occurred during the original traumatic event. These "fear structures" include information about stimuli, responses, and meaning and are composed of harmless stimuli that have been associated with danger and are reflected in the belief that the world is a dangerous place. This belief then manifests itself in cognitive and behavioral avoidance strategies that limit exposure to potentially corrective information that could be incorporated into and alter the fear structure. Because escape from and avoidance of feared situations are intrinsically rewarding (albeit temporarily), PTSD (as well as phobic disorders) can perpetuate without treatment.

Complicating matters in the treatment of trauma is that triggers are often subconscious. Stored memories are not always apparent in the conscious mind. A person might only realize something is a cue when that cue appears outside the traumatic event

Imaginal Prolonged Exposure (PE) is considered to be a leading evidence-based treatment for PTSD and entails engaging mentally with the fear structure through repeatedly revisiting the feared or traumatic event in a safe environment. The proposed mechanisms for symptom reduction involve activation and emotional processing, extinction/habituation of the anxiety, cognitive reprocessing of pathogenic meanings, the learning of new responses to previously feared stimuli, and ultimately an integration of corrective non-pathological information into the fear structure. One of the challenges associated with this treatment is the reliance on patients to be able to effectively imagine their traumatic experiences. Many patients, however, are unwilling or unable to do this. In fact, this very tendency to avoid the cues and reminders of the trauma is one of the cardinal symptoms of PTSD (along with hyperarousal, intrusive thoughts and dreams, alterations in cognitive/emotional experiences). Thus, VR was seen, early on, to be a potential tool for the treatment of PTSD and anxiety disorders; if an individual can become immersed in a feared virtual environment, activation and modification of the fear structure was possible.

From this, the use of VR to deliver PE (VRET) was the first psychological treatment area to gain traction clinically, perhaps in part due to the intuitive match between what the technology could deliver and the theoretical requirement of PE to systematically expose/engage users to progressively more challenging stimuli needed to activate and reprocess the fear structure. This is readily seen in the initial use of VR for delivering PE for other anxiety disorders, like specific phobias. In VR what clinicians can help the process along by putting people in simulations of their feared environment and then systematically making it a little bit more provocative once they've attained a certain level of fear reduction or extinction. If a patient has fear of flying, it is possible to put them in an airport or on an airplane in flight. Users can then experience a plane flight, they can turn their head and look around, see the passenger next to them, look out the window, etc., all in the safety of the clinical office. Once a patient has gotten through an "easy" flight and has shown a reduction in anxiety, the clinician could then introduce a little turbulence or a thunderstorm and begin the process anew in order to promote further anxiety reduction or fear extinction. With repeated exposures, the effect of reduced anxiety has been shown to transfer to real world flights and thereby helping people become more functional in engaging in the relatively safe activity of commercial air travel (which is statistically safer than driving an automobile!).

Similarly, PTSD PE treatment requires emotional processing of the fear structures to modify or extinguish their pathological elements so that the stimuli no longer invoke fear, any method capable of activating the fear structure and modifying it is predicted to improve symptoms of PTSD. The key to understanding why exposure therapy works so well in treating PTSD is recognizing the instinctive human response to experiencing trauma: avoidance. As with most psychological responses to stimuli, learned avoidance of threat evolved to protect us. It is the brain's way of making sure we do everything possible to avoid a similar incident. If the last time you awoke to the smell of smoke and your house was on fire, the smell of smoke in other situations is going to trigger an instinct to flee. There is no question that trauma-focused exposure is hard medicine for a hard problem. However, while avoidance is the biggest challenge to overcome in treating trauma, it is also the thing that VR therapy is arguably the most effective in preventing. Simply put, the use of VR is just another mechanism for delivering exposure based on the evidence-based trauma-focused approaches of prolonged exposure, cognitive processing therapy, or Eye Movement Desensitization and Reprocessing (EMDR), where people are encouraged to confront things that emotionally hurt them initially and process them in different ways. Thus, assisting a patient in the process of confronting and re-processing difficult emotional memories in VR has been shown to also be an effective approach in the treatment of PTSD.

In 2003, the University of Southern California Institute for Creative Technologies might also be of value as a research tool for measuring, documenting, and learning about PTSD. Using such a controlled stimulus environment to conduct studies that would help to better understand the brain and biological factors that could serve to further inform the prevention, assessment, and treatment of PTSD. As a treatment tool, BRAVEMIND was developed to address PTSD by offering a means by which the natural avoidance tendency could be overcome in trauma sufferers. The value for using VR for the treatment of PTSD is supported by previous reports in which patients with PTSD, who were unresponsive to previous imaginal PE therapy treatments, went on to respond successfully to Virtual Reality Exposure Therapy (VRET). As well, a number of clinical trials have also further supported its clinical efficacy (see recommended readings at the end of the chapter).

BRAVEMIND allows clinicians to gradually immerse patients into any of 14 virtual Iraq and Afghanistan environments representative of contexts where they experienced trauma in a controlled, stepwise fashion by providing the capability to control multisensory emotional stimuli and monitor the intensity of the patients' stress responses via psychophysiological assessment techniques (see Figures 1-7).

FIG 1. AFGHANISTAN CITY MARKET

FIG 2. AFGHANISTAN RURAL VILLAGE

FIG 3. IRAQ DRIVING (IED)

FIG 4. DISMOUNTED FOOT PATROL

FIG 5. CHECKPOINT ZONE

FIG 6. CLINICIAN INTERFACE

FIG 7. BRAVEMIND SYSTEM SETUP:

a. CLINICIAN INTERFACE FOR MODIFYING VR SETTINGS IN REAL-TIME
   TO MATCH USER EXPERIENCES;
b. SEATED USER WEARING A VR HEAD MOUNTED DISPLAY IN DRIVING
   SCENARIO WITH TRADITIONAL GAMEPAD;
c. USER IN WALKING SCENARIO WITH RIFLE MOUNTED MINI GAMEPAD

For example, the Iraq and Afghan City settings have a variety of elements including a marketplace, desolate streets, checkpoints, ramshackle buildings, warehouses, mosques, shops, and dirt lots strewn with junk. Access to building interiors and rooftops is available and the backdrop surrounding the navigable exposure zones creates the illusion of being embedded within a section of a sprawling densely populated mountainous or desert city. The user can also be positioned inside of a Humvee or MRAP (Mine-Resistant Ambush Protected) vehicle that supports the perception of travel within a convoy or as a lone vehicle with selectable positions as a driver, passenger or from the more exposed turret position above the roof of the vehicle. The number of soldiers in the cab can also be varied as well as their capacity to become wounded during certain attack scenarios (e.g., IEDs, rooftop/bridge attacks).

In addition to the visual stimuli presented in the VR Head-Mounted Display (HMD), directional 3D audio, vibrotactile, and olfactory stimuli (e.g., burning rubber, cordite, garbage, body odor, smoke, diesel fuel, Iraqi food spices, and gunpowder) can be delivered into the BRAVEMIND scenarios in real-time by the clinician. The presentation of all ambient and additive combat-relevant stimuli into the VR scenarios (e.g., helicopter flyovers, bridge attacks, exploding vehicles and IEDs) can be controlled in real time via a separate "Wizard of Oz" clinician's interface, while the clinician is in full audio contact with the patient.

The clinician's interface (see Figures 6 and 7a) is a key feature that provides a clinician with the capacity to customize the therapy experience to the individual needs of the patient. This interface allows a clinician to place the patient in VR scenario locations that resemble the setting in which the trauma-relevant events occurred, and ambient light and sound conditions can be modified to match the patient's description of their experience.

The clinician can then gradually introduce and control real time trigger stimuli (visual, auditory, olfactory and tactile), via the clinician's interface, to foster the anxiety modulation required to promote extinction learning and emotional processing in a customized fashion based on the patient's past experience and treatment progress. This package of controllable multi-sensory stimulus options was included in the design of BRAVEMIND system to allow a clinician the flexibility to engage users across a wide range of unique and highly customizable levels of exposure intensity. As well, these same features have broadened its applicability as a research tool for studies that require systematic control of stimulus presentation within combat relevant environments. The system has been deployed to over 100 VA Medical Centers, university clinics, and Army, Navy and Air Force medical centers to treat PTSD patients and is available to clinicians who can document their training in trauma-focused approaches like PE. A direct link to a YouTube channel with videos that illustrate features of this system and of former patients discussing their experience with the VRET approach can be found at: http://www.youtube.com/user/AlbertSkipRizzo.

The BRAVEMIND system is now further evolved to address the unique therapeutic needs of combat medics/corpsmen and persons who have experienced Military Sexual

Trauma (MST) with PTSD. This is of particular relevance for SMs who may face trauma from both the threat that is naturally inherent in the combat theater, as well as from the possible additive occurrence of sexual violations from within the ranks. Thus, MST can produce additional risk for the development of PTSD in a population that is already at high risk due to the existing occupational hazards present in the combat environment. This is an issue of significant concern for the Department of Defense (DoD). Thus, in addition to efforts aimed at reducing the incidence of MST with novel education and prevention programs, the U.S. Army funded the expansion of the BRAVEMIND system to address PTSD due to MST. This involved a significant effort to create new content within the existing BRAVEMIND scenarios such as barracks, tents, other living and work quarters, latrines, and other contexts that have been reported by MST victims as in-theatre locations where their sexual assault occurred. Moreover, based on interviews with MST victims, most occurrences of sexual trauma are NOT happening in the trenches of Afghanistan, but rather the more common contexts are in areas around military bases in the U.S.. Thus, stateside military base and civilian contexts were created including barracks, offices, a town bar area, abandoned lots, motel rooms, and civilian automobile settings. While both men and women can experience MST, the urgent need for this work is underscored by the growing role of women transitioning into full combat roles in the combat theatre, an area that up to now has been primarily the domain of men.

Prevention of PTSD with Pre-Deployment Resilience Training

Our lab is also working with the military to create realistic war-like experiences to train soldiers to better methods for coping with the physical, social, and emotional stress of the combat before they go to war. This is especially important when we look at the mental health statistics regarding SMs exposure to combat. One in five SMs who return from Afghanistan and Iraq have symptoms of PTSD or major depression and a widely cited 2016 VA study reported that in 2014 over 7,400 Veterans - 20 per day — took their own lives. Perhaps these numbers could be dramatically reduced with a focus on building psychological resilience in SMs prior to a combat deployment?

Psychological resilience has been defined as the dynamic process of positive adjustment to adverse events. Resilient individuals exhibit positive adaptation when they encounter significant adversity, tragedy, threats, or other sources of stress. In the context of exposure to traumatic events, an indicator of resilience would be considered the absence of psychiatric disorder symptoms, such as PTSD. A proactive approach for better preparing SMs for improving psychological resilience and effectively dealing with emotional challenges is needed in order to improve readiness and reduce the potential for later adverse psychological reactions such as PTSD and depression. The focus on resilience training prior to deployment has received increased emphasis emanating from the highest levels of command in the military. For example, in an 2011

American Psychologist article, General (R) George Casey made the case that "soldiers can be" better before deploying to combat so they will not have to "get" better after they "return" and then called for a shift in the military "...to a culture in which psychological fitness is recognized as every bit as important as physical fitness." In line with this view, the Army has aggressively pursued multiple programs to address this challenging issue. This includes revising the Comprehensive Soldier and Family Fitness (CSF2) program to include family members, launching the Ready and Resilient Campaign to guide the Army's efforts to improve the performance, resilience, and readiness of Soldiers, implementing Advanced Situational Awareness (ASA) training, and incorporating the Human Dimension within the Force 2025 vision. In essence, perhaps we can put ourselves out of a job treating PTSD on the backend, by doing a better job on the frontend by effectively preparing SMs before a deployment to be more resilience to stress.

These factors led to our lab placing a significant focus on retooling the **BRAVEMIND** PTSD treatment system for the purpose of pre-deployment resilience training with a program referred to as STRIVE: Stress Resilience in Virtual Environments. STRIVE emerged from 3D graphic content developed for the **BRAVEMIND VRET** simulations and was developed to foster resilience by creating a set of combat simulations that can be used as contexts for the experiential learning of psychoeducational, cognitive-behavioral, mindfulness, breathing exercises, and other emotional coping strategies. In STRIVE, users are immersed and engaged in a variety of narrative-based, virtual combat "missions" where they are confronted with emotionally challenging situations that are sometimes experienced in the combat environment. Interaction within such emotionally challenging scenarios aims to provide users with a more meaningful context in which to learn and practice psychoeducational and cognitive coping strategies that are believed to psychologically prepare them for a combat deployment.

To accomplish this, STRIVE was initially designed as a multi-episode interactive narrative in VR, akin to being immersed within a "Band of Brothers" type storyline of events that could occur during a combat deployment. At the end of each of the five to seven-minute episodes, an emotionally challenging event occurs, designed in part from feedback provided by SMs undergoing PTSD treatment (e.g., seeing/handling human remains, death/injury of a squad member, death/injury of a civilian child, disturbing culturally relative and morally challenging situations, etc.). At that point in the episode, the virtual world "freezes in place" and an intelligent virtual human (VH) "mentor" emerges from the midst of the chaotic VR scenario to guide the user through a variety of resilience-related psychoeducational and self-management tactics, as well as providing rational restructuring exercises for appraising and processing the virtual experience. The VH mentor presents resilience training content that is relevant to the VR context and narrative just experienced and draws on the types of strategies and content that has been endorsed as part of standard classroom-delivered DoD resilience training programs, as well as content that has been successfully applied in non-military contexts (e.g., humanitarian aid workers, sports psychology, etc.). In this fashion, STRIVE provides a digital "emotional obstacle course" that can be used as a tool for providing experiences that leverage narrative-based, context-relevant experiential learning of emotional coping strategies under very tightly controlled and scripted simulated conditions. Leveraging the power of narrative combined with the experiential learning made possible with simulation technology has always been at the core of the USC Institute for Creative Technologies' (ICT) mission. STRIVE is the embodiment of this mission applied to psychological resilience.

This work was supported by solid scientific research informed by a detailed theoretical basis. The VR simulation content we have developed for the BRAVEMIND PTSD exposure therapy treatment application and in the initial pilot versions of the STRIVE system are highly engaging, arousing and "emotiogenic". We hypothesize that these properties will bring the trainee into a highly "teachable" state of mind, in contrast to the neutral emotional background used in classroom or traditional web-based training that is commonly employed in existing programs. Our view is based on the well-known fact that emotional arousal facilitates learning, and, via a state dependent learning perspective, it is more likely that content learned in one emotional state or context would be more readily retrieved under similar emotional states that may be experienced in the combat environment. The use of an experiential VR STRIVE approach is also believed to further support resilience by leveraging the learning theory process of latent inhibition. Latent inhibition refers to the delayed fear learning that occurs as a result of pre-exposure to a similar stimulus without a consequence. Thus, the pre-exposure to a simulated combat context via STRIVE is hypothesized to decrease the likelihood of fear conditioning during the real combat event and reduce the probability of developing PTSD. Research thus far with STRIVE indicates that the content is emotionally evocative and SMs have rated the system to relevant and engaging.

We are currently in the process of rebuilding the STRIVE episodes to take advantage of recent VR technology developments that will allow for all SMs to have access to this form of training. The recent advances in VR computing and display technologies, coupled with the reduced costs of these hardware systems, will allow for widespread SM access to this kind of realistic, yet safe and engaging immersive VR training content, and do it at a dramatically lower cost. The technical development that ICT is aiming to leverage involves updating and adapting the STRIVE system content in a way that will allow it to be delivered in a low cost (<$200) "standalone" VR Head Mounted Display (HMD)—like the Samsung GearVR, Google Daydream, or Oculus Go. This class of emerging standalone HMDs have higher visual fidelity and better user comfort than any headset that was available to the BRAVEMIND or STRIVE project prior to 2016. Moreover, in contrast to the approximate $6,000 cost for the computing and VR HMD equipment needed to run the original BRAVEMIND/STRIVE location-based software, this effort will produce usable and engaging versions of the updated STRIVE episodes that can be delivered at a cost point that will allow every SM to possess their own personal display for experiencing the training content anytime/anyplace. Thus, by using this type of standalone VR HMD, we will eliminate the need for a computing workstation and generate the capability to deliver such training at a fraction of the previous cost. This would support wide scale dissemination and independent SM use and practice with any VR training content that does not require costly location-based training facilities and the additional costs for personnel to run and maintain such location-based systems. This is the future of Clinical Virtual Reality—Theory Informed, Research Supported, Readily Available, and Economically Feasible.

Conclusion

While VR may offer some "magic" in delivering this type of content, in the end the technology doesn't fix anyone—rather, VR should be viewed as a tool that extends the skills of a well-trained clinician. To design good clinical VR applications, one must always operate from a theoretical base of knowledge as to what we know works in the real world. How can we do it better, more effectively, more consistently, and in a more engaging way is where the VR "magic" occurs. With PTSD, the first thing to keep in mind is that we are never going to replicate an exact simulation of what the patient went through. However, we really don't need to as long as the virtual content has key similarities to the trauma context that is relevant to the patient and can serve as an emotionally evocative setting for activating their trauma memories. Although it might seem counter-intuitive to make someone go back and relive a traumatic experience, if you do it at a gradual pace and prevent avoidance with a good clinician in a safe environment, patients get better with time. They might get anxious at first, but anxiety extinguishes as they continue and can sometimes be replaced with a sense of empowerment, following effective confrontation of the traumatic event. We're also not aiming to erase memories of the trauma — people still remember what they've been through, but those memories don't have the same emotional potency to cause psychological distress as they had before treatment.

More recently, we have seen tremendous advances in the enabling technologies for creating VR experiences. This has resulted in the availability of lower cost and higher fidelity VR systems. This has also been primarily driven by investments from the gaming and entertainment industries and, along the way, it is resulting in better equipment, software, and computer graphics. However, the power and value of VR goes well beyond gaming and entertainment. It's in its potential to create new methods for testing, training, teaching, and treatment of clinical health conditions. Moreover, the clinical applications are far ranging, from PTSD to Autism, Pain Management to Physical Therapy, and in the use of artificially intelligent virtual humans in the role of virtual patients for clinical training or as healthcare support agents. The capacity to produce a controlled stimulus environment where users can confront their fears safely, or learn new ways socially interact with others via virtual human roleplaying, or even as a way to become distracted from acute pain, presents opportunities for advancing clinical care that didn't exist just 20 years ago.

This chapter provides a brief summary of applications that illustrate the current use of VR to address the behavioral healthcare needs of those suffering from the psychological effects of trauma. Since our work in this area was really instigated by the urgency to address the mental health needs of trauma exposed SMs and Veterans from the OIF/OEF and even Operation New Dawn (OND) combat theaters, it is only appropriate to put this work in a larger historical context, especially since it can help those outside those 'realms'. If one reviews the history of the impact of war on advances in clinical care it could be suggested that clinical use of VR may be an idea whose time has come. For example, during WW I, the Army Alpha/Beta Classification Test emerged from the need for better cognitive ability assessment; that development later set the stage for the civilian intelligence testing movement over the next 40 years. Later on, the birth of clinical psychology as a treatment-oriented profession was borne from the need to provide care to the many Veterans returning from World War II with "shell shock" or "battle fatigue" with the VA creating a clinical psychology intern program in the late 1940s. At the same time, the creation of the National Institute of Mental Health (NIMH) came from an executive order from President Harry Truman as a vehicle for addressing the challenge of "Combat Neurosis". More recently, the Vietnam War drove the recognition of PTSD as a definable and treatable clinical condition. In similar fashion, one of the clinical "game changing" outcomes of the OIF/OEF/OND conflicts could derive from the military's support for research and development to advance clinical systems that leverage new interactive and immersive technologies such as VR. Moreover, this may drive wider uptake of clinical VR use in the civilian sector as the technology becomes more common in society's digital landscape. Thus, as we have seen throughout history, innovations that emerge in military healthcare, driven by the urgency of war, typically have a lasting influence on civilian healthcare long after the last shot is fired.

**For further information on this work, please access the following video directory and papers.

Directory of MedVR Online Videos:

https://webdisk.ict.usc.edu/index.php/s/4q1sbMABegNNHnW
Rizzo, A. A., & Shilling, R. (2018). *Clinical virtual reality tools to advance the prevention, assessment, and treatment of PTSD.* European Journal of Psychotraumatology, 8(sup5), 1414560. Available at: https://webdisk.ict.usc.edu/index.php/s/SD4uggKn5vKRLXZ

Loucks, L., Yasinski, C., Norrholm, S., Maples-Keller, J., Post, L., Zwiebach, L., Fiorillo, D., Goodlin, M., Rizzo, A. A., & Rothbaum, B. O. (2018). *You can do that?!: Feasibility of virtual reality exposure therapy in the treatment of military sexual trauma.* Journal of Anxiety Disorders. Available at: https://webdisk.ict.usc.edu/index.php/s/RRHqKrBEwDNNBU5

Rizzo, A. A. & Koenig, S. (2017). *Is Clinical Virtual Reality Ready for Primetime?* Neuropsychology, 31(8), 877-899. Available at: https://webdisk.ict.usc.edu/index.php/s/3X3Wn2K6B5rPprX

CHAPTER 44 - WOODWORKING AND VETERANS

Kurt Ballash

Ballash Woodworks: How did it all get started? It all started with sourdough hard pretzels. Every time I walked into my grandfather's shop there was always this oversized tub of sourdough pretzels sitting on the work bench. Well, at the time the tub seemed oversized. I would munch away on this huge twisted pretzel and watch him and my father scurry around the shop for hours. I'm sure along the way there were lots of, "When are we leaving?" or "How much longer?" that seemed to interrupt the progress that needed to be made.

Memories that seem to go back as far as I can remember. By the time I was born my grandfather was already a Master Craftsman, and my father was well on his way. My grandfather started learning on his own before leaving home to serve during the Korean War. When he returned home he didn't want to return to the farm life so he started woodworking as a business. I heard stories of him riding a Harley Davidson to each job with a sidecar turned ladder rack right next to him.

My father started working with him in the late 70s and by the time I was born in 1984 they had already managed to scale into a 2,400 square foot facility. It looked like my grandfather had successfully changed the trajectory of our family. He took us out of farming and into woodworking. A decision without a doubt led by God knowing that woodworking would be the purpose I needed much later in life.

As a kid I remember annoying my father in the shop all the time with request to start nails or cut boards. I am sure my father never seen it that way though, he was just happy to be able to teach me. For me the hammer in my hands was heavy and foreign, so I would choke up on the handle grabbing close to the head. I thought this made things easier, but I didn't understand the physics behind the hammer. It would take me dozens of taps on the head of the nail to get the nail moving. My father would coach me and tell me to hold back further on the handle in order to get better swings. Now I was missing the head of the nail repeatedly. But you know what? I learned determination, perseverance, and how to swing a hammer when I was incredibly young.

I remember the first time I grabbed some hard maple to practice on. "Dad can you start some nails for me?" He laughed a little bit, at least in my memory, and he might have said something about the wood selection, but I didn't hear it. I was just staring at the nails he would tap into the hard maple sharply. They stood up straight, spaced out a couple inches apart, there must have been a dozen of them.

SMACK! A miss. Smack, smack. Ping!

The first nail I made contact with went shooting across the shop. I had hit it just enough to move it, just not enough to push it into the hard maple. The second nail started driving through the wood then bent over. I tried straightening the nail to attempt to drive it the rest of the way, but that wasn't working. You see, I was failing. But that failure stimulated learning. I thank God now for those opportunities now, because it paved the way for me to resume this trade after running from it for so long.

I didn't always want to be a woodworker. I wanted to get away from home to make my own path. I wasn't even very good in shop class, I never applied myself. I viewed working every day in a dusty shop as a dead end and not really leading towards a greater cause. How much more wrong could I have been?

I was in high school when it happened. The school rolled out large rear projection television into the cafeteria for the staff and students to stay informed on what was going on. Other kids in my school were crying, some were scared, some couldn't care less yet. The first tower had fallen. I watched the next plane strike the second tower. I watch my own countrymen and women jump from the windows to face a different death. Just thinking back to that day brings back tears for the families that were directly affected by the cowardly perpetrators.

I think this is when I knew where I was meant to go. I wanted to join the Navy and go be a SEAL. However, due to a couple of major mistakes I made as a juvenile, they said I wasn't the right fit, just in a not so nice way. Next up, the Army. I was deferred away from going into the 18X program (Army Special Forces) because my security clearance was going to be a huge hurdle. I was told by my recruiter not to apply for one and to establish a few years in service before attempting to breach into the Special Operations Command.

So, I enlisted as a Combat Engineer. I told him I wanted to build stuff and blow stuff up. I left for Basic Training in January of 2003 and traveled to the Fort Leonard Wood, Missouri. During Basic Training and Advanced Individual Training (AIT) I was selected to pilot and stand up a new military unit, the 67th Engineer Detachment.

If I remember correctly, I think two or three of us from my class were selected for this program. When we first arrived, we were checking into a one room office in a small office building on post. There were only about a dozen of us there and we were paving the way for a new military capability, using the Military Working Dog (MWD) as a counter mine asset. The British military had been using K-9s in this way to clear large suspected mined areas.

In the later portion of 2003, a group of seven of us were sent to Melton Mowbray in the United Kingdom to train with the Royal Army Vet Corps. We weren't just being trained on handling these MWDs, we were trained to train them. We taught the dogs scent discrimination, basic obedience, and the clearing patterns they were to use both on leash and off. We spent six months training our K-9 companions and created a bond with them in the process. I was assigned two dogs, both black labs. One was named Beanie, and the other Bruno. After finishing our training Bruno and I returned to the U.S. for our next mission.

In late 2004 I was deployed for my first rotation to Afghanistan with Bruno. We were primarily used to clear unsafe areas in and around Bagram and Kandahar for various expansion projects I am sure they have long since completed by now. Our team was also used in emergency extractions for mined areas. While landing, a C-130 had a tire blow which caused them to pull off the runway into an uncleared area we used to call "Charlie keyhole." My squad leader and I cleared a safe lane to the door which allowed them to exit the downed aircraft safely. After that extraction I was selected from a small group of handlers that supported a team of Special Forces in the Nangarhar Province.

I was introduced to the other side of war there. I was no longer behind safe high fencing and alarms; I was out on the very furthest reaches of the country with a team of 12 guys and a few support staff they kept on site. We lived in a what appeared to be a castle. We had the circular towers on each corner of our compound, each with some type of crew served weapon ready to be manned if needed. We had soft skin trucks with little to no armor and were told that speed was security.

This was where I started learning a lot more than handling a dog, I was retaught explosive calculations by the Weapons Sergeant. I learned ethernet cable network setup through the Communications Sergeant. I learned basic medical skills from their over qualified Medic. I was learning tactics from the Team Sergeant and the Commander.

I was attached to this team to assist in the vehicle control point set-up near our camp, as well as assist with mobile operations. I would bring my dog through after they finished clearing a compound of hostiles. While they were cleaning up the inside I was part of the outer security and then they would call my dog and I in to check for explosives.

At the age of 20 I was experiencing the full nature of war. The first time I reached down to pull a corpse from a vehicle the body felt like jello. This happened a few weeks before my 21st birthday. It was like every bone in the body had been pulverized or liquified and all that was left behind was a sack of meat and fluid. I was instructed to grab the clothes not the body as it was easier to drag to a cleared area.

Do you remember the first time your bravery was tested? The first time you had to look at paralyzing fear in the face. I have stood in front of judges that could tear me away from the comforts of home, I was an adrenaline chasing ATV rider as a kid, but never once had I faced true fear. The fear that will stop you dead in your tracks and cause the whole world to slow around you. The fear that initiates the bio-chemical reaction in your body telling you it's time to fight or hide. For me it was the first time I heard bullets impact the rock surfaces on the side of a mountain peak. The sound that pierces your ears when those tiny projects slice through the air at thousands of feet per second. I found out fear was no different from any other obstacle you'll face.

After returning from Afghanistan in early 2005 I started physically preparing to attend Special Forces Assessment and Selection. I went through my only divorce before starting the course and felt I was ready to tackle this mountain of a task. I was selected as a Team Medic and was about to go through two years or more of training. I was missing the fight.

I was dismissed from training near the end of the medic portion. I had made it through the patrol phases, SERE, and some language. I made it through the first six months of the medical course known as Special Operations Combat Medic (SOCM) and was into Special Forces Medical School. I was nearly done with training when I lost focus. I was distracted by a second job I had taken to help pay my bills and child support as a Physical Fitness Coach at a local gym, and my grades were suffering. I started watching my GPA slip from mid 90s to mid 70s. I failed.

I learned a lot in that failure but not until years later. At first, I was angry at myself and the "long tabbers", that were tab protecting in my eyes. Regardless, I re-enlisted as a 68WW1 (SOCM) and went to USASOC to support operations in Iraq as well as other key areas of interest in the region.

I went on to become a technically proficient Medic but wasn't a very good Soldier. I didn't like cutting my hair or wearing regulation boots. I didn't want to wear those stupid PT uniforms that chaffed the crap out of my chest. This was the next step backwards for me because with that lack of care came a level of recklessness. I was caught with steroids and demoted and later kicked out of USASOC for improper PT attire in a DFAC. Sounds stupid doesn't it? I can speculate that perhaps there was also some political maneuvering in there by some seniors I pissed off along my career thus far.

I ended up in the 82nd, a place where I was not very happy. I was destroyed. My motivation was gone, and I didn't fit in there. I wasn't indoctrinated into constantly berating your soldiers into forced compliance, and I certainly wasn't into the baby-sitter mentality they had there. Stare at the painted walls for hours waiting to be dismissed because something might come up. I mean in the age of cell phones you think that wouldn't be an issue, but there were also a lot of "shammers" in the larger units as well which complicated matters for leadership.

Regardless it was proven to me through my experience with the leadership that the seniors could not be trusted with anything. They would strive to find reasons to article 15 lower enlisted to buffer their "stats" to make them look better in front of the big-wigs upstairs. I left that place with a lot of anger inside of me that I couldn't really control. During my separation from service they attempted to down-grade my discharge to other than honorable for unstated reasons. It took my filing a complaint to get it rectified and I was never offered a reason on why they did that.

I was discharged honorably under a chapter 5-8 (Separation for the Convenience of the Government) in February 2013. After they lied to me during re-enlistment I no longer felt I could trust even my direct line supervisors, and if I couldn't trust them CONUS (in the Continental United States), how could I trust them OCONUS (outside the CONUS) when my life was in their hands. I refused to get a Family Care Plan for my youngest child and that led to my separation.

My grandfather had passed away from cancer around this time, and I inherited some of his tools from his boat work-shop. I started putting them to use while returning to work as a physical trainer at a local gym. I jumped from job to job until I landed in security contracting. The money was great, but I wasn't healing, and, in many ways, I was just running from the deeper issues. In between trips overseas I would continue to hone my skills as a tradesman and continue growing my reputation in my area.

It wasn't until I attended a retreat that I started healing. I started to see woodworking as a conduit through which I could stay busy, as well as give me time to meditate and work through the war scars in my head.

I think for many of us, being in the military becomes our purpose. It shapes who we are and how we react to everything around us. After service we lose that purpose and guidance and don't know how to channel the things we've learned into skills that help us succeed in the civilian world. We feel dirty for the things we've had to do and see, and sometimes we can't get those images out of our heads. When you're still serving you have guys around you to distract you from that noise, but when you are by yourself in your apartment, and don't have the interaction of like-minded individuals to distract you from those, you are forced to start healing or start running. Many run to a bottle of beer, or their drug of choice. This path most usually leads to destruction of their mind further, and unfortunately suicide. We lose more of our Soldiers here at home than we do overseas, all because we've lost that greater purpose.

What I learned to do is find something I was passionate about and make that my purpose. As a type 'A' personality, I like working with my hands and controlling the flow of work. I felt called to start a business doing what my family had been doing for generations now.

Perhaps when my grandfather left the farm years ago he was following his calling in order to set the foundation for what would save my life. I'm not saying when I started working in my shop that I instantly stopped all my destructive behaviors because He [God] knows I am as much of a sinner today as I've ever been. The main difference is I don't let those sins define what my purpose is. Through my years of working on my own I have learned to just try and be better today than I was yesterday. Woodworking allows me to quantify that in a way.

Throughout the course of my time as a woodworker I have had the chance to work with one of a kind pieces of wood. But nothing would ever prepare me for this project. I was contracted by a luxury home builder to create a fireplace mantle out of a piece of petrified wood recovered from the Cape Fear River. Being that the organic material in the wood had been replaced by inorganic material, is was no longer truly wood. It was a dense concentration of minerals and rock fragments. In order to cut it down to the correct dimensions I had to contract a local water jet operator that operated at 60,000 psi. Once the piece of petrified wood was cut the water jet left imperfections in the surface that needed to be corrected. During the polishing process I was watching sparks shoot out from the mantle. I washed down the surface to reveal that there were streaks of metal tracking through the center of the petrified wood. I guess the only thing I really regret about this project is that the customer was satisfied but I was not. When I envision a final project, I see something free of flaws and smooth. They were happy with the slightly rough edges left over from the water jet tracks. They enjoyed the rough appearance that was left behind and felt it enhanced the overall look they were going for. At the end of the day I had to be happy that the customer was happy. In fact, the exact words were "exceeded expectations."

Another project that meant a lot to me...I connected with a local Veteran who received a 1970 VW bus from his wife as a retirement present. This is a vehicle they use not only to drive around town, but also to go camping in. He had come to me looking to take this historic vehicle and add his own personal touch. He didn't care about rebuilding to historical accuracy, he wanted something that was unique. He bought a piece of live edge soft maple that had got gorgeous grain and color differentiation. He wanted to use this piece to replace the drop leaf table and spice rack as well as the center table. After a little wait the day for install was ready. He came over and left the keys to his van with me and got on his bike and rode away.

Two days later I was calling him back to set up a time for the reveal. He wanted to capture the reveal on video and also help me capture the moment to use in future videos or testimony advertisement. He hadn't seen any pictures in a while and was ready to view the transformation. I first opened the side door to the van and he instantly lit up with satisfaction and smiles. But the best part was yet to come.

When he first hired me for this project he wanted to do something special. He wanted to create a shifter knob that would allow his unit coin to sit inside of.

So, when I opened the front door and revealed the shifter knob, he began to weep. He was overcome with happiness in seeing his first unit coin was now a permanent addition to a van that it meant so much. I received a fair wage for this job, but nothing can ever offer greater payment than seeing true satisfaction on a customer's face when they see what you have created for them.

That is how I impact everyone I come into contact with. I pour my passion into every piece so they all hold a special place in my heart. The fact that he was a brother-in-arms made it so much better than just another random customer.

I can see in my final products what I used to call mission complete. We would take a moment to gather our thoughts and learn from our experience to get better. I do that now when I do my final look over. What did I do well? What can I improve on? Do those questions sound familiar? I could see that the more my mind was healing from war the better my final product was getting. I could approach projects with a calm mind and this allowed me to think through my projects more completely.

I was starting to see how the military had prepared me for entrepreneurship. A lot of what we learned as non-commissioned officers and even lower enlisted can be directly applied to successfully running your own business. The decision-making process, adapt and overcome, mission first mentality are all things that as Veterans of war we have become more experienced in a rather short period of time. But how could I use what I had learned to help other Veterans recover from their war injuries?

I started reaching out to other Veterans, inviting them to come hang out and learn. I really wanted to help them find their purpose and just hang out with other guys like me. I wanted to have someone to talk to when things were bothering me, as well as be an ear for them to share their burdens with. I've had multiple Veterans tell me how working with their hands is peaceful and calming. It provides instant gratification that combats stress, anxiety and depression. I have started to really understand how, with many hands, a heavy burden becomes light.

Thank You

To my unbelievably wonderful, committed and understanding husband Danny. Thank you for not only putting up with the countless hours I spent, day and night, working on this book, but also being there for me when I was deployed and gone on Active Duty throughout the years. We went through two deployments together and our marriage only became stronger because of it, despite the difficulty's PTSD can bring to a marriage and a relationship. Thank you for your understanding, your encouragement, your comfort and your helping hand through it all. Thank you also for never questioning my loyalty to our relationship...something I never did from the very first day we said our vows, if not before. Most of all, thank you for always and unfailingly being there to hold my hand and being my friend. That's how our relationship started, when you made me laugh...and that's what you still try to make me do every single day. That warms my soul and makes it so much lighter to carry, even on darkest days and difficult nights. I love you with all my heart.

Thank you to my mother Elizabeth LaCava and my Grandmother Isolde Weaver for raising me...both of you are now my Guardian Angels and more special to me than you could ever possibly know, in my dreams or visions; thank you to all of my family, including my father Loren Schmierer; my 'first' and second mother Paulette, for being there, whenever and wherever...no matter the circumstances, via phone, in person, and via text — I love you and miss you; my 'Grandfather' Jack Rasor. To my brother Daniel, you took a piece of my heart when you left us all, and I carry a piece of you with me always. I love and miss you so much...always my blessing...my brother.

To my newly discovered and 'extended' family and friends and the local Veterans community. Thank you for having 'my six' and being part of a very important support network.

Last but not least, thank you very much to Jeff Kamen for your guidance and encouragement along this path. Without your stalwart guidance and assistance this book would not have even been possible. I mean that from the bottom of my heart and from the depths of my soul. Your help, and the contributions from every single person in this book, all of whom were volunteers and received no compensation to assist with this endeavor, have earned my deepest possible thanks! Blessings and peace to you all. NAMASTE!

A Letter to My Friends

"Now, when I stand outside, I can actually feel the rain on my face...I can smell the rain...and I can tilt up my face and accept the feelings that come...even if there might still sometimes be tears that run down my cheeks along with the raindrops."
– Courtenay M. Nold

Dear Friends:

I hope that, by this time, the bricks that you built your wall up with to protect yourself from others, and even maybe to protect yourself from yourself, has been dismantled, brick-by-brick...even if might have had to put one back once in a while. That wall was there to protect you when you needed it, and you were able to take it down when you were ready and had the tools to build your own brick path towards recovery. My hope is that, by this time, your personal copy of this book is dog-eared and bookmarked throughout. I hope...better yet...I dream...that the ideas, concepts, and advances represented in this book have taken you places you have never before imagined you could go on your very own road...your own path...to personal recovery. Because it is your path and no one else's. You must always recognize and discover your own right path for yourself. My hope is that, like my own, that your trust has been restored in yourself, as well as others. I pray that you have found what 'colors your world'. I also hope you have shared the information you have gained with friends...or maybe even got them a copy of this book so they could have one of their own...if you knew it could help them as much as it has helped you.

As I was sitting earlier, staring down at my hands, and struggling a bit with writer's block, I started to realize how very far I have come on a personal basis, in the process of compiling this book. I pressed my hands together...fingertips touching...just feeling the sensation of my skin...my fingers...of mindfulness and just being there in that moment. I was able to feel the air from the fan blowing through my hair and was aware of the tension throughout my body. These were all things I wasn't aware of nor able to do a year ago. The ability to practice mindfulness has made a huge difference in my life and has helped me to recognize and reduce chronic pain areas and stress. Refer back to chapters 1, 6, 13, 32, 35 and 43 to review information on mindfulness.

The BIPRI Headband, an FDA-registered device, used for migraine relief, provides a 100% drug-free way to interrupt pain while also providing sensory distraction. For someone like me who is already wary of taking more medications than I have to, the capability to use this device for massage therapy and migraine relief has been a true lifesaver...often making my days go from just being bearable to being relaxing and enjoyable (actually what I would see as being normal again) in a single sitting. You can read more about **BIPRI** at www.bipri.com and via the **BIPRI** specific links in chapter 45.

TouchPoints provide me with dual vibrations that helps to reduce and even eliminate my fight-or-flight reaction in stressful situations. For me, this is usually any time I am around large crowds or a lot of noise. TouchPoints reduce not only the perception of stress, but also the associated bodily reactions that come with them. Basically, my TouchPoints have managed to bring me out of my head and into my body again...no longer reacting on an emotional level but a logical and mindful level instead. You can read more about TouchPoints at ilovetouchpoints.com and via the TouchPoint specific links in chapter 45.

While I have not personally experienced the benefits of Hyperbaric Oxygen Therapy (HBOT), due to non-availability and locality issues on an individual basis, I would be remiss to leave this particular topic out of the book...so here it is in short order. Please look into HBOT and advocate for it in your state and at your VA, if you aren't already doing so. H.R. 4370 was brought to amend title 38, United States Code [introduced 09/18/2019], to direct the VA to provide HBOT to Veterans with TBI or PTSD. There is a lot of information out there in support these efforts, and many advocates out there in the medical fields who are doing outstanding work in their particular fields as well. While this is still considered off-label, it may only be a matter of time, and constant effort our parts, as well as the medical and the VA, in addition to our congressional advocates, to take this a step closer to reality for the people who really need it. Just one of those extraordinary individuals making a big difference with HBOT is Raymond 'Ray' Crallé, RPT (USMC, Ret.), a leading Physical Therapist specializing in Neuro-Rehabilitation as well as Sport Rehabilitation, has worked with children and adults with various disabilities as well as Polo players, NFL football players, NHL hockey players and other athletes from around the world. He takes a particular interest in Veterans, and a video relating to his work can be found here: https://www.youtube.com/watch?v=azR_Q7Niq1g#action=share. In addition, you can location his current practice website here: http://www.orccahbo.com. One very important change relating to HBOT is the approval of HBOT care in the state of Florida. The Bill reflected at the end of this chapter explains the specific of this extraordinary change in the care of veterans.

More recent news involves that of COVID-19. Of course, the story here is what was happening behind the smile — the daily rocket attacks striking the unconscious like a timpani drum roll quiet louder...louder...louder...louder. Building until it was easily observable as the beast that is Post-Traumatic Stress Disorder (PTSD). This scourge that has blindsided the world, much like Agent Orange continues to blindside our nation's Veterans, and will continue to do so for years to come, psychologically and physically.

Psychotherapists at the VA began seeing increasing stress on their PTSD patients as soon as the coronavirus threat manifested as a serious life-threatening reality very quickly claiming more American lives than were lost in the terrorist attacks of 9/11/2001. Speaking with us privately, those same psychotherapists said millions of Americans and others around the world who never before experienced PTSD are about to get a dose of it that could last a lifetime because of the global shocks of COVID-19.

On the presidential and emergency channels, the following actions have taken place. "According to the FEMA COVID-19 Emergency Declaration," [Release date: March 13, 2020] "On March 13, 2020, the President declared the ongoing Coronavirus Disease 2019 (COVID-19) pandemic of sufficient severity and magnitude to warrant an emergency declaration for all states, tribes, territories, and the District of Columbia pursuant to section 501 (b) of the Robert T. Stafford Disaster Relief and Emergency Assistance Act, 42 U. S. C. 5121-5207 (the "Stafford Act")." Additional information can be found at: https://www.fema.gov/news-release/2020/03/13/covid-19-emergency-declaration.

"The COVID-19 viral disease that has swept into at least 114 countries and killed more than 4,000 people is now officially a pandemic, the World Health Organization announced Wednesday. "This is the first pandemic caused by a coronavirus," WHO Director-General Tedros Adhanom Ghebreyesus said at a briefing in Geneva. It's the first time the WHO has called an outbreak a pandemic since the H1N1 "swine flu" in 2009. Even as he raised the health emergency to its highest level, Tedros said hope remains that COVID-19 can be curtailed. And he urged countries to take action now to stop the disease. "WHO has been in full response mode since we were notified of the first cases." Additional information is contained at: https://www.npr.org/sections/goatsandsoda/2020/03/11/814474930/coronavirus-covid-19-is-now-officially-a-pandemic-who-says.

"Prominent national-religious rabbi Shmuel Eliyahu has called for Israelis to join him at the Western Wall on Sunday afternoon for a mass prayer rally on behalf of those infected with the coronavirus.
Eliyahu, the head of the Community Rabbinical Association and chief rabbi of Safed, is organizing the gathering together with the Israeli branch of the Orthodox Union, an American Modern Orthodox synagogue network.

"As the sons of the patriarch Abraham, we have an obligation to everyone created in the image of God. The job of the Jewish people is to pray for the good of the entire world," he said in a statement calling for people to gather Sunday at 4:30 p.m. at the Jerusalem holy site. "The fact that our prayers have a huge impact requires us to pray for peace and good in the world," he continued, referring to the Jews as a "light unto the nations.'"" Article references available here: https://www.timesofisrael.com/rabbis-call-for-mass-western-wall-prayer-for-coronavirus-patients/

"In Rome, the first signs of change came from overhead. Shortly before cocktail hour on Monday, the thrum-thrum-thrum of a helicopter could be heard above the winding lanes of the 2,000-year-old historic center. The police were keeping an eye on the Trastevere neighborhood, where smoke billowed from the windows of a jail as inmates rioted, protesting cramped conditions that put them at risk of coronavirus infection.

About the same time, the stock market was opening in New York, ushering in a week that would become the worst rout in more than three decades. A few hours later, Italian Prime Minister Giuseppe Conte gathered journalists for a televised, prime-time press conference. Rules that only 48 hours earlier had been imposed on Milan, Venice and other cities in the North—travel was restricted, schools were shut, and even the opera was called off—would be extended nationwide. The world's eighth biggest economy, with more than 60 million inhabitants, entered virtual quarantine. It was like flicking a switch." More information can be found here: https://finance.yahoo.com/news/italy-nightmare-offers-chilling-preview-050009137.html.

"Health officials take for granted that COVID-19 will continue to infect millions of people around the world over the coming weeks and months. However, as the outbreak in Italy shows, the rate at which a population becomes infected makes all the difference in whether there are enough hospital beds (and doctors, and resources) to treat the sick.
In epidemiology, the idea of slowing a virus' spread so that fewer people need to seek treatment at any given time is known as "flattening the curve." It explains why so many countries are implementing "social distancing" guidelines — including a "shelter in place" order that affects 6.7 million people in Northern California, even though COVID-19 outbreaks there might not yet seem severe.

Here's what you need to know about the curve, and why we want to flatten it. The curve takes on different shapes, depending on the virus's infection rate. It could be a steep curve, in which the virus spreads exponentially (that is, case counts keep doubling at a consistent rate), and the total number of cases skyrockets to its peak within a few weeks. Infection curves with a steep rise also have a steep fall; after the virus infects pretty much everyone who can be infected, case numbers begin to drop exponentially, too.

The faster the infection curve rises, the quicker the local health care system gets overloaded beyond its capacity to treat people. As we're seeing in Italy, more and more new patients may be forced to go without ICU beds, and more and more hospitals may run out of the basic supplies they need to respond to the outbreak. A flatter curve, on the other hand, assumes the same number of people ultimately get infected, but over a longer period of time. A slower infection rate means a less stressed health care system, fewer hospital visits on any given day and fewer sick people being turned away.

For a simple metaphor, consider an office bathroom. "Your workplace bathroom has only so many stalls," Charles Bergquist, director of the public radio science show "Science Friday" tweeted. "If everyone decides to go at the same time, there are problems. If the same number of people need go to the restroom but spread over several hours, it's all ok."" More information can be obtained on this topic here: https://www.livescience.com/coronavirus-flatten-the-curve.html.

COVID-19 has made all of us victims of PTSD most of us won't realize it for months or years down the line.

While this is a small blessing in my own 'fight,' it is pretty major in my daily existence. My nightmares are much less now...thanks to a change in medications. After the first day...I thought maybe it was a fluke. After the 2nd a blessing...and each following day I felt progressively better. While the nightmares are not totally gone they are much less now...and that in itself is a true gift.

I am not done walking my own path. I would imagine that you aren't either. I am willing to bet however, that you are a lot farther on than you were when you started reading this book! No matter what your PTSD is from, let's all continue to fight this fight together. You are strong and radiate strength. No matter what you've been through, you are a survivor. You adapted and overcame and found your own path. Advocate for your needs and reach your future. Take care of yourself, and ask for help when you need to. Lastly, accept things aren't always easy and you aren't always in control. I thought about this being a TAPS to PTSD, and, for some of you it may be. Some of you may be able to place this book on your bookshelf and...maybe...leave it there for a long time...while you experience the renewed life you are leading now. For others, it may still be an on-going fight. It doesn't matter at all which one of these you might be. What does matter is that you are still in the fight and that your eyes are open to all the wonderful options that are out there and available to help you all.

Never, ever give up that fight. My heart is lighter every moment...every second...and filled with happiness when I think about how much I know this book can, and will, help each and every one of you.

Biography

I call what I do 'caring to make a change'. Any change. I have wanted to make things better in the world since I was a little girl and tried to save earthworms from the sidewalks...not having the heart to leave them to their deaths. I still save spiders instead of killing them and avoid stepping on bugs...and I still save those little, and not so little earthworms from sidewalks once in a while too. It's not their fault they got a little lost. I wasn't so nice to roaches. They met their fates in glue traps and underfoot in well-deserved crunchy splats.

I liken this to when I was on deployment, and took possibly undue joy from the knowledge that, at the end of a rocket, deployed by a drone, there would be a well-deserved 'splat,' or at the least some very bad injuries, for anyone who was found at the coordinates from which the rockets were being fired. In my mind I thought of this as the Decon formation. It meant there was one less asshole killing and injuring the people I served alongside. It was one less chance that I could also get killed too. It was one less splat on our side of the fence.

The same can be said for those with PTSD. It's not their fault. PTSD, in any form, and from any cause, is not their fault. Mine potentially originated from issues in childhood and bloomed into a full-fledged wildflower patch of issues when I deployed to Afghanistan. It was after that deployment that I sustained a TBI, brain lesions and had to deal with a bunch of other health related issues that flowered out of a now fertile medical ground of injury (moral, mental and otherwise), pain and anguish. While I am dealing much better with my 'flowers' now, and able to 'pick some of them' to place in a vase and enjoy, I still deal with significant issues.

One thing that has always helped me, especially during my almost 15 years in the Navy, during which I advanced from 3rd Class Petty Officer (Yeoman) to Chief Petty Officer E7 and then Limited Duty Officer (Lieutenant Junior Grade) O2; was being able to help...to guide others, along their own path. To help them off the sidewalks, so to speak. Not that I am calling anyone a worm...just using an analogy.

Through the years, since I was only a junior Petty Officer, I chose to mentor others in their own careers, to help them to advance. I started by helping develop study guides, then group training sessions that I conducted, then rotational training sessions so others would also be engaged, and so on. That expanded into a Navy Mentor website that I singlehandedly managed for four years. I picked up a highly competitive assignment as a Navy Leadership facilitator as a First Class Petty Officer (which was an additional duty assignment as I was in the Navy Reserve at that time).

This allowed me to expand my abilities and reach even more individuals, along with a co-facilitator, teaching leadership concepts and providing mentorship to future Navy leaders in both the Active and Reserve Navy sectors. It was one of my most meaningful assignments aside from my Afghanistan deployment.

Since this time, or actually interwoven in it, I have been mentoring individuals online. They could be anyone really. A majority are individuals who have health or physical issues related to PTSD, have or are dealing with MST, or need positive encouragement in general.

My book Total War on PTSD contains 44 chapters by experts in their fields who donated their expertise to benefit those suffering from PTSD and MST.

I have been on Military Network Radio, hosted by Linda Kreter, which can be accessed here:
http://bit.ly/MNR-CourtenaysWarOnPTSD.

I have contributed articles to the Association of the United States Navy (AUSN) NAVY Magazine and AT EASE! Veteran's Magazine. I am a featured author and poet in the anthology 'Veterans Unchained', a #1 Amazon Bestseller, published in 2022. I have had poems included in 'Father', a Poetry Society of Indiana Publication. Last but not least, I published my first book of poetry via Southern Arizona Press, under the title of *Removing Interference: From Words of Life*, available from Amazon at: https://www.amazon.com/dp/1960038303 or directly from the publisher at https://www.southernarizonapress.com/store/Removing-Interference--From-Words-of-Life-p571439759. I hold a B.S. in Organizational Security and Management. A Certified Paralegal, I served in the U.S. Navy and Navy Reserve for almost fifteen years (now retired). I regularly publish poems on the Poetry Society of Indiana's Facebook page at: www.facebook.com/PoetrySocietyIN. I also write poetry on and curate/administer my Poetry Warrior page at: https://www.facebook.com/groups/945323226710286.

I strive to offer anyone who wants encouragement and support through visual art and the written word. I seek to help anyone who needs a way to fight their 'demons' and win...and see the sunshine again.

Maybe we could add a couple drone strikes in for good measure and see where that takes us. Total War on PTSD!

"We are all broken...that's how the light gets in." - Earnest Hemingway